Analytic Geometry

Harold D. Larsen
Rinehart Mathematical Tables, Formulas, and Curves, ENLARGED EDITION
Horace C. Levinson
The Science of Chance
Neal H. McCoy and Richard E. Johnson
Analytic Geometry
Kenneth S. Miller
Engineering Mathematics
John T. Moore
Fundamental Principles of Mathematics
William K. Morrill
Plane Trigonometry, REVISED EDITION
John A. Northcott
Mathematics of Finance
Plane and Spherical Trigonometry, REVISED EDITION
Lewis M. Reagan, Ellis R. Ott, and Daniel T. Sigley
College Algebra, REVISED EDITION
Paul R. Rider and Carl H. Fischer
Mathematics of Investment
Robert L. Swain
Understanding Arithmetic
Gerhard Tintner
Mathematics and Statistics for Economists
Walter W. Varner
Computing With Desk Calculators

Analytic Geometry

by

Neal H. McCoy

and

Richard E. Johnson

Department of Mathematics
Smith College

Rinehart & Company, Inc.
New York

Sixth Printing, February 1960

Preface

The emphasis throughout this book is on an *understanding* of the basic principles of analytic geometry. Considerable care is taken with the proofs of the main theorems, so that the student may develop an appreciation of the logical structure of a mathematical proof. As an aid to full understanding, numerous illustrative examples are worked out in detail and many exercises of varying degrees of difficulty are included at appropriate places in the text.

The principal definitions and theorems are set off and numbered for easy reference. A few sections are marked *optional*, and these may be omitted without affecting the continuity of the text. The results obtained in these sections are never referred to except possibly in another optional section.

In conformity with tradition, the conics are treated rather fully, but some of this material may be omitted at the option of the instructor. For example, in a short course, the focus-directrix property of the ellipse and hyperbola may be omitted entirely. The eccentricity and directrices of an ellipse or hyperbola are not mentioned in the text, or in the illustrative examples, except in Sections 35, 38, 39, and 58. However, in some other sections there are a few exercises in which these concepts occur; so a little care may be necessary in assigning problems.

In the Appendix to this book is a list of facts and formulas for purpose of reference. In addition, the Appendix includes a table of the values of the trigonometric functions and a table of logarithms. Answers are given to the odd-numbered exercises.

We wish to thank our former colleague, Miss Anne F. O'Neill, for permission to use material from our joint book, *Fundamentals of College Mathematics* (Rinehart & Company, Inc., 1953). With some modifications and a few additions, the material of the first seven chapters is taken from this text.

We are also greatly indebted to Dr. C. V. Newsom, the mathematical consultant of Rinehart & Company, for a very careful reading of our manuscript. His many suggestions have resulted in a considerable improvement in the final product.

N. H. M.

R. E. J.

Northampton, Massachusetts
January, 1955

Foreword to the Student

In studying mathematics, it is important to try to understand every new concept at the time it is introduced. The suggestions listed below are designed to help the student develop suitable study habits, habits that may bring about the desired mastery of the subject.

I. FIRST, spend a few minutes reviewing previous material. Look over anything you have already studied which still seems difficult or confusing. If explanations were made in class the previous day, be sure that you understand them.

II. NEXT, read carefully and critically the material assigned. In particular, do the following:

1. Have pencil and paper handy, and work out all details not given in the book. Many simple algebraic steps are necessarily omitted; work through them.

2. Look up references to previous numbered items only if you need to. In many cases you should be able to understand the argument without looking them up.

3. If there are points which you do not understand, try to find *exactly* what they are and be prepared to ask about them when you come to class. For example, if you do not understand the proof of a theorem, find the *first* sentence or formula that is not clear.

4. Learn the exact definitions of all new terms. How can you understand what is being said if you do not know the meanings of the words being used?

5. Pay special attention to the illustrative examples, and be sure that you understand them.

6. Now close the book and see if you can write out the definitions and statements of the theorems. Also see if you can write out an outline of the main points in the proofs.

III. Now, try the exercises that have been assigned.

1. Try to remember the necessary formulas, and look them up only when necessary.

2. Look up the answer only *after* you have obtained an answer of your own.

Contents

3. EQUATIONS AND GRAPHS

4. THE CIRCLE

5. THE CONIC SECTIONS

6. TRANSFORMATION OF COORDINATES

7. GRAPHS OF EQUATIONS OF THE SECOND DEGREE

8. ALGEBRAIC AND TRANSCENDENTAL CURVES

9. POLAR COORDINATES

10. PARAMETRIC EQUATIONS

11. TANGENTS TO THE CONIC SECTIONS

12. SOLID ANALYTIC GEOMETRY

APPENDIX

INDEX

Analytic Geometry

chapter 1

Coordinate Lines
and Planes

1. INTRODUCTION

The elementary geometry taught in secondary schools is often called *Euclidean* geometry, after the Greek mathematician Euclid (300 B.C.), who wrote the first systematic treatise on the subject. We assume that the reader is familiar with the principal definitions and theorems of Euclidean geometry.

In analytic geometry the methods of algebra are combined with those of Euclidean geometry in the solution of geometry problems. By this combination of algebraic and geometric methods it is possible to solve many problems that could not be solved by the techniques of Euclidean geometry alone.

The fundamental ideas of analytic geometry are usually attributed to the French mathematician and philosopher Descartes (1596–1650). The key to the expression of geometric facts in algebraic form lies in the representation of a point in the plane by means of a pair of real numbers called the *coordinates* of the point. Although the reader has previously met this concept, we devote this first chapter to a detailed discussion of coordinates and to the proof of a few fundamental theorems.

2. THE COORDINATE LINE

We consider a fixed plane the lines and points of which are assumed to satisfy the postulates of Euclidean geometry. Henceforth, in the absence of a statement to the contrary, we shall be considering lines and points of this plane.

Any two points A and B determine a line l (Figure 1), namely, the line passing through A and B. The points A and B determine not only the line l but also the **segment** AB of l. If the segments AB and CD, on the same line or on different lines, are congruent, we shall write $AB = CD$.

1

If a point A is on a line l, instead of saying that the line l *passes through* the point A, we shall usually say that the line l is *on* the point A. Thus, for example, in Figure 1 the line l is the line on the points A and B.

On a given line l, select any two distinct point O and I. Starting with these two points, we shall indicate how it is possible to associate with

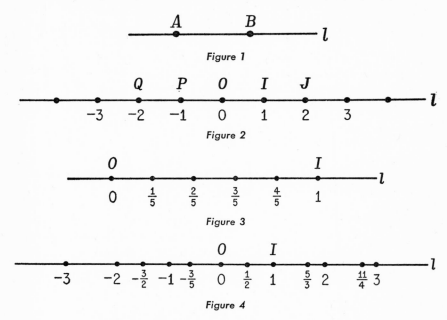

Figure 1

Figure 2

Figure 3

Figure 4

every point on l a real number and, conversely, with every real number a point on l.

For convenience of description, we think of l as a horizontal line with I to the right of O, as in Figure 2. With the point O we associate the number 0 and with I the number 1. With the point J to the right of I such that $OI = IJ$ we associate the number 2, and so on for the other positive integers. We select the point P to the left of O such that $PO = OI$, and associate with P the number -1. If Q is to the left of P such that $QP = OI$, we associate with Q the number -2, and so on for the other negative integers. In this way the integers are associated with equispaced points on l.

Let n be a positive integer, and let us divide the segment OI into n congruent segments. To the mth point of this subdivision (counting from left to right) we assign the rational number m/n. For example, if $n = 5$, we get the division of OI indicated in Figure 3. The same process can be carried out for the segments IJ, OP, PQ, and so on, thus associating a point on l with each rational number. Some examples are given in Figure 4.

The other points on l have irrational numbers associated with them. Without further discussion, we now *assume* that every point on l has a real number assigned to it and, conversely, that every real number is assigned to some point on l. This fact will be described by saying that l has a *coordinate system* on it, and l will be called a **coordinate line.** The number a assigned to the point A is called the **coordinate** of A. Thus, in Figure 2, O has coordinate 0, I has coordinate 1, J has coordinate 2, P has coordinate -1, and so on.

In making the horizontal line l into a coordinate line, we have done so in such a way that the points to the right of O have positive coordinates, and those to the left of O have negative coordinates. This fact is sometimes expressed by saying that l is *directed toward the right*.

3. DISTANCES ON A COORDINATE LINE

We now make the following definition, which is suggested by the way that coordinates were introduced.

1·1 Definition

*The **length** of the segment AB of a coordinate line l is denoted by $|AB|$, and is defined as the absolute value* of $b - a$, that is,*

$$|AB| = |b - a|,$$

where a and b are the coordinates of A and B, respectively.

The length of the segment AB will sometimes be referred to as the **distance** between the points A and B.

It is evident that the length of a segment is a positive number, and since $|b - a| = |a - b|$, the length of the segment AB can be described

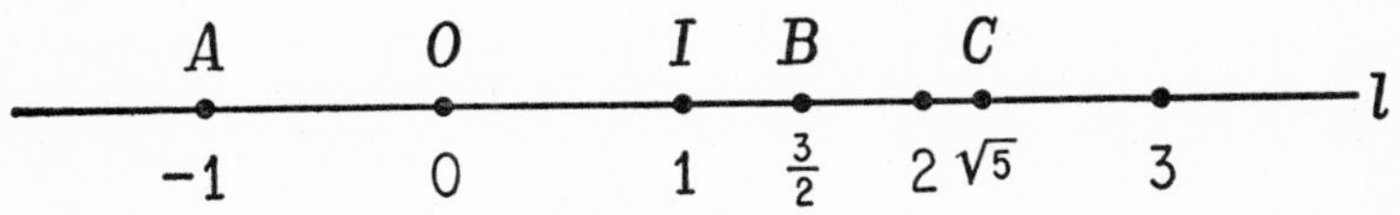

Figure 5

as the absolute value of the difference of the coordinates of A and B, with the difference taken in either order. The segment OI has length 1; the segment OA has length $|a|$.

To illustrate this concept, let A, B, and C have coordinates as specified in Figure 5. Then

---

* Simple properties of absolute values, as well as many other concepts from algebra and trigonometry, are listed in an appendix, "Facts and Formulas for Reference."

$$|AB| = \left|\frac{3}{2} - (-1)\right| = \frac{5}{2}, \qquad |CI| = |1 - \sqrt{5}| = \sqrt{5} - 1,$$

$$|IA| = |-1 - 1| = 2, \qquad |OC| = |\sqrt{5} - 0| = \sqrt{5}.$$

It may be well to emphasize the distinction between AB and $|AB|$. The first of these is a geometric entity, namely, a segment of a line; the second, being the length of a segment, is a *number*. It is true, however, that congruent segments have equal length, and conversely; that is, $AB = CD$ if and only if $|AB| = |CD|$.

We now define another number associated with two points on a coordinate line.

1·2   Definition

*The **directed distance** from the point A to the point B on a coordinate line is denoted by* $\overline{AB}$, *and is defined as*

$$\overline{AB} = b - a,$$

where a and b are the respective coordinates of A and B.

The *directed distance* from A to B differs from the *distance* between A and B in that the directed distance may be a negative number, whereas the distance must be a positive number.

If B is to the right of A, so that $b > a$, $|AB| = b - a$, and thus

$$\overline{AB} = |AB|.$$

On the other hand, if B is to the left of A, so that $a > b$, $|AB| = a - b$. However, by 1·2, we have $\overline{AB} = b - a$, so that in this case,

$$\overline{AB} = -|AB|.$$

Knowing the directed distance from A to B, we know not only the length of the segment AB but also whether B is to the right or left of A. For example, if $\overline{AB} = -3$, then we know that the distance between A and B is 3, and that B is to the left of A. It is important to observe that *the directed distance from the point O to any point A is just the coordinate a of A;* that is,

$$\overline{OA} = a - 0 = a.$$

As illustrations of directed distances, let A, B, and C be as in Figure 5. Then

$$\overline{AB} = \frac{3}{2} - (-1) = \frac{5}{2}, \qquad \overline{BA} = -1 - \frac{3}{2} = -\frac{5}{2},$$

$$\overline{CI} = 1 - \sqrt{5}, \qquad \overline{OA} = -1 - 0 = -1.$$

From the definition of directed distance, for any two points A and B on a coordinate line,

$$\overline{AB} = -\overline{BA}.$$

Some other properties of directed distances are given in the following example, and in the exercises below.

Example 1

Prove that for any three points A, B, and C on a coordinate line,

$$\overline{AB} + \overline{BC} = \overline{AC}.$$

Solution: To prove this, let A, B, and C have respective coordinates a, b, and c. Since

$$\overline{AB} = b - a, \qquad \overline{BC} = c - b, \qquad \overline{AC} = c - a,$$

we see at once that

$$\overline{AB} + \overline{BC} = (b - a) + (c - b) = c - a = \overline{AC},$$

and the proof is completed.

EXERCISES

1. Let O, I, A, B, C, and D be the points on a coordinate line with respective coordinates 0, 1, 3, -2, 1/2, and $-4/3$. Draw a figure showing these points, and find each of the following: $\overline{AB}$, $\overline{BA}$, $|AB|$, $\overline{OD}$, $|OC|$, $|IC| + |CA|$, $\overline{IC} + \overline{CA}$, $|DO| - |OB|$, $\overline{ID} + |ID|$, $\overline{AB} + \overline{BC} + \overline{CD}$.

2. Let O, A, B, C, D, and E be the points on a coordinate line with respective coordinates, 0, -5, 4, 3/2, $-\sqrt{3}$, and $-11/5$. Draw a figure showing these points, and find each of the following: $\overline{OC}$, $\overline{OD}$, $|BE|$, $|AC|$, $\overline{AC} + \overline{CE}$, $|AC| + |CE|$, $\overline{AD} + \overline{BC}$, $\overline{DE} - \overline{ED}$, $|OD| + |DO|$, $|AB| + |BD| + |DE|$.

3. Let P, Q, R, S, and T be the points on a coordinate line with respective coordinates -7, $-9/4$, $-1/2$, 4, and 13/3. Draw a figure showing these points, and find each of the following: $\overline{PS}$, $|RT|$, $\overline{RQ}$, $|SQ|$, $\overline{TR} + \overline{RS}$, $|TQ| + |QR|$, $|PR| + |RT|$, $\overline{PR} + \overline{RT} + \overline{TP}$, $|PR| + |QS| + |RT|$, $|PT| - |TS|$.

4. Let U, V, W, X, and Y be the points on a coordinate line with respective coordinates $3\sqrt{2}$, $\sqrt{5}$, 1, -2, and -7. Draw a figure showing these points, and find each of the following: $|UW|$, $\overline{VY}$, $\overline{XV}$, $|UV| + |VW|$, $\overline{UW} + \overline{WV}$, $|VW| + |WY|$, $|XY| + |YU|$, $\overline{UX} + \overline{VW} + \overline{XV}$, $\overline{UY} + \overline{VX} + \overline{YX}$, $\overline{UY} + \overline{YW} + \overline{WX} + \overline{XV}$.

5. If A, B, and C are three points on a coordinate line, under what conditions on these points is it true that $|AB| + |BC| = |AC|$?

In each of the following three exercises, prove that the given equation holds for any four points A, B, C, and D on a coordinate line.

6. $\overline{AB} + \overline{BC} + \overline{CD} = \overline{AD}.$

7. $\overline{AB} \cdot \overline{CD} + \overline{AC} \cdot \overline{DB} + \overline{AD} \cdot \overline{BC} = 0.$

8. $\overline{DA}^2 \cdot \overline{BC} + \overline{DB}^2 \cdot \overline{CA} + \overline{DC}^2 \cdot \overline{AB} = \overline{AB} \cdot \overline{BC} \cdot \overline{AC}.$

4. DIVISION OF A SEGMENT IN A GIVEN RATIO

If A and B are points on a coordinate line, we first show how to find the coordinate of the midpoint C of the segment AB.   Let A, B, and C have

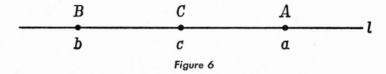

Figure 6

coordinates a, b, and c, respectively (Figure 6).   Obviously, then,

$$\overline{AC} = \overline{CB}$$

regardless of whether B is to the left or right of A.   Since $\overline{AC} = c - a$ and $\overline{CB} = b - c$, it follows that

$$c - a = b - c$$

or

$$c = \frac{1}{2}(a + b).$$

We have therefore proved the following theorem.

1·3 Theorem

If A and B have respective coordinates a and b, then the midpoint of AB has coordinate $(a + b)/2$.

For example, if A has coordinate -1, and B has coordinate 4, the midpoint of AB has coordinate $(-1 + 4)/2$, or $3/2$.

At times it is desirable to have a rule for finding the coordinate of the point dividing a segment in some way other than in half (for example, a

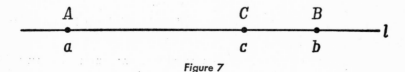

Figure 7

point of trisection of a given segment).   To find such a general rule, assume that A, B, and C are distinct points and that C divides the segment AB in the ratio r; that is assume that

$$\frac{\overline{AC}}{\overline{CB}} = r.$$

Although we say that C "divides the segment AB," we do not mean to imply that C is necessarily between A and B. As far as we are concerned, C is *any* point on the coordinate line distinct from A and B (Figure 7). As usual, let a, b, and c be the coordinates of A, B, and C, respectively. Since we are assuming that $\overline{AC}/\overline{CB} = r$, it follows at once that

$$\frac{c - a}{b - c} = r,$$

or

$$c - a = r(b - c).$$

From this, we can obtain c by the following calculations:

$$\begin{aligned} c - a &= rb - rc, \\ c + rc &= a + rb, \\ (1 + r)c &= a + rb, \\ c &= \frac{a + rb}{1 + r}. \end{aligned}$$

We have proved the following theorem.

1·4 Theorem

If A, B, and C are three distinct points on a coordinate line with A and B having coordinates a and b, respectively, and if

$$\frac{\overline{AC}}{\overline{CB}} = r,$$

then the point C has coordinate c given by

$$c = \frac{a + rb}{1 + r}.$$

Example 2

If A has coordinate $-3/5$ and B has coordinate 3, find the coordinate c of the point C nearer A which trisects AB.

Solution: Clearly, in this case, $\overline{CB} = 2 \cdot \overline{AC}$ (Figure 8); so $r = \overline{AC}/\overline{CB} = 1/2$. Using 1·4, we find at once that

$$c = \frac{-\dfrac{3}{5} + \dfrac{1}{2} \cdot 3}{1 + \dfrac{1}{2}},$$

or $c = 3/5$. One can check this answer by computing $|AC|$ and $|AB|$, verifying that $|AC| = |AB|/3$.

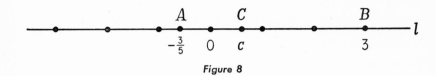

Figure 8

Example 3

If A and B have respective coordinates -1 and 3, find the coordinate c of the point C such that $\overline{AC}/\overline{CB} = -2$.

Solution: Using 1·4, we have $a = -1$, $b = 3$, $r = -2$. Accordingly, we find that

$$c = \frac{-1 + (-2)\cdot 3}{1 - 2},$$

from which it easily follows that $c = 7$ (Figure 9). As a check, it is easy to verify that $\overline{AC} = 8$, $\overline{CB} = -4$, so $\overline{AC}/\overline{CB} = -2$, as required.

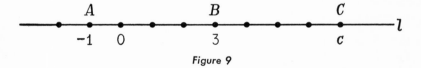

Figure 9

In this last example, with r a negative number, we found that C was *outside* the given segment AB. The reader may verify that this will always be the case if r is negative, for this would imply that $\overline{AC}$ and $\overline{CB}$ have opposite signs. On the other hand, if r is a positive number, C will be *within* the given segment AB. (Why?)

Note that 1·3 is the special case of 1·4 in which $r = 1$; for if $\overline{AC}/\overline{CB} = 1$, then certainly C is the midpoint of AB.

EXERCISES

In each of Exercises 1–10, A, B, and D are the points on a coordinate line with respective coordinates 2, 5, and -6.

1. Find the coordinate of the bisector of AB.

2. Find the coordinates of the points of trisection of AD.

3. Find the coordinates of the points of trisection of BD.

4. Find the coordinate of the point C if $\overline{AC}/\overline{CB} = -3$.

5. Find the coordinate of the point C if $\overline{AC}/\overline{CD} = \sqrt{2}$.

6. Find the coordinate of the point C if $\overline{AC}/\overline{CB} = 2$.

7. Find the coordinate of the point C if $\overline{AC}/\overline{CB} = -99/100$.

8. In what ratio r does D divide the segment AB?

9. In what ratio r does B divide the segment DA?

10. In what ratio r does A divide the segment BD?

In each of Exercises 11–20, P, Q, and R are the points on a coordinate line with respective coordinates 7, -3, and 1.

11. Find the coordinate of the bisector of PR.

12. Find the coordinates of the points of trisection of PQ.

13. Find the coordinate of the point S if $\overline{PS}/\overline{SQ} = 4$.

14. Find the coordinate of the point S if $\overline{QS}/\overline{SR} = -1$.

15. Find the coordinate of the point S if $\overline{PS}/\overline{SR} = \sqrt{3}$.

16. Find the coordinate of the point S if $\overline{RS}/\overline{SQ} = -1/2$.

17. Find the coordinate of the point S if $\overline{PS}/\overline{PR} = 3$.

18. In what ratio r does P divide the segment RQ?

19. In what ratio r does Q divide the segment PR?

20. In what ratio r does R divide the segment QP?

21. If A, B, and C are any three points on a coordinate line and P, Q, and R are the respective midpoints of the segments BC, CA, and AB, prove that the midpoint of CR coincides with the midpoint of PQ.

In each of Exercises 22–24, A, B, and C are three points on a coordinate line such that $\overline{AC}/\overline{CB} = r$. Find:

22. $\overline{AB}/\overline{CB}$.   23. $\overline{AC}/\overline{AB}$.   24. $\overline{BC}/\overline{BA}$.

5. RECTANGULAR COORDINATE SYSTEM

If u is a line and E is a point, let v be the line on E perpendicular to u, as indicated in Figure 10. Then the point A of intersection of u and v is called the **projection** of the point E on the line u. This concept will be used presently.

We now consider a coordinate line l which we think of as a horizontal line directed toward the right. Let k be the line on the point O perpendicular to l; thus k appears as a vertical line (Figure 11). Select the point L on k above the point O such that $OL = OI$, and give L the coordinate 1. Then k can be made into a coordinate line in exactly the same way as was l. Clearly, k is directed upward; that is, the points with positive coordinates are above the point O. We will follow the usual convention of calling the horizontal line l the *x-axis* and the vertical line k the *y-axis*. These two axes are frequently called the *coordinate axes*.

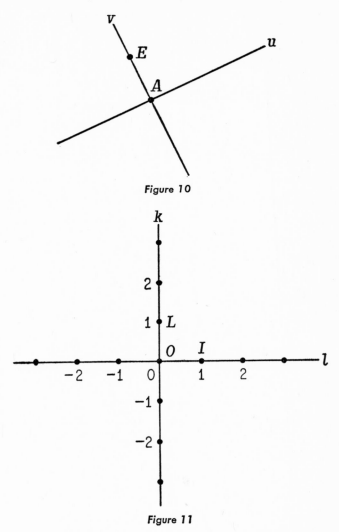

Figure 10

Figure 11

If E is any point in the plane, let A and B denote the projections of E on the *x*-axis and *y*-axis, respectively (Figure 12). If A has coordinate a on the *x*-axis, and B has coordinate b on the *y*-axis, then a and b are called the **coordinates** of the point E. We call a the **x-coordinate** of E and b the **y-coordinate** of E, and denote the point E by (a, b) or by $E(a, b)$. Since $a = \overline{OA}$ and $b = \overline{OB}$, we may also denote the point E by $(\overline{OA}, \overline{OB})$. Some examples of coordinates are given in Figure 13.

The point $(1, 0)$ is just the point I on the x-axis.   If A is a point on the x-axis with coordinate a, then A has coordinates $(a, 0)$ in the plane. Similarly, the point B on the y-axis with coordinate b has coordinates

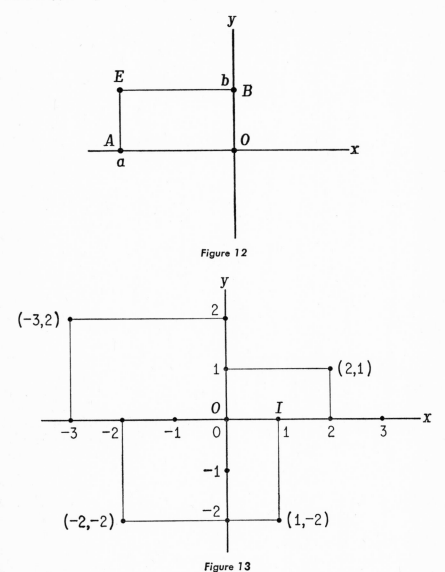

Figure 12

Figure 13

$(0, b)$ in the plane.   The point O has coordinates $(0, 0)$; it is called the **origin.**

The axes divide the plane into the familiar four quadrants, defined as follows (Figure 14):

I. The points $E(a, b)$, where $a > 0$ and $b > 0$.
II. The points $E(a, b)$, where $a < 0$ and $b > 0$.
III. The points $E(a, b)$, where $a < 0$ and $b < 0$.
IV. The points $E(a, b)$, where $a > 0$ and $b < 0$.

A point is either on an axis or in one of the four quadrants.

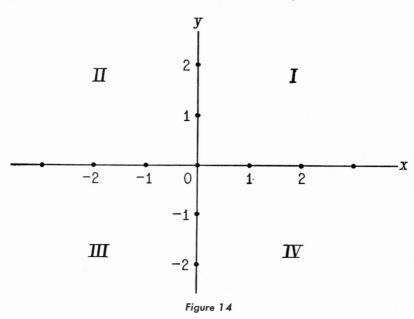

Figure 1 4

The x- and y-axes are said to introduce a *rectangular coordinate system* on the plane. Thus every point on the plane can be described by a pair of real numbers, the coordinates of the point; moreover, every pair of real numbers describes a point on the plane. A plane having a rectangular coordinate system on it will be called a **coordinate plane.** This representation of points on a plane by pairs of real numbers is the basis of plane analytic geometry. Until the last chapter of this book, when we shall briefly introduce the subject of solid analytic geometry, we shall always be working in a coordinate plane.

6. USE OF COORDINATE PAPER

For convenience in drawing figures in which it is necessary to locate a number of points with specified coordinates, there is available a special paper, called *coordinate paper* or *graph paper*, which is ruled into small squares. In using such paper, one first chooses x- and y-axes and draws them in somewhat heavier than the other lines. It is then a very simple matter to find the points with given coordinates, or as we sometimes say, to "plot" the points. Some examples of plotting and a sample of coordinate paper, are shown in Figure 15.

Although use of coordinate paper is not absolutely essential in the study of analytic geometry, an accurate figure is frequently of great help

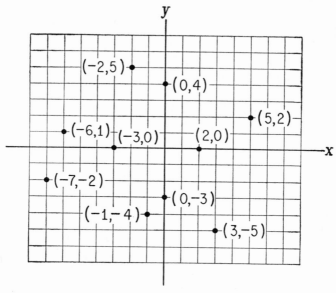

Figure 15

as a check on algebraic calculations. Accordingly, the student should develop the habit of drawing reasonably accurate figures, either with or without the use of graph paper.

EXERCISES

1. Plot the points $(4, 1)$, $(-1, -3)$, $(2, -5)$, $(-3, 3)$, $(0, 2)$, $(-3, 0)$.

2. Plot the points $(1/2, 3)$, $(-2/3, -1)$, $(4, -5/2)$, $(-5, 3/4)$, $(0, 0)$, $(1/2, 0)$.

3. Sketch the triangle with vertices $A(1, 3)$, $B(-1, 5)$, and $C(4, 7)$.

4. Sketch the triangle with vertices $A(2, 3)$, $B(2, -2)$, and $C(-4, 3)$, and find its area.

5. Sketch the quadrilateral with vertices $A(1, -3/2)$, $B(3, 3/4)$, $C(-2, 4)$, and $D(-3, 0)$.

6. Find the lengths of the sides of the triangle with vertices $A(4, -2)$, $B(4, 5)$, and $C(-3, -2)$.

7. Sketch the rectangle with vertices $A(2, -8)$, $B(2, -2)$, $C(8, -2)$, and $D(8, -8)$, and find its area.

8. If $(-1, -1)$, $(-1, 4)$, and $(3, -1)$ are three vertices of a rectangle, find the fourth vertex.

9. The points $(4, 1)$ and $(-1, -2)$ are opposite vertices of a rectangle whose sides are parallel to the coordinate axes. Find the other vertices.

10. If $(-3, -2)$, $(2, -2)$, and $(0, 1)$ are three vertices of a parallelogram, find the fourth vertex. Is the answer unique?

11. Describe the line parallel to the x-axis and on the point $(0, 2)$ in terms of the coordinates of its points.

12. Describe the line parallel to the y-axis and on the point $(-3, 0)$ in terms of the coordinates of its points.

7.   THE DISTANCE FORMULA

In Section 3 we showed how to find the distance between two points on a coordinate line. Starting with a coordinate plane, we shall show presently how to find the distance between any two points on the plane.

Before proceeding, we introduce a convenient notation that will be used in this and later sections. If, for example, we are considering two or more fixed, but arbitrary, points in the plane, instead of using different letters to designate the points we may use the same letter with a numerical subscript. Thus P_1 and P_2 may indicate any two points, and it is convenient to use (x_1, y_1) and (x_2, y_2) as their respective coordinates. Here x_1 and y_1 are to be considered as fixed real numbers, just as we have been using the letters a and b; and similarly for x_2 and y_2.

Now let $P_1(x_1, y_1)$ and $P_2(x_2, y_2)$ be any two points on the coordinate plane (Figure 16). The projections of P_1 on the x- and y-axes are denoted by A_1 and B_1, respectively; those of P_2 by A_2 and B_2, respectively. Let l be the line on P_2 parallel to the x-axis, and k the line on P_1 parallel to the y-axis. If C is the point of intersection of l and k, evidently C has coordinates (x_1, y_2). By construction, $|CP_2| = |A_1A_2|$ and, by 1·1, $|A_1A_2| = |x_2 - x_1|$. Hence

$$|CP_2| = |x_2 - x_1|;$$

and similarly,

$$|CP_1| = |y_2 - y_1|.$$

Hence, by the Pythagorean theorem applied to the right triangle P_1CP_2, we see that

$$|P_1P_2|^2 = |x_2 - x_1|^2 + |y_2 - y_1|^2.$$

But

$$|x_2 - x_1|^2 = (x_2 - x_1)^2 \qquad \text{and} \qquad |y_2 - y_1|^2 = (y_2 - y_1)^2,$$

and thus we obtain

$$|P_1P_2| = \sqrt{(x_2 - x_1)^2 + (y_2 - y_1)^2}.$$

We have therefore proved the following result.

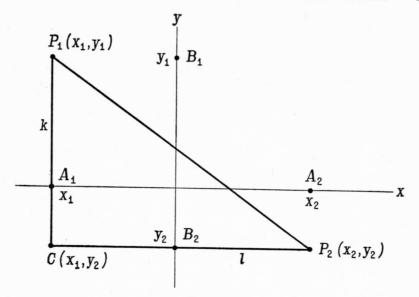

Figure 16

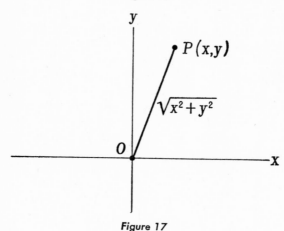

Figure 17

1·5 Distance formula

If $P_1(x_1, y_1)$ and $P_2(x_2, y_2)$ are any two points on the plane, the distance $|P_1P_2|$ between P_1 and P_2 is given by

$$|P_1P_2| = \sqrt{(x_2 - x_1)^2 + (y_2 - y_1)^2}.$$

An important special case occurs if either P_1 or P_2 is the origin. Denoting the other point by $P(x, y)$ (Figure 17), it follows that the distance between the origin and the point $P(x, y)$ is

$$|OP| = \sqrt{x^2 + y^2}.$$

Example 4

Find the distance between the points $A(-4, -2)$ and $B(3, 5)$.

Solution: We identify one of these points (it does not matter which one) with $P_1(x_1, y_1)$ and the other with $P_2(x_2, y_2)$, and use the distance formula. Thus we obtain

$$|AB| = \sqrt{(-4 - 3)^2 + (-2 - 5)^2}$$
$$= \sqrt{98} = 7\sqrt{2}.$$

Example 5

Show that $A(-1, 3)$, $B(4, 1)$, and $C(2, -4)$ are the vertices of a right triangle.

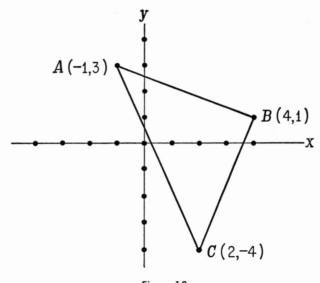

Figure 18

Solution: The given points are plotted and the triangle shown in Figure 18. By the distance formula,

$$|AB| = \sqrt{(-1 - 4)^2 + (3 - 1)^2} = \sqrt{29},$$
$$|BC| = \sqrt{(4 - 2)^2 + (1 + 4)^2} = \sqrt{29},$$
$$|AC| = \sqrt{(-1 - 2)^2 + (3 + 4)^2} = \sqrt{58}.$$

Since $|AB|^2 + |BC|^2 = |AC|^2$, the triangle ABC is a right triangle with right angle at B. Note that the triangle is also an isosceles triangle.

EXERCISES

In each of Exercises 1–6, find the distance between the given points.

1. $(1, 3)$, $(8, 9)$.   2. $(-5, -4)$, $(-2, 5)$.   3. $(3/2, 3/4)$, $(-5/3, -2)$.

4. $(8, -2)$, $(-7, 3)$.   5. $(\sqrt{8}, 3)$, $(-\sqrt{2}, -5)$.   6. $(3, \sqrt{3})$, $(\sqrt{2}, -\sqrt{6})$.

In each of Exercises 7–10, find the lengths of the sides of the triangle with the given vertices.

7. $A(1, 1)$, $B(2, 5)$, $C(7, 3)$.   8. $A(3, -2)$, $B(-2, -4)$, $C(-7, 5)$.

9. $A(4, 2)$, $B(-7, 3)$, $C(-7, -3)$.   10. $A(-1/2, 3)$, $B(1, -2/3)$, $C(7/2, 8/3)$.

In each of Exercises 10–20, the given points are the vertices of a right triangle or an isosceles triangle or both. Determine which it is, and find the area of each right triangle.

11. $(-2, 1)$, $(2, -3)$, $(6, 5)$.   12. $(-5, -3)$, $(-7, 3)$, $(2, 6)$.

13. $(7, 0)$, $(4, 1)$, $(6, 7)$.   14. $(-1, 5)$, $(1, 1)$, $(5, -1)$.

15. $(-1/2, 1)$, $(1/2, -2)$, $(11/2, 3)$. 16. $(7, 8)$, $(5, 2)$, $(0, 7)$.

17. $(5, 1)$, $(1, -5)$, $(-5, -1)$.   18. $(-1, -2)$, $(-2, 0)$, $(-4, -1)$.

19. $(0, -2)$, $(\sqrt{3}, -1)$, $(0, 2)$. 20. $(1, 1)$, $(6, -1)$, $(4, -6)$.

21. Show that the three points $A(-4, -6)$, $B(1, 0)$, and $C(11, 12)$ are collinear.

22. Are the three points $A(-2, -4)$, $B(3, 7/2)$, and $C(1, 1/2)$ collinear?

23. Are the three points $A(-1/3, -3)$, $B(2, 4)$, and $C(5/2, 11/2)$ collinear?

24. If $(0, 0)$ and $(a, 0)$ are two vertices of an equilateral triangle, find the third vertex.

25. Find the real number k so that $A(4, 0)$, $B(k, 0)$, and $C(0, -6)$ are the vertices of a right triangle with right angle at C.

26. Find the fourth vertex of the rectangle having $(-3, -1)$, $(-5, 5)$, and $(4, 8)$ as three of its vertices.

27. Which of the following points are on the circle of radius 5 with center at the origin?

$(-3, 4)$, $(2, \sqrt{20})$, $(-4, -3)$, $(\sqrt{21}, -2)$, $(0, 6)$.

Give conditions on x and y so that the point $P(x, y)$ shall be on this circle.

28. Which of the following points are equidistant from the points $A(-1, 3)$ and $B(2, 0)$?

$(-2, -1)$, $(1/2, 3/2)$, $(3, 3)$, $(7, 9)$, $(13, 14)$.

Give conditions on x and y so that the point $P(x, y)$ shall be equidistant from A and B.

29. Let l be the line on the points $(-2, 5)$ and $(2, 1)$. Prove that the point $P(x, 3 - x)$ is on l for every choice of x.

30. Let x and y be any numbers satisfying the equation $x^2 + y^2 + 4x = 0$. Prove that the point $P(x, y)$ is on the circle of radius 2 and with center $(-2, 0)$.

31. Prove that the distance formula 1·5 is valid even if the line on P_1 and P_2 is parallel to a coordinate axis.

8. DIRECTED DISTANCES ON ANY LINE

In Section 3 we defined directed distances on a coordinate line.   Directed distances can be defined in a natural way on any line that is parallel to a coordinate axis.   If, for example, A and B are two points on a line l that is parallel to the x-axis, as in Figure 19, and A' and B' are the respective

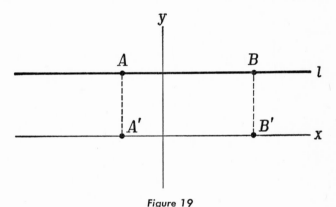

Figure 19

projections of A and B on the x-axis, we define the directed distance $\overline{AB}$ from A to B to be $\overline{A'B'}$.   In this case, therefore, $\overline{AB}$ is the x-coordinate of B minus the x-coordinate of A.   Similar considerations apply to the case in which the line l is parallel to the y-axis.

Although there is no such natural way to define directed distances on a line l that is not parallel to a coordinate axis, it is possible to do so by assigning a direction to l as follows. Let C and D be two distinct points on l (Figure 20).   If we think of a point moving along l, it may move in such a way as to go from C to D or from D to C.   Thus there are two possible directions on l, and we choose one of them and indicate it by an arrowhead on l.   In Figure 20, the chosen direction is *from D to C*. Although the choice of direction is quite arbitrary, when it is once made we consider it to be fixed, and we say that l is a *directed line* having the direction of the arrowhead.   Now, following the procedure suggested by the definition of directed distances on a coordinate line, we make the following definition.   If A and B are any two points on l, the directed distance $\overline{AB}$ from A to B is $|AB|$ or $-|AB|$ according as a point moving along the line from A to B would go in the direction of the arrowhead or in the opposite direction. In Figure 20, clearly $\overline{CD} = -|CD|$, whereas $\overline{DC} = |DC|$.

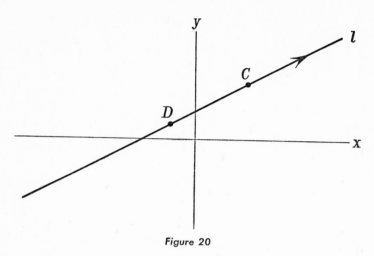

Figure 20

It is easy to see that if A and B are any two points on a directed line, then always

$$\overline{AB} = -\overline{BA}.$$

Also, if A, B, and C are any three points on a directed line, then

$$\overline{AB} + \overline{BC} = \overline{AC}.$$

These, of course, are properties that have already been observed for directed distances on a coordinate line.

The following section is one of the few in this book in which we shall have occasion to use directed lines that are not parallel to a coordinate axis. However, we shall often use directed distances on lines that are parallel to a coordinate axis and, as indicated at the beginning of this section, any such line will always be considered to have the direction of the coordinate axis to which it is parallel.

9. DIVISION OF A SEGMENT IN THE PLANE IN A GIVEN RATIO

Theorem 1·3 may be used to find the coordinates of the midpoint of any segment of a line l parallel to one of the coordinate axes, and Theorem 1·4 may be used to find the point which divides a segment of such a line in any given ratio. In this section we obtain formulas which apply even if the line l is not parallel to a coordinate axis.

Let l be a line that is not parallel to either coordinate axis, and let

$P_1(x_1, y_1)$ and $P_2(x_2, y_2)$ be arbitrary fixed points on l (Figure 21). We assign a direction to l (it does not matter which of the two possible directions is chosen), so that we can use directed distances. We wish to find the point $P(x, y)$ which "divides the segment P_1P_2 in the ratio r"; that is, we wish to find P on l such that

$$\frac{\overline{P_1P}}{\overline{PP_2}} = r.$$

To do this, let P_1', P_2', and P' be the respective projections of P_1, P_2, and P on the x-axis. Thus P_1', P_2', and P' are points on a coordinate line (the x-axis) with coordinates x_1, x_2, and x, respectively. Now since the

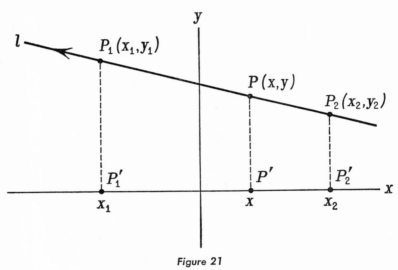

Figure 21

line on P_1 and P_1', the line on P_2 and P_2', and the line on P and P' are all parallel, and these parallel lines are cut by two transversals, namely, l and the x-axis, it follows from elementary geometry that

$$\frac{|P_1P|}{|PP_2|} = \frac{|P_1'P'|}{|P'P_2'|}.$$

Moreover, $\overline{P_1P}/\overline{PP_2}$ is positive if and only if P is between P_1 and P_2, and $\overline{P_1'P'}/\overline{P'P_2'}$ is positive if and only if P' is between P_1' and P_2'. But clearly P' is between P_1' and P_2' if an only if P is between P_1 and P_2. Thus these ratios always have the same sign and therefore

$$\frac{\overline{P_1P}}{\overline{PP_2}} = \frac{\overline{P_1'P'}}{\overline{P'P_2'}}.$$

Hence, from our hypothesis, it follows that

$$\frac{\overline{P_1'P'}}{\overline{P'P_2'}} = r,$$

and we can apply 1·4 (with $a = x_1$, $b = x_2$, $c = x$) to obtain

$$x = \frac{x_1 + rx_2}{1 + r}.$$

Similarly, y can be found by taking projections on the y-axis. We have proved the following theorem.

1·6 Theorem

If $P_1(x_1, y_1)$, $P_2(x_2, y_2)$ and P are three distinct points on a directed line, and if

$$\frac{\overline{P_1P}}{\overline{PP_2}} = r,$$

then the point P has coordinates

$$\left(\frac{x_1 + rx_2}{1 + r}, \frac{y_1 + ry_2}{1 + r}\right).$$

In the proof of this theorem we have assumed that the line l on P_1 and P_2 is not parallel to a coordinate axis. However, the conclusion is valid in this case also.

A special case of 1·6 which is frequently used is the case in which P is the midpoint of the segment P_1P_2. This implies that $r = 1$, and we obtain at once the following result.

1·7 Midpoint Formula

If $P_1(x_1, y_1)$ and $P_2(x_2, y_2)$ are any two points on a coordinate plane, then the midpoint of the segment P_1P_2 has coordinates

$$\left(\frac{x_1 + x_2}{2}, \frac{y_1 + y_2}{2}\right).$$

We now illustrate the use of these results by some examples.

Example 6

Given the points $A(7, 5)$ and $B(-6, 1)$, find the midpoint of the segment AB.

Solution: By 1·7, the midpoint of AB has coordinates

$$\left(\frac{7 - 6}{2}, \frac{5 + 1}{2}\right),$$

or $(1/2, 3)$.

Example 7

Let l be the line on the points $P_1(7, 9)$ and $P_2(-2, 3)$. Find the point P on l for which $\overline{P_1P}/\overline{PP_2} = -4$.

Solution: In 1·6, we let $r = -4$ and find that P has coordinates

$$\left(\frac{7 + (-4)\cdot(-2)}{1 - 4}, \frac{9 + (-4)\cdot 3}{1 - 4}\right),$$

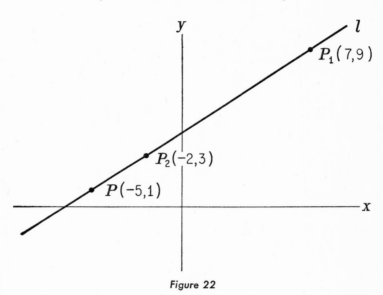

Figure 22

or $(-5, 1)$. These points are plotted in Figure 22. Note that P is outside the segment P_1P_2 because r is negative.

Example 8

A triangle has vertices $A(-1, 2)$, $B(3, 4)$, and $C(1, -6)$. Verify that the medians of this triangle intersect at a point two thirds of the distance from each vertex to the midpoint of the opposite side.

Solution: The triangle is shown in Figure 23. By 1·7, we find at once the midpoints of the sides as indicated on the figure. Let us now find the coordinates of the point P on the median AE which is two thirds of the distance from A to E. Clearly, P is such that $\overline{AP}/\overline{PE} = 2$, and thus by 1·6 (using A as P_1 and E as P_2), we find that P has coordinates

$$\left(\frac{-1 + 2\cdot 2}{1 + 2}, \frac{2 + 2(-1)}{1 + 2}\right),$$

or $(1, 0)$. We omit further details, but a similar calculation will show that the point two thirds of the distance from B to F has these same coor-

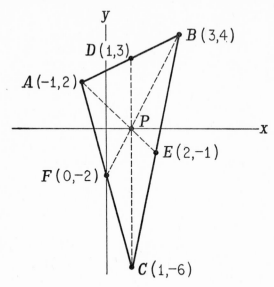

Figure 23

dinates, as does the point two thirds of the distance from C to D. Hence the three medians intersect at the desired point.

EXERCISES

In each of Exercises 1–4, find the points of trisection of P_1P_2.

1. $P_1(4, -1)$, $P_2(7, 5)$.
2. $P_1(-5, 2)$, $P_2(8, -4)$.

3. $P_1(1/2, 3/2)$, $P_2(-5/2, -7)$.
4. $P_1(\sqrt{2}, -3)$, $P_2(-\sqrt{8}, 5/2)$.

5. Given the points $P(-1, -4)$ and $Q(-6, 2)$, find the point R such that $\overline{PR}/\overline{RQ} = 1/5$.

6. Given the points $A(3, 7)$ and $B(-2, 4)$, find the point C such that $\overline{AC}/\overline{CB} = 3$.

7. If $A(-4, 3)$, $B(3, 2)$, and C are collinear, and B is the midpoint of AC, find the coordinates of C.

8. If $A(-2, 5)$, $B(1, 2)$, and C are collinear, with B between A and C, and if $|AC| = 3|AB|$, find the coordinates of C.

9. If $P(-3, -6)$, $Q(4, 2)$, and R are collinear, with R between P and Q, and if $|PQ| = 4|RQ|$, find the coordinates of R.

10. If $P(0, 4)$, $Q(5, 0)$, and R are collinear, with P between R and Q, and if $|RP| = 10|PQ|$, find the coordinates of R.

In each of Exercises 11–14, find the lengths of the medians of the triangle with the given vertices.

11. $A(0, 0)$, $B(-2, 6)$, $C(4, 4)$.
12. $A(-3, -1)$, $B(1, 7)$, $C(9, -3)$.

13. $A(-4, 3)$, $B(3, 3)$, $C(6, -8)$.
14. $A(12, 3)$, $B(-1, -3)$, $C(-12, 8)$.

15. Show that the three points $P(-3, -4)$, $Q(2, 6)$, and $R(0, 2)$ are collinear, and find the value of $\overline{PR}/\overline{RQ}$.   Also find the value of $\overline{PQ}/\overline{QR}$.

16. Show that the three points $A(5, -2)$, $B(1, 2)$, and $C(-2, 5)$ are collinear, and find the value of $\overline{AB}/\overline{BC}$.   Also find the value of $\overline{AC}/\overline{CB}$.

17. If P, Q, and R are three collinear points and if $\overline{PR}/\overline{RQ} = r$, what is the value of $\overline{PR}/\overline{PQ}$?   What is the value of $\overline{PQ}/\overline{QR}$?

18. Let $A(3, 5)$, $B(-2, 6)$, and $C(1, -4)$ be the vertices of a triangle.   If P is the midpoint of AC and Q is the midpoint of BC, verify that $|PQ| = |AB|/2$.

19. Let $O(0, 0)$, $A(a, 0)$, and $B(b, c)$ be the vertices of a triangle, where a, b, and c are positive numbers.   Find the area of the triangle the vertices of which are the midpoints of the sides of OAB.   Show that it is one fourth the area of the given triangle.

20. If $P_1(x_1, y_1)$, $P_2(x_2, y_2)$, and $P_3(x_3, y_3)$ are the vertices of a triangle, prove that the point

$$\left(\frac{x_1 + x_2 + x_3}{3}, \frac{y_1 + y_2 + y_3}{3} \right)$$

is a point of trisection of the three medians of the triangle.

21. Prove that Theorem 1·6 is valid even if the segment P_1P_2 is parallel to a coordinate axis.

chapter 2

The Line

In the present chapter we shall make a detailed study of lines in a coordinate plane.

10. INCLINATION AND SLOPE

A number of different angles can be associated with two lines l_1 and l_2 intersecting at a point V. Of all the possible angles with vertex V and sides on l_1 and l_2, it is frequently convenient to select one for special consideration. Accordingly, we make the following definition.

2·1 Definition

*If l_1 and l_2 are intersecting lines, the **angle from l_1 to l_2** is the angle of least positive measure* having its initial side on l_1 and terminal side on l_2. In case l_1 and l_2 are parallel, the angle from l_1 to l_2 is defined as the angle of zero measure.*

In reality there are two angles from l_1 to l_2 that satisfy the definition, namely, the angles θ_1 and θ_2 in Figure 24; similarly, there are two angles from l_2 to l_1, that is, ϕ_1 and ϕ_2 in the figure. Since $\theta_1 = \theta_2$ and $\phi_1 = \phi_2$, it obviously makes no difference whether we consider θ_1 or θ_2 as the angle from l_1 to l_2, and whether we consider ϕ_1 or ϕ_2 as the angle from l_2 to l_1.

From the definition it follows that the angle from any line to any other line is either $0°$, or a positive angle of measure less than $180°$. Notice also that if l_1 and l_2 are not parallel, the sum of the measures of the angles from l_1 to l_2 and from l_2 to l_1 is $180°$ (in Figure 24, $\theta_1 + \phi_1 = 180°$).

---

* It will be recalled that an angle is considered to have positive measure if it is generated by a counterclockwise rotation from the initial side to the terminal side. See the appendix, "Facts and Formulas for Reference."

We shall follow the usual practice of denoting angles by Greek letters. A list of these letters and their names will be found in the appendix.

2·2   Definition

*The angle from the x-axis to a line l is called the **inclination** of the line l.*

It is important to observe that if x' is a line parallel to the x-axis, the angle from x' to l is also the inclination of l. In Figures 25 and 26 the angle α is the inclination of the line l.

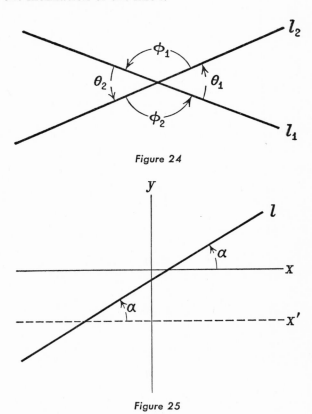

Figure 24

Figure 25

2·3   Definition

*The **slope** m of a line l is the tangent of its inclination α, that is,*

$$m = \tan \alpha.$$

The range of values of the inclination α of a line l is such that $0° \leqq \alpha < 180°$. If $0° < \alpha < 90°$, the line extends upward to the right and its slope is positive (Figure 25); if $\alpha > 90°$ the line extends upward to the left and its slope is negative (Figure 26). Since $\tan 0° = 0$, lines parallel to the x-axis have zero slope; and since $\tan 90°$ does not exist, lines parallel to the y-axis have no slope.　Moreover, the *only* angle α between $0°$ and $180°$ for which tan α does not exist is $\alpha = 90°$; hence the statement that a line has no slope is equivalent to the statement that the inclination of the line is $90°$, or that the line is parallel to the y-axis.　It

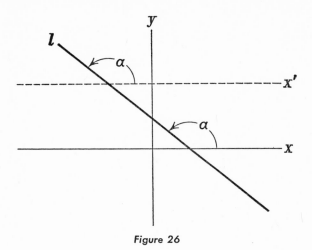

Figure 26

may be well to emphasize that a line with a zero slope *does* have a slope, namely, zero.

The definition of slope implies that *two lines with the same inclination have the same slope*.　It is important to observe also that *two lines with the same slope have the same inclination*.　This follows from the fact that if m is *any* real number, there is precisely *one* angle α in the range $0° \leqq \alpha < 180°$ such that tan $\alpha = m$.

The meaning of slope may perhaps be clarified by consideration of the problem of constructing a line on a given point and having a given slope.

Example 1

Construct the line on the point $P(1, 2)$ having slope $2/3$.

Solution:　It is only necessary to move 3 units to the right of P and 2 units up to obtain another point $Q(4, 4)$ on the line, as indicated in Figure 27.　The line on P and Q is then the required line, since clearly tan $\alpha = 2/3$.　Another way of expressing the fact that the slope of a line is $2/3$ is to say that the y-coordinate of a point on the line is increased 2 units whenever the x-coordinate is increased 3 units, or that the y-coordinate increases at the rate of $2/3$ of a unit per unit increase in the x-coordinate.

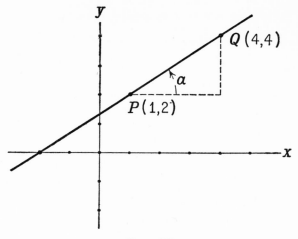

Figure 27

Example 2

Construct the line on the point $P(1, 2)$ having slope $-2/3$.

Solution: This time we pass from P to a new point R on the line by moving 3 units to the left and 2 units up (Figure 28), and the line on P and R is the required line.   If β is the supplement of α, as indicated, evidently $\tan \beta = 2/3$.   Since $\alpha = 180° - \beta$, $\tan \alpha = -\tan \beta = -2/3$, as desired.

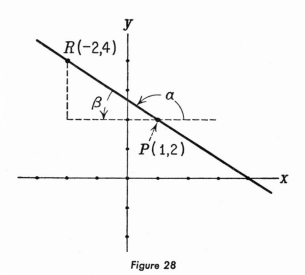

Figure 28

11. SLOPE OF THE LINE ON TWO POINTS

We shall now prove the following important theorem.

2·4   Theorem

Let l be the line on the two distinct points $P_1(x_1, y_1)$ and $P_2(x_2, y_2)$.
(1)   If $x_1 = x_2$, the line has no slope.
(2)   If $x_1 \neq x_2$, the line l has slope m given by the formula

$$m = \frac{y_2 - y_1}{x_2 - x_1}.$$

Proof: Part (1) follows at once from the observation that if $x_1 = x_2$, the line on $P_1(x_1, y_1)$ and $P_2(x_2, y_2)$ is parallel to the y-axis, and therefore has no slope.

To prove part (2), let us first suppose that $y_2 \geqq y_1$, that is, that P_2 is either above P_1 or on a horizontal line with P_1 (Figure 29).   Construct

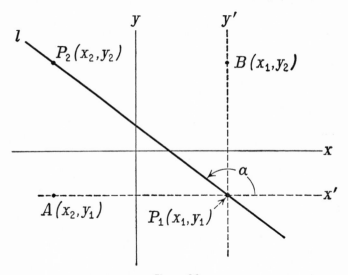

Figure 29

lines x' and y' on P_1 parallel to the x- and y-axes, respectively.   Let A and B be the projections of P_2 on the lines x' and y', respectively.   The angle α from x' to l is the inclination of l.   Now let us consider the lines x' and y' as new coordinate axes in the plane.   This is to allow us to find $\tan \alpha$, for angle α is in standard position relative to the lines x' and y'. What are the coordinates of P_2 relative to the *new* axes?   They are evidently $(\overline{P_1A}, \overline{P_1B})$.   Thus we have

$$\tan \alpha = \frac{\overline{P_1B}}{\overline{P_1A}}.$$

Since $\overline{P_1A} = x_2 - x_1$, $\overline{P_1B} = y_2 - y_1$, and $m = \tan \alpha$, the desired conclusion follows.

Should P_1 be above P_2, and therefore $y_1 > y_2$, a similar argument would show that

$$m = \frac{y_1 - y_2}{x_1 - x_2}.$$

But

$$\frac{y_1 - y_2}{x_1 - x_2} = \frac{y_2 - y_1}{x_2 - x_1};$$

hence the correctness of the formula is independent of the relative positions of P_1 and P_2. This completes the proof of the theorem.

Example 3

Find the slope and inclination of the line on $(-2, 2)$ and $(3, -1)$.

Solution: If, in applying 2·4, we let $(-2, 2)$ be P_1 and $(3, -1)$ be P_2, we find

$$m = \frac{-1 - 2}{3 - (-2)} = -\frac{3}{5}.$$

Had we chosen $(3, -1)$ as P_1 and $(-2, 2)$ as P_2, we would have found

$$m = \frac{2 - (-1)}{-2 - 3} = -\frac{3}{5},$$

as before.   Since m is negative, the inclination α of the line lies between $90°$ and $180°$.   From Table I (see Appendix) we find that the *acute* angle whose tangent is $3/5$ is approximately $30°$ $58'$; hence $\alpha = 180° - 30°$ $58' = 149°$ $2'$.

This example illustrates one of the reasons why slopes are used much more frequently than inclinations in analytic geometry.   For if a line is defined by two points, it is a simple matter to find the exact slope of the line, but usually we can find only an approximation of the inclination, and even this requires the use of tables.

EXERCISES

Construct each of the following lines:

1. On $(-1, 2)$ with slope 4.
2. On $(-1, 2)$ with slope 1/4.
3. On $(3, 0)$ with slope $-1/2$.
4. On $(4, -2)$ with slope 10.
5. On $(3, 7)$ with slope 0.
6. On $(-1, -1)$ with slope -1.
7. On $(1/2, 2)$ with slope 3.
8. On $(1, 2)$ with no slope.

Find the slope and inclination of each of the following lines:

9. On $(1, -2)$ and $(2, 3)$.   10. On $(3, 3)$ and $(-5, 2)$.

11. On $(-2, -2)$ and $(3, -2)$.   12. On $(1, \sqrt{2})$ and $(-\sqrt{2}, 1)$.

13. On $(0, 13)$ and $(-13, 0)$.   14. On $(-3, 7)$ and $(10, 4)$.

15. On $(1/2, 2/3)$ and $(2/3, 1/2)$.   16. On $(5/2, -6)$ and $(-3/2, 4)$.

17. Find the slopes of the sides and of the medians of the triangle whose vertices are $A(-1, 2)$, $B(3, -4)$, and $C(1, 6)$.

18. Find the slopes of the sides and of the medians of the triangle whose vertices are $A(2, 5)$, $B(4, -1)$, and $C(6, 3)$.

19. Find the inclination and slope of a line l if the angle from l to the y-axis has measure $120°$.

20. The inclination of the line l is twice the inclination of the line l_1. If the line l has slope -4, what is the slope of the line l_1?

12. PARALLEL AND PERPENDICULAR LINES

It has already been observed that if two lines have the same slope they have the same inclination, and conversely. Furthermore, two lines are parallel if and only if they have the same inclination. (Why?) This proves the first part of the following important result.

2·5 Theorem

Let l_1 and l_2 be lines with slopes m_1 and m_2 respectively. Then
(1) l_1 and l_2 are parallel if and only if $m_1 = m_2$,
(2) l_1 and l_2 are perpendicular if and only if $m_1 m_2 = -1$.

To prove part (2), let us first assume that l_1 and l_2 are perpendicular, and let α_1 and α_2 be the respective inclinations of l_1 and l_2. Now $\alpha_1 \neq \alpha_2$, since l_1 and l_2 are not parallel; so either $\alpha_1 > \alpha_2$ or $\alpha_2 > \alpha_1$. Let us suppose that the notation is so chosen that $\alpha_2 > \alpha_1$, as in Figure 30. On the point of intersection of l_1 and l_2 construct a line x' parallel to the x-axis. Then α_1 and α_2 are the angles from x' to l_1 and l_2, respectively, and

$$\alpha_2 = \alpha_1 + 90°.$$

Since $\tan(\alpha_1 + 90°) = -\cot \alpha_1$, we conclude that

$$\tan \alpha_2 = -\cot \alpha_1 = -\frac{1}{\tan \alpha_1}.$$

But $\tan \alpha_2 = m_2$ and $\tan \alpha_1 = m_1$; therefore, we have

$$m_2 = -\frac{1}{m_1},$$

or $m_1m_2 = -1$, which is the desired result.

Conversely, suppose that the two lines l_1 and l_2 are such that

$$m_1m_2 = -1.$$

We wish to show that l_1 and l_2 are perpendicular. Since m_1m_2 is negative, one of the numbers, m_1 or m_2, is positive and the other is negative. Assume that the notation is so chosen that m_2 is negative and m_1 is posi-

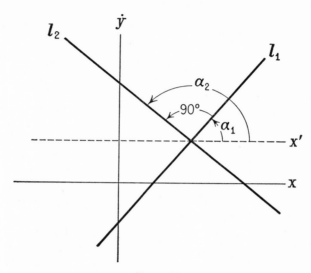

Figure 30

tive. If α_1 and α_2 are the respective inclinations of l_1 and l_2, so that $m_1 = \tan \alpha_1$ and $m_2 = \tan \alpha_2$, then necessarily $0° < \alpha_1 < 90°$ and $90° < \alpha_2 < 180°$. Since $\tan \alpha_1 \tan \alpha_2 = -1$,

$$\tan \alpha_2 = -\frac{1}{\tan \alpha_1} = -\cot \alpha_1.$$

However,

$$\tan (\alpha_1 + 90°) = -\cot \alpha_1,$$

and thus

$$\tan \alpha_2 = \tan (\alpha_1 + 90°).$$

Moreover, both α_2 and $\alpha_1 + 90°$ lie between 90° and 180°. It follows that $\alpha_2 = \alpha_1 + 90°$, and the angle from l_1 to l_2 is 90°. Hence the lines l_1 and l_2 are perpendicular, and the theorem is proved.

We may point out that the relation $m_1m_2 = -1$ can be put in either of the forms, $m_1 = -1/m_2$, $m_2 = -1/m_1$. In words, this may be expressed as follows: *Two lines are perpendicular if and only if the slope of either is the negative reciprocal of the slope of the other.*

Some simple cases are not covered by the above theorem, namely, those in which at least one of the given lines has no slope. If, say, l_1 has no slope, then l_1 is parallel to the y-axis and l_2 will be parallel to l_1 if and only if l_2 has no slope. Also, if l_1 has no slope, a line l_2 will be perpendicular to l_1 if and only if l_2 is parallel to the x-axis and therefore has zero slope.

Example 4

Find the slope of a line which is perpendicular to the line on the points $(2, 3)$ and $(-4, 1)$.

Solution: By 2·4, the slope of the line on the given points is

$$\frac{3 - 1}{2 - (-4)} = \frac{2}{6} = \frac{1}{3}.$$

Hence the slope of a line perpendicular to this line must be the negative reciprocal of $1/3$, namely, -3.

EXERCISES

In each of Exercises 1–8, find the slopes of the altitudes of the triangle whose vertices are the three given points.

1. $A(-1, -2)$, $B(3, 5)$, $C(5, 1)$.
2. $A(2, 5)$, $B(4, -1)$, $C(6, 3)$.

3. $A(3, -4)$, $B(-1, 2)$, $C(1, 6)$.
4. $A(7, 1)$, $B(12, -2)$, $C(8, -5)$.

5. $A(-1, 1)$, $B(1, 2)$, $C(2, 5)$.
6. $A(-6, 1)$, $B(-5, 2)$, $C(-3, 6)$.

7. $A(3/5, 0)$, $B(1, -1/2)$, $C(10/3, 3)$.
8. $A(0, \sqrt{2})$, $B(3, 0)$, $C(5, 2\sqrt{2})$.

9. Use slopes to show that the point $(7, 9)$ is on the perpendicular bisector of the segment joining $(-2, 1)$ and $(6, -3)$.

10. Verify that the triangle with vertices $A(-7, 4)$, $B(1, -3)$, and $C(0, 12)$ is a right triangle, and find its area.

11. Is the triangle with vertices $A(1, 5)$, $B(3, 9)$, and $C(-5, 8)$ a right triangle? Is the triangle with vertices $A(1, 0)$, $B(1, 4)$, and $C(-2, 1)$ a right triangle?

12. Is the quadrilateral with vertices $A(1, 1)$, $B(6, 0)$, $C(7, 4)$, and $D(2, 5)$ a parallelogram? Is it a rectangle?

13. Show, by means of slopes, that the points $(1, 1)$, $(-2, 7)$, and $(10, -17)$ are on the same line.

14. If a, b, and c are any real numbers, show that the points $(a, b + c)$, $(b, c + a)$, and $(c, a + b)$ are on the same line.

15. In the triangle with vertices $A(2, 2)$, $B(6, 0)$, and $C(5, 3)$, show that one of the medians is an altitude, and find the area of the triangle.

16. A quadrilateral has vertices $A(-2, 1)$, $B(3, 6)$, $C(6, 3)$, and $D(5, 0)$. Show that the midpoints of the sides of this quadrilateral are the vertices of a parallelogram.

17. The consecutive vertices of a quadrilateral are $A(-2, -4)$, $B(-3, 4)$, $C(10, 20)$, and $D(5, 0)$. Show that the diagonals of this quadrilateral are perpendicular.

18. Show that $A(-3, -10)$, $B(1, 2)$, $C(4, 5)$, and $D(1, -4)$ are the vertices of a trapezoid, and verify that the line joining the midpoints of the nonparallel sides is parallel to the parallel sides.

19. The vertices of a triangle are $A(7, 5)$, $B(-1, 2)$, and $C(c, 0)$. Determine c so that the triangle shall have a right angle at B.

20. Let $P_1(x_1, y_1)$, $P_2(x_2, y_2)$, and $P_3(x_3, y_3)$ be the vertices of any triangle. Show that the line joining the midpoints of P_1P_2 and P_1P_3 is parallel to P_2P_3, and that its length is equal to one-half the length of P_2P_3.

13. THE ANGLE FROM ONE LINE TO ANOTHER

It is frequently necessary to find the angle from one line to another, as defined in 2·1, and we now proceed to determine a formula for this purpose.

2·6 Theorem

Let l_1 and l_2 be lines with slopes m_1 and m_2, respectively, and let θ be the angle from l_1 to l_2. If $m_1m_2 = -1$, $\theta = 90°$. Otherwise, θ is the angle such that

$$\tan \theta = \frac{m_2 - m_1}{1 + m_2m_1}, \qquad 0° \le \theta < 180°.$$

Proof: We first dispose of two simple cases. First, if $m_1m_2 = -1$, 2·5 shows that l_1 and l_2 are perpendicular and hence $\theta = 90°$. Second, if $m_1 = m_2$, 2·5 shows that l_1 and l_2 are parallel and hence, by Definition 2·1, $\theta = 0$. Since $\tan 0° = 0$, the above formula is therefore true in this case.

Henceforth in the proof we assume that l_1 and l_2 are neither parallel nor perpendicular. On the point of intersection of l_1 and l_2 construct a line x' parallel to the x-axis. If α_1 and α_2 are the respective inclinations of l_1 and l_2, then α_1 is the angle from x' to l_1 and α_2 is the angle from x' to l_2. Since α_2 and α_1 are unequal, we must have either $\alpha_2 > \alpha_1$ or $\alpha_1 > \alpha_2$. These two possible cases are illustrated in Figures 31 and 32. If $\alpha_2 > \alpha_1$, as in Figure 31, we see that $\theta = \alpha_2 - \alpha_1$; if $\alpha_1 > \alpha_2$, as illustrated in Figure 32, it is clear that $\theta = (180° + \alpha_2) - \alpha_1 = 180° + (\alpha_2 - \alpha_1)$. However,

$$\tan [180° + (\alpha_2 - \alpha_1)] = \tan (\alpha_2 - \alpha_1),$$

so that in either case above,

2·7 $$\tan \theta = \tan (\alpha_2 - \alpha_1).$$

Using a known formula from trigonometry, we have

$$\tan (\alpha_2 - \alpha_1) = \frac{\tan \alpha_2 - \tan \alpha_1}{1 + \tan \alpha_2 \tan \alpha_1} = \frac{m_2 - m_1}{1 + m_2 m_1},$$

and this completes the proof.

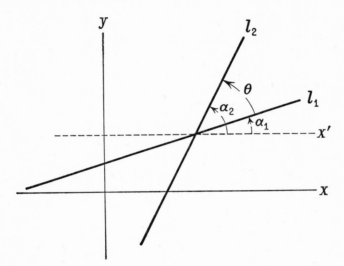

Figure 31

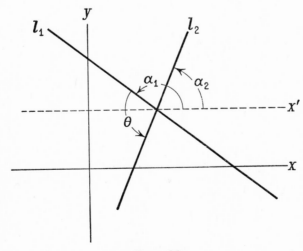

Figure 32

Of course, the reason that we had to consider separately the case in which $m_1 m_2 = -1$ is that the denominator of the formula for $\tan(\alpha_2 - \alpha_1)$ becomes zero, and hence $\tan \theta$ does not exist. In a certain sense the formula is still correct, since the only positive angle $\theta < 180°$ such that $\tan \theta$ does not exist is $90°$, which is now the angle from l_1 to l_2. However, if in using the formula the denominator becomes zero, it is enough to observe that $m_1 m_2 = -1$, and thus 2·5 shows that the lines are perpendicular.

In the proof of 2·6 it is assumed that the lines l_1 and l_2 have slopes, that is, that neither is parallel to the y-axis. Let us now consider briefly the situation in which l_1 is parallel to the y-axis, and therefore $\alpha_1 = 90°$. The proof of 2·6 down to Equation 2·7 still holds, and thus

$$\tan \theta = \tan(\alpha_2 - 90°),$$

so that

$$\tan \theta = -\cot \alpha_2 = -\frac{1}{\tan \alpha_2} = -\frac{1}{m_2}.$$

We have thus shown that *the angle from a line l_1 parallel to the y-axis to a line l_2 (with slope $\neq 0$) is the angle θ between $0°$ and $180°$ such that*

2·8
$$\tan \theta = -\frac{1}{m_2}.$$

By a similar argument it can be shown that *the angle from l_1 (with slope $\neq 0$) to a line l_2 parallel to the y-axis is the angle θ between $0°$ and $180°$ such that*

2·9
$$\tan \theta = \frac{1}{m_1}.$$

Example 5

Find the angles of the triangle with vertices $A(-2, 4)$, $B(4, -1)$, and $C(8, 2)$.

Solution: The triangle is sketched in Figure 33. First we find that the line l_1 on A and C has slope $m_1 = -1/5$, the line l_2 on A and B has slope $m_2 = -5/6$, and the line l_3 on B and C has slope $m_3 = 3/4$. The angle θ_1 at vertex A is formed by going from l_2 to l_1 (remember, the rotation must be *counterclockwise*), and therefore

$$\tan \theta_1 = \frac{m_1 - m_2}{1 + m_1 m_2} = \frac{-\dfrac{1}{5} - \left(-\dfrac{5}{6}\right)}{1 + \left(-\dfrac{1}{5}\right)\left(-\dfrac{5}{6}\right)}$$

$$= \frac{19}{35} = .5429,$$

correct to four decimal places.   From Table I we find

$$\theta_1 = 28° \ 30',$$

approximately.   Similarly,

$$\tan \theta_2 = \frac{m_2 - m_3}{1 + m_2 m_3} = -4.2222,$$

$$\tan \theta_3 = \frac{m_3 - m_1}{1 + m_3 m_1} = 1.1176,$$

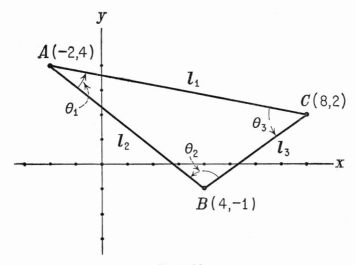

Figure 33

and the angles are approximately

$$\theta_2 = 103° \ 19', \qquad \theta_3 = 48° \ 11'.$$

As a check, note that the sum of the angles is 180° (in some cases, the sum might be slightly different from 180°, owing to the approximations involved).

EXERCISES

In each of Exercises 1–6, find the angles of the triangle whose vertices are the three given points.

1. $A(-3, 0)$, $B(2, 5)$, $C(5, 1)$.
2. $A(-4, 1)$, $B(3, -1)$, $C(0, 6)$.
3. $A(-8, -3)$, $B(-2, -1)$, $C(-6, -5)$.
4. $A(3, 1)$, $B(3, 5)$, $C(7, -1)$.
5. $A(-1, 4)$, $B(2, -1)$, $C(10, 3)$.
6. $A(2, 2)$, $B(3, -1)$, $C(8, 2)$.

7. For the triangle of Exercise 1, find the angle from the median drawn from A to the altitude drawn from B.

8. For the triangle of Exercise 3, find the angle from the median drawn from A to the median drawn from B.

9. Use 2·6 to show that the triangle with vertices $A(0, -4)$, $B(5, 6)$, and $C(-2, 7)$ has two equal angles. Are tables necessary?

10. The vertices of a quadrilateral are $A(7, 3)$, $B(0, 2)$, $C(4, -1)$, and $D(6, 0)$. Show, without use of tables, that the opposite angles of this quadrilateral are supplementary.

11. The line k has an inclination of 105°, and the line l has an inclination of 10°. What is the measure of the angle from the line k to the line l? What is the measure of the angle from the y-axis to the line k? What is the measure of the angle from the line l to the x-axis?

12. The line k is the line on the points $(-2, 4)$ and $(5, -1)$. Find the slope of a line l such that the measure of the angle from the line l to the line k is 45°.

13. Let k be the line on the points $A(1, 2)$ and $B(7, 10)$, and l the line on the points $C(a, 0)$ and $B(7, 10)$. Determine a so that the angle from the line l to the line k will have a measure of 135°.

14. Write out the proof of 2·9.

14. THE EQUATION OF A LINE

As an illustration of the next concept to be introduced, let us consider the line l which bisects the first and third quadrants, that is, the line on the origin with an inclination of 45° (Figure 34). From the simple geometry

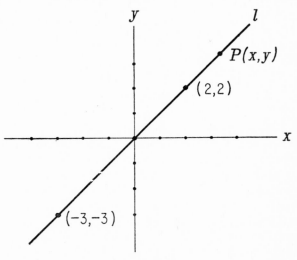

Figure 34

of the figure it is apparent that if $P(x, y)$ is *any* point on l then $x = y$. Furthermore, any point (x, y) with $x = y$ is necessarily on l, and thus the points whose coordinates satisfy the equation $x = y$ are just the points on l and no others. Accordingly, we shall say that the equation $x = y$ (or $x - y = 0$) is the *equation* of the line l. This is an example of an important general concept described in the following definition.

2·10　Definition

　　*The **equation of a line** l is an equation in x and y with the following two properties:*
　　(1)　*If (x, y) is a point on l, then (x, y) satisfies the equation.*
　　(2)　*If (x, y) satisfies the equation, then the point (x, y) is on l.*

　　It may be pointed out that equations which differ somewhat in form may each be the equation of the same line. For example, the line l at the beginning of this section has the equation $x - y = 0$. However, the

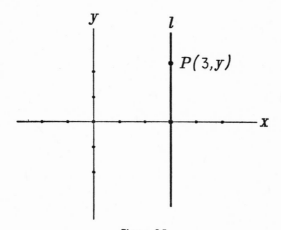

Figure 35

equation $2(x - y) = 0$ is an equation of the same line, since $2(x - y) = 0$ if and only if $x - y = 0$. More generally, it is clear that in the equation of a line one may multiply (or divide) throughout by any real number other than zero and still have an equation of the same line.

　　We shall presently introduce methods of finding the equation of any line, but first we observe that the problem is very simple if the line is parallel to either axis. If, for example, l is a line parallel to the y-axis and 3 units to the right of the y-axis, as in Figure 35, then a point is on l if and only if its x-coordinate is 3. Thus the equation of l is just $x = 3$. In general, any line parallel to the y-axis has an equation of the form

$$x = c,$$

where c is a real number; and any line parallel to the x-axis has an equation of the form

$$y = d,$$

where d is a real number. In particular, *the equation of the y-axis is $x = 0$, and the equation of the x-axis is $y = 0$.*

15.   THE POINT-SLOPE FORM

Let l be a line on the point $P_1(x_1, y_1)$, having the slope m. Let $P(x, y)$ be a point on l distinct from $P_1(x_1, y_1)$, as indicated in Figure 36. Since,

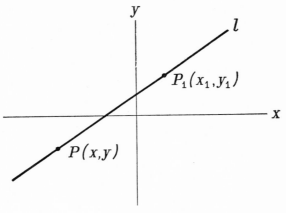

Figure 36

by assumption, l has a slope, l is not parallel to the y-axis, and therefore $x \neq x_1$. Hence, by 2·4 (2), the slope of l must be

$$\frac{y - y_1}{x - x_1}.$$

But it is given that l has slope m, and therefore we must have

$$m = \frac{y - y_1}{x - x_1},$$

or

2·11 $$y - y_1 = m(x - x_1).$$

We shall now prove that 2·11 is the *equation* of the line on $P_1(x_1, y_1)$ having the slope m. The above calculations show that the coordinates of every point (x, y) on l other than (x_1, y_1) satisfy this equation; it is obvious by direct substitution that $x = x_1$, $y = y_1$ also satisfies the equation. Hence 2·11 is satisfied by the coordinates of *every* point on *l*. To complete the proof that 2·11 is the equation of *l*, we need to verify part (2) of 2·10. To this end, suppose that (x_2, y_2) satisfies 2·11, that is, that

$$y_2 - y_1 = m(x_2 - x_1),$$

and let us show that the point $P_2(x_2, y_2)$ is necessarily on the line *l*. If $x_2 = x_1$, then $y_2 = y_1$, and P_2 coincides with P_1, which is on *l*. If $x_2 \neq x_1$, we can solve the preceding equation for m and obtain

$$m = \frac{y_2 - y_1}{x_2 - x_1}.$$

Now m is given as the slope of *l*, and 2·4 shows that

$$\frac{y_2 - y_1}{x_2 - x_1}$$

is the slope of the line on P_2 and P_1. Thus these two lines have the same slope and also have the point P_1 in common. Hence they coincide, and $P_2(x_2, y_2)$ is on *l*, as required. This completes the proof that 2·11 is the equation of *l*.

The equation 2·11 is usually called the **point-slope form** of the equation of a line. It furnishes a convenient means of writing the equation of a line if one knows a point on the line and is given, or can find from what is given, the slope of the line.

Example 6

Find the equation of the line on the points $(-1, 2)$ and $(3, 4)$.

Solution: By 2·4, we find the slope of the line to be $1/2$. Now using 2·11 with $m = 1/2$ and taking (x_1, y_1) to be the point $(-1, 2)$, we find the desired equation

$$y - 2 = \frac{1}{2}(x + 1),$$

which upon simplification becomes

$$x - 2y + 5 = 0.$$

As a check, one can now substitute the coordinates of both the given points and verify that they satisfy the equation. The reader may verify that if (x_1, y_1) is taken as the other given point $(3, 4)$ the same equation is obtained.

16. THE SLOPE-INTERCEPT FORM

A special case of the point-slope form of the equation of a line is frequently useful. Let *l* be a line which is not parallel to the *y*-axis, as in Figure 37, and hence l has a slope m.   Now l will intersect the y-axis at a point with coordinates $(0, b)$; it is customary to call b the **y-intercept** of the line l. (In like manner, if l intersects the x-axis at the point $(a, 0)$, a is called the

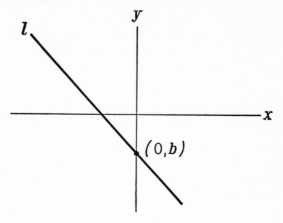

Figure 37

x-intercept of l.)   Since we know that the point $(0, b)$ is on l and that l has slope m, we can use 2·11 to find at once that the equation of l is

$$y - b = m(x - 0),$$

or

2·12 $y = mx + b.$

This is usually called the **slope-intercept form** of the equation of a line.   The word *intercept* here refers to the y-intercept.

Consider again the line whose equation was found above to be

$$x - 2y + 5 = 0.$$

If we solve this equation for y, we obtain

2·13 $y = \dfrac{1}{2}x + \dfrac{5}{2}.$

It is clear that this equation is of the form 2·12 with $m = 1/2$ and $b = 5/2$; in other words, 2·13 is the slope-intercept form of the equation of this line.

If one has a given line segment, for example, the side of a triangle, it is sometimes convenient to refer to the equation of the line on which the segment lies as the equation of the line segment.

Example 7

In the triangle with vertices $A(2, 0)$, $B(-1, 6)$, and $C(4, 10)$, find the equation of the altitude from A.

Solution: The triangle is drawn in Figure 38.   By 2·4, the slope of side *BC* is found to be 4/5.   Now the altitude from *A* is the line *l* on *A* perpendicular to the line on *B* and *C*.   Thus the slope of *l* is −5/4, by 2·5.

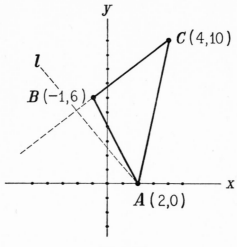

Figure 38

The point-slope form of the equation of a line, Equation 2·11, gives the equation of *l* as

$$y - 0 = -\frac{5}{4}(x - 2),$$

which simplifies to

$$5x + 4y - 10 = 0.$$

EXERCISES

Find the equation of each of the following lines:

1. On $(-1, 2)$ and $(4, 3)$.

2. On $(1, -2)$ and $(-3, 1)$.

3. With slope 3/2 and y-intercept -5.

4. On $(2, -4)$ with slope $-2/3$.

5. With x-intercept a and slope m.

6. With x-intercept 3 and y-intercept -4.

7. On $(-2, 3)$ and with an inclination of 135°.

8. On $(3, 1)$ and $(3, 4)$.

9. With x-intercept a and y-intercept b.

10. With x-intercept 4 and no y-intercept.

11. On $(1, 3)$ and rising 3 units for each unit increase in x.

12. On $(-1, 2)$ and falling 2 units for each unit increase in x.

13. On $(2, -1)$ and $(-4, -1)$.

14. On $(4, 4)$ and with an inclination of $60°$.

15. On $(1/2, -1/3)$ and with slope $3/5$.

16. Parallel to the y-axis and 2 units to the left of it.

In each of Exercises 17–22 the three given points are the vertices of a triangle. Find the equations of the three sides, of the three medians, of the three altitudes, and of the three perpendicular bisectors of the sides.

17. $A(-3, 1)$, $B(0, 5)$, $C(3, -1)$.   18. $A(2, 0)$, $B(-4, 2)$, $C(-2, -6)$.

19. $A(6, 2)$, $B(1, -1)$, $C(6, -5)$.   20. $A(1, 1)$, $B(5, 4)$, $C(8, 0)$.

21. $A(-4, -2)$, $B(1, 4)$, $C(5, -2)$.   22. $A(3/2, 2)$, $B(5, 0)$, $C(3, -1/2)$.

23. Find the equation of the line l on the origin such that the angle from l to the line on $(-3, 1)$ and $(4, 2)$ has measure $135°$.

24. Find the equation of the line l on the point $(-1, 2)$ such that the angle from l to the line on $(3, 2)$ and $(-1, 4)$ has measure $45°$.

17. EQUATIONS OF THE FIRST DEGREE

An equation of the form

2·14 $$Ax + By + C = 0,$$

where A, B, and C are given real numbers with A and B *not both zero*, is called an **equation of the first degree.** We shall now prove the following result.

2·15 Theorem

Every line has an equation of the first degree and, conversely, every equation of the first degree is the equation of some line.

Proof: The results of the preceding section show that any line not parallel to the y-axis has an equation of the form $y = mx + b$, or, if we prefer,

$$mx - y + b = 0;$$

hence its equation is of the first degree. Furthermore, a line parallel to the y-axis has an equation of the form

$$x - c = 0,$$

which again is an equation of the first degree. We have therefore proved the first part of the theorem, namely, that every line has an equation of the first degree.

To prove the second part of the theorem we need to show that any equation

$$Ax + By + C = 0$$

of the first degree is the equation of a line. If $B \neq 0$, we can write the equation in the form

$$y = -\frac{A}{B}x - \frac{C}{B},$$

and by a comparison with 2·12 we recognize this as the slope-intercept form of the equation of a line with slope $-A/B$ and y-intercept $-C/B$. If $B = 0$, then $A \neq 0$, since we have assumed that A and B are not both zero, and we can write the equation in the form

$$x = -\frac{C}{A}.$$

We recognize that this is the equation of a line parallel to the y-axis. This completes the proof of the theorem.

The proof of this theorem brought out the following important fact. If

$$Ax + By + C = 0$$

is the equation of a line, and $B \neq 0$, then *the slope of the line is* $-A/B$. This fact is of frequent application and should be kept in mind. In a numerical case, instead of using this formula, it is perhaps as convenient to write the equation in slope-intercept form; the coefficient of x is then the slope of the line.

In view of 2·15, an equation of the first degree is often called a *linear equation*. Also, as a matter of terminology, it is sometimes convenient to refer to the line with equation $Ax + By + C = 0$ simply as the *line* $Ax + By + C = 0$.

Several different points will be illustrated by the following example.

Example 8

(1) Draw the line $2x - y + 7 = 0$. (2) What is the slope of this line? (3) Are the following points on this line: $(20, 46)$, $(-10, -13)$?

Solution: (1) As a simple way of drawing the line, let us find two points on the line. Frequently, the x- and y-intercepts are most convenient to use. To find the x-intercept, let $y = 0$ in the given equation and find $x = -7/2$; therefore the x-intercept is $-7/2$. Similarly, let $x = 0$ and find that the y-intercept is 7. The line on the points $(-7/2, 0)$ and $(0, 7)$, sketched in Figure 39, is the desired line. Of course, we may find as many other points as we wish.   For example, if we let $x = 1$ in the given equation, we find $y = 9$; therefore $(1, 9)$ must also be on the line.

(2) By solving for y, we find that the slope-intercept form of the equation is

$$y = 2x + 7;$$

hence the slope is 2.

(3) By 2·10, the point $(20, 46)$ is on the line if and only if the coor-

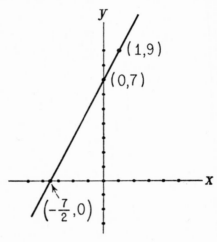

Figure 39

dinates of this point satisfy the equation of the line.   A simple calculation shows that

$$2 \cdot 20 - 46 + 7 \neq 0,$$

and therefore this point is not on the line.   Since

$$2(-10) - (-13) + 7 = 0,$$

the point $(-10, -13)$ *is* on the line.

EXERCISES

For each of the lines of Exercises 1–10, find the intercepts, draw the line, write the equation in slope-intercept form, and determine the slope.

1. $2x + 5y + 3 = 0.$
2. $x - 3y + 7 = 0.$
3. $x + y + 1 = 0.$
4. $-2x + y + 2 = 0.$
5. $x - y + 12 = 0.$
6. $10x + y - 5 = 0.$
7. $5x + 2y = 0.$
8. $3x - y + 4 = 0.$
9. $x + 4y - 2 = 0.$
10. $4x + 2y - 1 = 0.$

In each of Exercises 11–16, find the equations of the lines on the given point that are respectively parallel and perpendicular to the given line.

11. $(-3, 2)$, $3x - 7y + 4 = 0$.   12. $(0, 1)$, $-x + 4y - 6 = 0$.

13. $(3, -2)$, $2x + 5 = 0$.   14. $(1, 2)$, $x - 2y + 6 = 0$.

15. $(-2, 3)$, $5x + y + 1 = 0$.   16. $(0, 1)$, $-7x + 2y - 3 = 0$.

17. If l is a line with equation $Ax + By + C = 0$, show that the equation of the line on the point $P(x_1, y_1)$ parallel to l is $Ax + By = Ax_1 + By_1$.

18. If l is a line with equation $Ax + By + C = 0$, show that the equation of the line on the point $P(x_1, y_1)$ perpendicular to l is $Bx - Ay = Bx_1 - Ay_1$.

19. Work Exercises 11–16 using the results of Exercises 17 and 18.

20. Find the angle from the line with equation $2x + y - 4 = 0$ to the line with equation $y - 2x + 5 = 0$.

21. Find the angle from the line with equation $2x - 5y + 1 = 0$ to the line with equation $3x + y - 7 = 0$.

22. If lines k and l have the respective equations $Ax + By + C = 0$ and $Dx + Ey + F = 0$, show that the angle θ from k to l satisfies the equation

$$\tan \theta = \frac{AE - BD}{AD + BE}.$$

18.   INEQUALITIES OF THE FIRST DEGREE

It is clear that a line divides the plane in which it lies into two regions such that every point of the plane not on the line lies in one of these regions. Thus, if a line is not parallel to the y-axis, every point of the plane not on the line is either above the line or below the line.   We know that the points *on* the line are characterized by the fact that their coordinates satisfy the equation of the line.   The next theorem will show how to characterize the points above (or below) the line in terms of an *inequality* satisfied by their coordinates.

2·16   Theorem

Let l denote the line with equation

$$Ax + By + C = 0,$$

with $B > 0$.

   (1)   *If $P(x_1, y_1)$ is a point which is above the line l, then*

$$Ax_1 + By_1 + C > 0.$$

   (2)   *If $P(x_1, y_1)$ is a point which is below the line l, then*

$$Ax_1 + By_1 + C < 0.$$

Proof: On $P(x_1, y_1)$ draw a line k parallel to the y-axis intersecting the line l in the point R (Figure 40). Now the x-coordinate of R is the same as the x-coordinate of P, namely, x_1. Let us denote the y-coordinate of R by y_2 so that R is the point (x_1, y_2). To prove part (1) of the theorem, let us take the point P *above* l, so that $y_1 > y_2$. Now it is given that $B > 0$, and hence

$$By_1 > By_2.$$

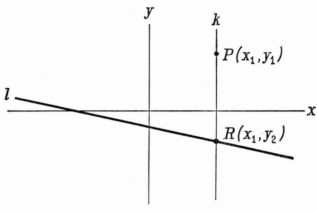

Figure 40

Let us add $Ax_1 + C$ to both sides of this inequality, thus obtaining

$$Ax_1 + By_1 + C > Ax_1 + By_2 + C.$$

Since the point $R(x_1, y_2)$ is *on* the line l, its coordinates must satisfy the equation of l; that is,

$$Ax_1 + By_2 + C = 0.$$

From the preceding inequality we therefore conclude that

$$Ax_1 + By_1 + C > 0,$$

and the proof of part (1) is completed.

If the point $P(x_1, y_1)$ is below the line l, then $y_1 < y_2$. The proof of part (2) then follows by a simple modification of the above argument, and we omit the details.

The converses of 2·16 (1) and (2) are easily seen to be true, and we state them in the following theorem.

2·17   Theorem

Let l denote the line with equation

$$Ax + By + C = 0,$$

with B > 0.

(1) *If x_1 and y_1 are real numbers such that*

$$Ax_1 + By_1 + C > 0,$$

then the point $P(x_1, y_1)$ is above the line l.
   (2) *If x_1 and y_1 are real numbers such that*

$$Ax_1 + By_1 + C < 0,$$

then the point $P(x_1, y_1)$ is below the line l.

Proof: To prove part (1) it is only necessary to observe that if $Ax_1 + By_1 + C > 0$, then $P(x_1, y_1)$ cannot be on the line l (why?), and by 2·16 (2) it cannot be below l; hence it must be above l. Part (2) is proved in a similar way.

It may be emphasized that 2·16 and 2·17 can be used only after the equation of the given line has been put in the form $Ax + By + C = 0$ with $B > 0$. Of course, this is impossible in case $B = 0$, but then the line l would be parallel to the y-axis and it is nonsense to talk about a point being above or below l. (See Exercise 13 on page 50.)

Example 9

Find whether each of the points $(10, 18)$, $(-12, -14)$, $(50, 80)$, and $(-100, -152)$ is above or below the line l whose equation is

$$3x - 2y + 7 = 0.$$

Solution: In order to use 2·17, which requires that B be positive, we write the equation of l in the form

$$-3x + 2y - 7 = 0.$$

It is easy to verify that

$$-3(10) + 2(18) - 7 = -1,$$

and since $-1 < 0$, 2·17 (2) states that the point $(10, 18)$ is *below* the line l.
   Similarly, we find

$$-3(-12) + 2(-14) - 7 = 1,$$
$$-3(50) + 2(80) - 7 = 3,$$
$$-3(-100) + 2(-152) - 7 = -11.$$

Thus the points $(-12, -14)$ and $(50, 80)$ are *above* the line l, and the point $(-100, -152)$ is *below* l.

EXERCISES

In each of Exercises 1–10, determine whether each of the specified points is above or below the given line.

1. $3x + 11y - 44 = 0$; $(10, 1)$, $(-4, 6)$, $(5, 3)$.

2. $x - 4y + 5 = 0$; $(14, 5)$, $(-32, -7)$, $(-39, -8)$.

3. $10x - 12y + 17 = 0$; $(5, 5)$, $(-20, -15)$, $(100, 84)$.

4. $5x + 14y - 11 = 0$; $(11, -3)$, $(-4, 2)$, $(20, -7)$.

5. $150x + 23y - 147 = 0$; $(2, -6)$, $(-3, 24)$, $(10, -54)$.

6. $14x - y + 40 = 0$; $(6, 43)$, $(-2, 13)$, $(-5, -29)$.

7. $x + 2y - 12 = 0$; $(7, 3)$, $(14, -1)$, $(-8, 11)$.

8. $29x - 17y + 31 = 0$; $(0, 2)$, $(-3, -3)$, $(20, 30)$.

9. $112x - 25y + 1 = 0$; $(1, 5)$, $(3, 13)$, $(-5, -4)$.

10. $3x + 5y - 113 = 0$; $(20, 10)$, $(50, -6)$, $(-100, 81)$.

11. Show that the point $(101, 50)$ lies between the parallel lines

$$x - 2y + 1 = 0,$$
$$2x - 4y - 3 = 0.$$

12. If r and s are any positive real numbers, show that the line with equation

$$3x - 4y + \frac{7r + 15s}{r + s} = 0$$

lies between the parallel lines with equations $3x - 4y + 7 = 0$ and $3x - 4y + 15 = 0$.

13. Let l denote the line with equation $Ax + C = 0$, with $A > 0$. Show that if $P(x_1, y_1)$ is a point which is to the right of l, then $Ax_1 + C > 0$, whereas if $P(x_1, y_1)$ is to the left of l, then $Ax_1 + C < 0$.

14. Write out the proof of Theorem 2·16 (2).

19.   POINT OF INTERSECTION

A problem of frequent occurrence is that of finding the coordinates of the point of intersection of two nonparallel lines with known equations. By Definition 2·10 of the equation of a line, the point of intersection will be characterized by the fact that its coordinates satisfy each of the equations of the given lines. The problem of determining the point of intersection is therefore simply that of solving the two equations simultaneously.

Example 10

Find the point of intersection of the lines $x - 2y + 1 = 0$ and $2x + 3y - 7 = 0$.

Solution: If we multiply the first equation by 2 and subtract its members from those of the second equation, we get $7y - 9 = 0$, or $y = 9/7$. Now, substituting this value of y in either of the given equations, we find $x = 11/7$. Hence $(11/7, 9/7)$ is the point of intersection.

EXERCISES

Find the point of intersection of each of the following pairs of lines:

1. $2x - y + 1 = 0,$
   $x + y - 4 = 0.$

2. $x - 4y + 2 = 0,$
   $2x + y - 1 = 0.$

3. $x + y - 3 = 0,$
   $5x + 2y - 12 = 0.$

4. $3x + 2y + 6 = 0,$
   $5x - 3y - 4 = 0.$

5. $x - y + 1 = 0,$
   $7x + 2y - 1 = 0.$

6. $3x - 2y + 4 = 0,$
   $2x + y - 3 = 0.$

7. In the triangle with vertices $A(-1, 1)$, $B(5, 2)$, and $C(3, -1)$, find the equations of the perpendicular bisectors of the three sides and show that these three lines meet on a point. Verify that this point is equidistant from the three vertices, and hence is the center of the circumscribed circle.

8. In the triangle of the preceding exercise, find the equations of the three altitudes and then show that the altitudes meet on a point.

In each of Exercises 9–14, find the vertices of the triangle whose sides have the given equations.

9. $x - 5y + 11 = 0, 8x + 3y + 2 = 0, 9x - 2y - 30 = 0.$

10. $2x - 7y + 11 = 0, 9x - 2y - 39 = 0, 7x + 5y + 9 = 0.$

11. $6x + 26y - 63 = 0, 28x + 15y + 25 = 0, 19x - 24y - 40 = 0.$

12. $x + 3y - 4 = 0, 2x - 2y + 5 = 0, 5x - y + 9 = 0.$

13. $4x + 14y - 27 = 0, x - 2y - 4 = 0, 8x + 6y + 1 = 0.$

14. $7x - 2y + 3 = 0, x - 4y + 9 = 0, 3x - y + 11 = 0.$

15. The vertices of a parallelogram are $A(-2, 1)$, $B(6, 11)$, $C(12, 9)$, and $D(4, -1)$. Find the point of intersection of the diagonal BD with the line on A and the midpoint of side CD. Verify that this point of intersection is a point of trisection of the diagonal BD.

16. Find the projection of the point $(0, -4/3)$ on each of the sides (extended if necessary) of the triangle with vertices $A(-2, 0)$, $B(4, 0)$, and $C(0, 6)$. Show that these three points lie on a line.

20. DISTANCE OF A POINT FROM A LINE

If l is a given line (Figure 41) and P is a given point, let us denote by Q the projection of P on l. By the *distance of the point P from the line l* we shall mean $|PQ|$; in other words, the distance is to be measured along a perpendicular to the line l. We shall now prove the following theorem which furnishes a convenient means of determining the distance of a point from a line.

2·18   Theorem

The distance d of the point $P(x_1, y_1)$ from the line l with equation

2·19
$$Ax + By + C = 0$$

is given by the formula

$$d = \frac{|Ax_1 + By_1 + C|}{\sqrt{A^2 + B^2}}.$$

Proof: The method of proof consists in finding the equation of the line k on $P(x_1, y_1)$ which is perpendicular to l, and then solving this equation simultaneously with the equation of the line l in order to find the coor-

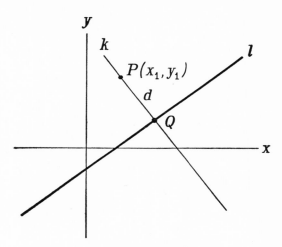

Figure 41

dinates of Q (Figure 41).   The familiar formula for the distance between two points then gives the desired result.   We shall now carry out these calculations in some detail.

If l is not parallel to a coordinate axis, its slope is $-A/B$, and the slope of k is therefore B/A.   Hence k has as its equation

$$y - y_1 = \frac{B}{A} (x - x_1),$$

which becomes upon simplification

2·20
$$Bx - Ay + Ay_1 - Bx_1 = 0.$$

It is left for the reader to verify that 2·20 is the equation of k even if l is parallel to a coordinate axis.

To find the coordinates of Q, we shall solve Equations 2·19 and 2·20 simultaneously. If, throughout, we multiply 2·19 by B and 2·20 by A and subtract corresponding members, we obtain

$$(A^2 + B^2)y + BC - A^2y_1 + ABx_1 = 0,$$

from which it follows that

2·21
$$y = \frac{A^2y_1 - ABx_1 - BC}{A^2 + B^2}.$$

Similarly, if, throughout, we multiply 2·19 by A and 2·20 by B and add corresponding members, we obtain

2·22
$$x = \frac{B^2x_1 - ABy_1 - AC}{A^2 + B^2}.$$

The coordinates of Q are therefore given by 2·21 and 2·22, so that the distance d between the points P and Q may be found by the usual distance formula as follows:

$$
\begin{aligned}
d^2 &= \left[\frac{B^2x_1 - ABy_1 - AC}{A^2 + B^2} - x_1\right]^2 + \left[\frac{A^2y_1 - ABx_1 - BC}{A^2 + B^2} - y_1\right]^2 \\
&= \left[\frac{A(Ax_1 + By_1 + C)}{A^2 + B^2}\right]^2 + \left[\frac{B(Ax_1 + By_1 + C)}{A^2 + B^2}\right]^2 \\
&= (A^2 + B^2)\left[\frac{Ax_1 + By_1 + C}{A^2 + B^2}\right]^2 = \frac{(Ax_1 + By_1 + C)^2}{A^2 + B^2}.
\end{aligned}
$$

It follows at once that d is the positive square root of this last expression and hence is merely

$$\frac{|Ax_1 + By_1 + C|}{\sqrt{A^2 + B^2}}.$$

The proof of the theorem is therefore completed.

Example 11

Find the distance of the point $(-3, -2)$ from the line $4x - 5y - 7 = 0$.

Solution: We apply the theorem just proved, using $P(x_1, y_1)$ as the point $(-3, -2)$, and identifying the equation $Ax + By + C = 0$ with the equation $4x - 5y - 7 = 0$. This gives

$$d = \frac{|4(-3) - 5(-2) - 7|}{\sqrt{4^2 + (-5)^2}} = \frac{|-9|}{\sqrt{41}},$$

or

$$d = \frac{9\sqrt{41}}{41}.$$

EXERCISES

In each of Exercises 1–10, find the distance of the given point from the given line.

1. $3x - 4y - 7 = 0$, $(-1, 2)$.   2. $2x + 5 = 0$, $(3, -2)$.

3. $2x - 3y - 11 = 0$, $(0, 1)$.   4. $-x + 2y - 3 = 0$, $(1, -3)$.

5. $12x - 5y + 4 = 0$, $(0, 2)$.   6. $x + y - 1 = 0$, $(-3, 5)$.

7. $4x + 3y - 5 = 0$, $(-3, 7)$.   8. $x - 3y + 5 = 0$, $(3, -4)$.

9. $2y - 3 = 0$, $(7, -6)$.   10. $6x - 8y + 3 = 0$, $(1/2, -3/2)$.

11. Use 2·18 to find the length of the altitude from B in the triangle with vertices $A(-1, 1)$, $B(5, 2)$, and $C(3, -1)$; then find the area of the triangle.

12. Find the area of the triangle with vertices $A(-2, 1)$, $B(3, 3)$, and $C(0, -2)$.

13. Find the area of the triangle with vertices $A(-2, 1)$, $B(1, 7)$, and $C(5, 2)$.

14. Find the area of the triangle with vertices $A(5, -2)$, $B(0, -7)$, and $C(1, 9)$.

15. Find the area of the triangle with vertices $A(-4, -1)$, $B(-1, 5)$, and $C(4, -3)$.

16. Find the distance between the parallel lines
$$5x - 12y + 2 = 0,$$
$$5x - 12y - 7 = 0.$$

17. Find the distance between the parallel lines
$$4x + 3y - 7 = 0,$$
$$8x + 6y - 5 = 0.$$

18. Find the distance between the parallel lines
$$x - 2y + 11 = 0,$$
$$-x + 2y - 13 = 0.$$

19. The distance of the point $(5, -2)$ from the line l is 4, and l is parallel to the line with equation $3x - 4y + 7 = 0$. Find the equation of the line l (two answers).

20. In the arbitrary triangle with vertices $P_1(x_1, y_1)$, $P_2(x_2, y_2)$, and $P_3(x_3, y_3)$, find the length of the altitude from P_2 by 2·18 and then show that the area of the triangle is equal to the absolute value of
$$\frac{1}{2}[(x_3 - x_1)(y_2 - y_1) - (x_2 - x_1)(y_3 - y_1)].$$

21. NORMAL FORM OF EQUATION OF A LINE (OPTIONAL)

In this section we give an alternate approach to the problem of finding the distance of a point from a line. The method is based on another form of the equation of a line, called the *normal form* of the equation. The word "normal" is here used in the sense of "perpendicular."

Let l be an arbitrary line, let k be the line on the origin perpendicular to l, and let N be the point of intersection of k and l. If α is the inclination of k, we shall consider k to be a directed line having the direction from O along the terminal side of angle α in standard position,* as in Figures 42 and 43. We set $p = \overline{ON}$, and observe that p is positive if the

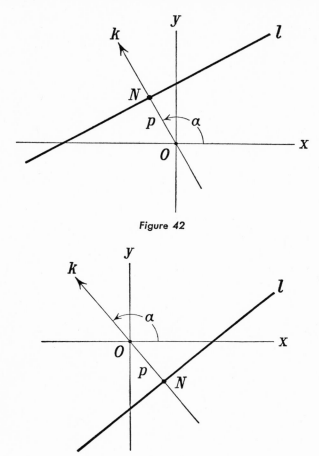

Figure 42

Figure 43

origin is below line l (Figure 42), and that p is negative if the origin is above line l (Figure 43).

We now proceed to find the equation of line l in terms of α and p. Since k has slope $\tan \alpha$ and l is perpendicular to k, it follows by 2·5 that l

---

* In view of the definition (2·2) of the inclination of a line, the above statement is equivalent to saying that if k does not coincide with the x-axis, k is directed upward; whereas if k coincides with the x-axis, it is directed to the right.

has slope $-\cot\alpha$. The next step in finding the equation of l is to show that the point N on l has coordinates $(p\cos\alpha, p\sin\alpha)$. In the case illustrated in Figure 42, this result follows at once from the definitions of the trigonometric functions, since N is a point on the terminal side of angle α in standard position. In the case illustrated in Figure 43, we observe that N is a point on the terminal side of angle $180° + \alpha$ in standard position, and hence N has coordinates $(|ON|\cos(180° + \alpha), |ON|$ $\sin(180° + \alpha))$. However, $\cos(180° + \alpha) = -\cos\alpha$, $\sin(180° + \alpha) = -\sin\alpha$, and in this case $p = -|ON|$; hence again N has coordinates $(p\cos\alpha, p\sin\alpha)$. Also, if l happens to pass through the origin, N coincides with O and $p = 0$; so in every possible case N has coordinates $(p\cos\alpha, p\sin\alpha)$.

Since we now know the slope of l and the coordinates of a point on l, we can use 2·11 and find its equation to be

$$y - p\sin\alpha = -\cot\alpha(x - p\cos\alpha).$$

If we replace $\cot\alpha$ by $\cos\alpha/\sin\alpha$ and use the identity $\sin^2\alpha + \cos^2\alpha = 1$, this reduces to

2·23
$$x\cos\alpha + y\sin\alpha - p = 0.$$

This is the **normal form** of the equation of the line l.

Next, we indicate how one can easily find the normal form of the equation of a line l whose equation is already known in some other form. Suppose that l has the equation

2·24
$$Ax + By + C = 0.$$

Then if s is any nonzero real number, l also has the equation

2·25
$$sAx + sBy + sC = 0,$$

and we proceed to determine s so that 2·25 will coincide with Equation 2·23. For this to be true we must have

$$sA = \cos\alpha, \qquad sB = \sin\alpha, \qquad sC = -p.$$

Squaring and adding the first two of these equations, we find that

$$s^2(A^2 + B^2) = \sin^2\alpha + \cos^2\alpha = 1;$$

hence

$$s = \frac{1}{\pm\sqrt{A^2 + B^2}}.$$

Moreover, since $0° \leqq \alpha < 180°$, we must have $\sin\alpha \geqq 0$. Hence, if $B \neq 0$, sB must be positive and therefore s must have the same sign as B. If $B = 0$, the line l is parallel to the y-axis (why?) and $\alpha = 0$. Thus Equation 2·23 becomes just $x - p = 0$. Therefore if $B = 0$, Equation 2·24 can be written in normal form simply by dividing by A. We summarize these results as follows. *If* 2·24 *is the equation of a line l, and* $B \neq 0$, *the normal form of the equation of l is*

$$\frac{A}{\pm \sqrt{A^2 + B^2}} x + \frac{B}{\pm \sqrt{A^2 + B^2}} y + \frac{C}{\pm \sqrt{A^2 + B^2}} = 0,$$

with the sign of the radical chosen to be the same as the sign of B. If $B = 0$ in 2·24, *the normal form of the equation of l is*

$$x + \frac{C}{A} = 0.$$

Example 12

A line l has equation $3x - 4y + 6 = 0$. Write this equation in normal form, and determine α and p.

Solution: In this case $A = 3$, $B = -4$, and $C = 6$. Accordingly, we divide by $-\sqrt{9 + 16} = -5$, the negative sign being chosen because B is negative. Thus the normal form of the equation of l is

$$-\frac{3}{5} x + \frac{4}{5} y - \frac{6}{5} = 0.$$

Identifying this with 2·23, we find that $\cos \alpha = -3/5$, $\sin \alpha = 4/5$, and $p = 6/5$. Since $\cos \alpha$ is negative, it is clear that α is a second quadrant angle. From Table I it follows easily that $\alpha = 126° 52'$, approximately. We may remark that since p is positive the origin is below l, as can be easily verified by drawing the figure.

We conclude this section with an application of the normal form of the equation of a line to the problem of finding the distance of a point from a line. Let l be a line whose equation in normal form is Equation 2·23, and let $P(x_1, y_1)$ be a given point. If k is the line on the origin perpendicular to l (Figure 44), we consider all lines parallel to k to have the direction of k. Thus if Q is the projection of P on l, l' is the line on P that is parallel to l, and M is the intersection of l' and k, then $\overline{QP} = \overline{NM}$. We define the distance $\bar{d}$ *from* the line l *to* the point $P(x_1, y_1)$ to be the directed distance $\overline{QP}$, and now prove the following theorem.

2·26 Theorem

Let l be a given line, $P(x_1, y_1)$ be a given point, and $\bar{d}$ be the distance from the line l to the point P. If the normal form of the equation of l is

$$x \cos \alpha + y \sin \alpha - p = 0,$$

then

$$\bar{d} = x_1 \cos \alpha + y_1 \sin \alpha - p.$$

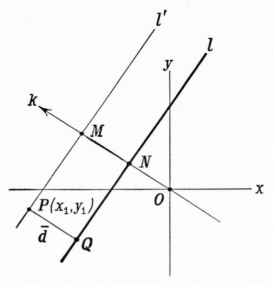

Figure 44

To prove this, we observe that in the notation of Figure 44 the normal form of the equation of line l' is

$$x \cos \alpha + y \sin \alpha - \overline{OM} = 0.$$

Since $P(x_1, y_1)$ is on this line, we must therefore have

$$x_1 \cos \alpha + y_1 \sin \alpha - \overline{OM} = 0.$$

But on the directed line k, $\overline{OM} = \overline{ON} + \overline{NM}$, and thus

$$x_1 \cos \alpha + y_1 \sin \alpha - \overline{ON} = \overline{NM}.$$

However, $\overline{ON} = p$ and $\overline{NM} = \overline{QP} = \bar{d}$; thus

$$\bar{d} = x_1 \cos \alpha + y_1 \sin \alpha - p.$$

The theorem is therefore established.

It may be remarked that $\bar{d}$ is positive or negative depending on whether $P(x_1, y_1)$ is above or below the line l (assuming, of course, that l is not parallel to the y-axis). Thus Theorem 2·26 not only gives the distance of the point from the line but also tells whether the point is above or below the line. Thus the results of this section combine the results of Sections 18 and 20.

EXERCISES

In each of Exercises 1–8, sketch the line and then find the normal form of its equation.

1. $\alpha = 30°,\ p = 4.$

2. $\alpha = 135°,\ p = -2.$

3. $\alpha = 90°,\ p = -5.$

4. $\alpha = 120°,\ p = 7.$

5. $\alpha = 135°,\ p = 1.$

6. $\alpha = 0°,\ p = -10.$

7. $\alpha = 60°,\ p = -3.$

8. $\alpha = 45°,\ p = 0.$

In each of Exercises 9–18, change the equation of the line into normal form and find α and p.

9. $x + y - 3 = 0.$

10. $x - y + 4 = 0.$

11. $3x - 4y + 7 = 0.$

12. $4x + 3y - 5 = 0.$

13. $3y - 2 = 0.$

14. $2x + 3 = 0.$

15. $5x - 12y = 0.$

16. $2x - y + 5 = 0.$

17. $x + \sqrt{3}\,y - 4 = 0.$

18. $\sqrt{3}\,x - y + 7 = 0.$

19. Find the normal form of the equation of the line on the point $(6, 8)$ which is perpendicular to the line joining this point to the origin.

20. Find the equation of the line with inclination $60°$ if the distance from the origin to the line is 6.

21. Find the equation of the line parallel to the line $3x - y + 2 = 0$ and such that the distance from the origin to the line is -2.

22. Find the equations of the lines on the point $(1, -7)$ such that the distance from each line to the origin is 5.

22. APPLICATIONS TO ELEMENTARY GEOMETRY

Many problems of Euclidean geometry can easily be solved by the methods of analytic geometry developed in this chapter.   An important observation is that geometrical properties of figures are not affected by the position of the coordinate axes, and a convenient choice of axes may greatly simplify the calculations.

Example 13

Prove that the altitudes of any triangle meet on a point.

Solution: Let us consider any triangle with vertices A, B, and C.   We now choose coordinate axes in the plane, and a convenient choice is the following: Let the x-axis be chosen as the line on A and B, and the y-axis be chosen on C (Figure 45).   Clearly this choice can be made for any triangle.   The coordinates of the vertices are then of the form $A(a,\ 0)$, $B(b,\ 0)$, and $C(0,\ c)$.   Note that no assumptions are made about the sign or magnitude of the numbers a, b, and c, except the obvious ones that $a \neq b$ and $c \neq 0$.   Now, by our choice of axes it is clear that the altitude of the triangle from C has the equation $x = 0$.   Simple calculations show that the altitude from A is $bx - cy - ab = 0$, and from B is

$ax - cy - ab = 0$. Obviously, the point $(0, -ab/c)$ lies on all three altitudes and hence is their common point of intersection.

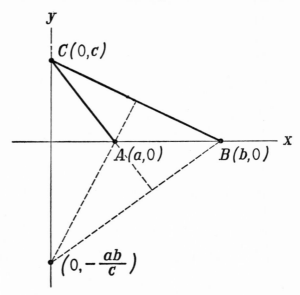

Figure 45

Example 14

Prove that a quadrilateral with diagonals that bisect each other is a parallelogram.

Solution: For the given quadrilateral, designated as $ABCD$, let A be the origin and the line on AB be the x-axis. The coordinates of the vertices are then as indicated in Figure 46. Now $(b/2, c/2)$ is the midpoint

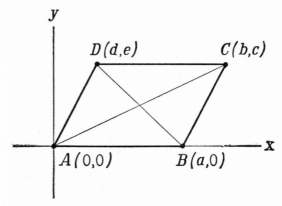

Figure 46

of the diagonal AC, and $((a + d)/2,\ e/2)$ is the midpoint of the diagonal BD. These midpoints must coincide in view of what is given, and thus we must have

$$\frac{b}{2} = \frac{a + d}{2} \quad \text{and} \quad \frac{c}{2} = \frac{e}{2},$$

or

$$b = a + d \quad \text{and} \quad c = e.$$

Since $c = e$, side CD has slope zero and is therefore parallel to side AB. If $d \neq 0$, the slope of side AD is e/d, and the slope of BC is $c/(b - a)$. However, in view of the relationships between the coordinates, it follows that

$$\frac{c}{b - a} = \frac{e}{d},$$

and thus the sides AD and BC are parallel. If $d = 0$, one readily sees that AD and BC are parallel to the y-axis. Thus, in every case, the figure is a parallelogram, and the proof is completed.

EXERCISES

1. Show that by a proper choice of coordinate axes the vertices of any triangle have coordinates $(0, 0)$, $(d, 0)$, and (e, f). Then work through Example 13 above, using this choice of coordinate axes.

2. Prove that an isosceles triangle has two equal medians.

3. Prove that any triangle which has two equal medians is an isosceles triangle.

4. Show that by a proper choice of coordinate axes the vertices of any parallelogram have coordinates of the form $(0, 0)$, $(a, 0)$, (b, c), and $(a + b, c)$.

5. Prove that the diagonals of a parallelogram bisect each other.

6. Prove that the sum of the squares of the lengths of the sides of any parallelogram equals the sum of the squares of the lengths of the diagonals.

7. Prove that the figure obtained by joining in order the midpoints of the sides of any quadrilateral is a parallelogram.

8. Show that the lines joining the midpoints of opposite sides of any quadrilateral intersect at a point which bisects both lines. Show also that this same point bisects the line joining the midpoints of the diagonals of the quadrilateral.

9. Prove that a parallelogram with perpendicular diagonals is a rhombus.

10. Prove that a trapezoid with diagonals of equal length is an isosceles trapezoid.

11. Prove that in a triangle the sum of the squares of the lengths of the medians is three fourths the sum of the squares of the lengths of the sides.

12. Prove that the distance between the midpoints of the nonparallel sides of a trapezoid equals half the sum of the lengths of the parallel sides.

13. The vertices of any parallelogram are A, B, C, and D. Show that the diagonal BD intersects the line on A and the midpoint of side CD at a point of trisection of the diagonal BD.

14. Complete the proof of the following statements. In any triangle the altitudes meet on a point, the medians meet on a point, and the perpendicular bisectors of the sides meet on a point. The three points just described lie on a line.

chapter 3

Equations and Graphs

In the previous chapter, we considered some special equations in x and y, namely, those of the form $Ax + By + C = 0$. This chapter is devoted to a preliminary study of the graphs of more complicated equations in x and y, with special attention to general methods of obtaining some of the salient features of their graphs. Also presented in this chapter is a brief discussion of the equation of a given locus.

23. THE GRAPH OF AN EQUATION

Given the equation

$$y = x^2 - 4,$$

and a point $P(a, b)$ in the coordinate plane, the coordinates (a, b) of P are said to *satisfy* the equation if

$$b = a^2 - 4.$$

Note that the latter equation is obtained from the former by replacing x with a the x-coordinate of P) and y with b (the y-coordinate of P). Thus, for example, the coordinates of $P(3, 5)$ *satisfy* the given equation, since

$$5 = 3^2 - 4.$$

On the other hand, the coordinates of $Q(4, 11)$ *do not satisfy* the given equation, since

$$11 \neq 4^2 - 4.$$

With this example in mind, let us define what is meant by the graph of an equation.

3·1 Definition

*The **graph of an equation** in x and y is the totality of points $P(x, y)$ in the coordinate plane with coordinates which satisfy the equation.*

Thus, in the example above, the point $P(3, 5)$ is on the graph of the given equation, whereas the point $Q(4, 11)$ is not. Many other points on the graph of the equation $y = x^2 - 4$ can be found simply by replacing x by random numbers and solving the resulting equations for y. For example, replacing x by 7 we obtain the equation

$$y = 7^2 - 4 = 45.$$

Consequently, $(7, 45)$ is a point on the graph of this equation. It is apparent that we could never find *all* the points on the graph of this equation, so in this sense it is impossible to determine its graph. However, the graph of this equation can be described geometrically, as will be shown in a later chapter.

One of the important problems of analytic geometry is that of determining the nature of the graph of a given equation. We know from the preceding chapter that the graph of an equation of the first degree is a line. In later chapters, the graph of an equation of the second degree (as in the example above) will be shown to be of a particular type (usually a parabola, hyperbola, ellipse, or circle).

It is frequently convenient to refer to the graph of an equation as a **curve.** Since an equation may be of the first degree, in which case the graph is a line, a line is a special case of a curve as here defined.

24. INTERCEPTS

As we pointed out above, it usually is possible to find any number of isolated points on the graph of a given equation by replacing x (or y) by numbers and solving the resulting equations for y (or x). If, in particular, we replace x by 0 and solve for y, we find all the points on the graph that have x-coordinate equal to 0, that is, all points of the graph on the y-axis. These points are called the **y-intercepts*** of the graph. Similarly, if in the given equation we let $y = 0$ and solve the resulting equation for x, we find the **x-intercepts** of the graph, that is, the points of the graph on the x-axis.

Example 1

Find the x- and y-intercepts of the graph of the equation

$$x^2 = 2x - y.$$

Solution: On replacing x by 0, we obtain the equation

$$0^2 = 2 \cdot 0 - y,$$

---

* In the previous chapter the *y-coordinates* of the points of intersection of the curve with the y-axis were called the y-intercepts. It is sometimes convenient to call the points themselves the y-intercepts. The context will always make it clear which meaning is intended.

which, when solved for y, yields $y = 0$. Thus $P(0, 0)$ is the only y-intercept of the given curve. If we replace y by 0, we get

$$x^2 = 2x - 0.$$

Solving this equation for x as indicated below,

$$x^2 - 2x = 0,$$
$$x(x - 2) = 0,$$

we see that $x = 0$ or $x = 2$. Thus $P(0, 0)$ and $Q(2, 0)$ are the x-intercepts of the curve.

Although we might be able to find the intercepts and many other points on the graph of a given equation, having done so, we might still have only a vague idea of the general nature of the graph we seek. For this reason, we shall now consider some additional methods that may be used to obtain information about the graph of a given equation.

25. EXTENT

One of the general properties of a curve that we shall discuss is the **extent** of a curve. In seeking the extent of a curve, we are first of all looking for the part of the plane in which the curve lies. The curve might be **bounded;** that is, it might be completely contained in some rectangular region of the plane. On the other hand, the curve might not be bounded, but might be completely above some line $y = b$ or completely to the right of some line $x = a$, and so on.

Another feature of a curve that may be associated with the concept of extent is the nature of the curve far away from the origin of the coordinate system. What can be said about the y-coordinates of those points on a given curve with large (positive or negative) x-coordinates? Conversely, what can be said about the x-coordinates of those points with large y-coordinates?

Some examples will now be given to illustrate the concept of extent of a curve, as well as some other concepts related to the graph of an equation.

Example 2

Discuss the graph of the equation

$$y = x^2 - 4.$$

Solution: If we let $y = 0$ in this equation, we obtain

$$x^2 = 4.$$

Thus $x = \pm 2$, and the x-intercepts of the curve are

$$(2, 0) \qquad \text{and} \qquad (-2, 0).$$

The *y*-intercept, found by letting $x = 0$, is easily seen to be $(0, -4)$. These and some other points on the curve, obtained by giving the indicated values to x and solving the resulting equations for y, are listed in the following table.   In other words, by reference to the table, we see

x	-3	$-5/2$	-2	$-3/2$	-1	$-1/2$	0	$1/2$	1	$3/2$	2	$5/2$	3
y	5	$9/4$	0	$-7/4$	-3	$-15/4$	-4	$-15/4$	-3	$-7/4$	0	$9/4$	5

that $(-3, 5)$, $(-5/2, 9/4)$, $(-2, 0)$, and so on, are points on the curve.

Let us now discuss the extent of the curve.   Solving the given equation for x^2, we obtain

$$x^2 = y + 4.$$

If we give y a value less than -4, x^2 will equal a negative number in the resulting equation.   Such an equation has no real solution, and therefore we conclude that no point on the curve has a *y*-coordinate less than -4.   If, for example, $y = -5$, then the resulting equation in x is

$$x^2 = -1.$$

Certainly this equation has no real solution.   Thus the curve is *above* the line $y = -4$.   Evidently the *y*-intercept $(0, -4)$ is the *lowest* point on the curve.

For any $y > -4$, there are two corresponding points on the curve,

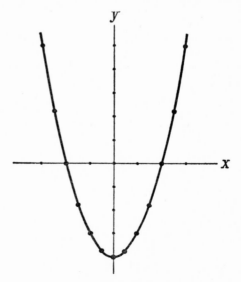

Figure 47

namely, the points with x-coordinates $\pm \sqrt{y+4}$. Moreover, as we give $|x|$ larger and larger values, the corresponding values of y become larger and larger. This fact suggests that the curve rises from the point $(0, -4)$ both to the right and to the left.

Since there is a point on the curve with *any* given x-coordinate, and two points with any given y-coordinate greater than -4, it is evident that the curve is not bounded; that is, no rectangle can be constructed that will completely contain the graph of the given equation.

The facts stated above suggest a graph as sketched in Figure 47. This curve is called a *parabola*. The symmetry of the graph about the y-axis stems from the fact that if a is any real number, the point on the curve with $x = a$ has the same y-coordinate (namely, $a^2 - 4$) as the point with $x = -a$. The concept of symmetry will be discussed in the following section.

Example 3

Discuss the graph of the equation

$$x^2 + y^2 = 4.$$

Solution: The intercepts are easily seen to be $(2, 0)$, $(-2, 0)$, $(0, 2)$, and $(0, -2)$. A few other points on the curve are as follows:

$$(1, \sqrt{3}), \quad (\sqrt{3}, 1), \quad (-1, \sqrt{3}), \quad (1, -\sqrt{3}), \quad (\sqrt{2}, \sqrt{2}), \quad (-\sqrt{2}, \sqrt{2}).$$

If we solve the equation for y, we obtain

$$y = \pm \sqrt{4 - x^2}.$$

Since $4 - x^2$ is a negative number if $|x| > 2$, y is not a real number, and

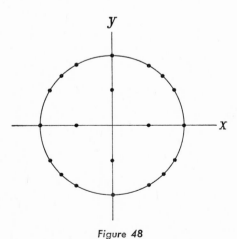

Figure 48

thus there are no points on the curve for $|x| > 2$, that is, for $x > 2$ or $x < -2$. Similarly, solving the equation for x, we find

$$x = \pm \sqrt{4 - y^2},$$

and we see that there are no points on the curve for $y > 2$ or $y < -2$. We conclude that the curve is contained in the rectangle with sides $x = \pm 2$, $y = \pm 2$, and so is bounded.

If we plot the intercepts and other points already found (using 1.7 as an approximation of $\sqrt{3}$), the curve appears to be a circle (Figure 48). As a matter of fact, it *is* the circle with center at the origin and radius 2, for if (a, b) is any point 2 units from the origin, then (by the distance formula)

$$a^2 + b^2 = 4.$$

Thus (a, b) satisfies the equation $x^2 + y^2 = 4$, and (a, b) is therefore on the graph of the equation.   Conversely, any point on the graph must be just 2 units from the origin (why?), and thus the graph is precisely this circle.

Example 4

Discuss the graph of the equation

$$xy = 1.$$

Solution: This equation can not be satisfied for $x = 0$ or $y = 0$; hence its graph has no intercepts.   Corresponding values of x and y must both

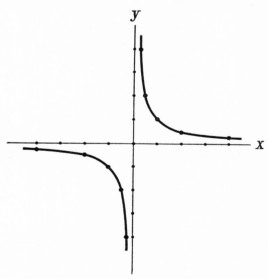

Figure 49

be positive or negative (since their product is positive), and therefore the curve appears in the first and third quadrants only.   If we write the equation in the form $y = 1/x$, it is clear that when $|x|$ is a large number, $|y|$ is a small number, and when $|x|$ is a small number, $|y|$ is a large number. Clearly the curve is not bounded.   Some points on the curve are given in the following table.

x	-100	-4	-2	-1	$-1/2$	$-.01$	$.01$	$1/2$	1	2	4	100
y	$-.01$	$-1/4$	$-1/2$	-1	-2	-100	100	2	1	$1/2$	$1/4$	$.01$

A sketch of the graph is shown in Figure 49. This curve, composed of two branches, is called a *hyperbola*.

Example 5

Discuss the graph of the equation

$$(y + x)(y - x^2 + 4) = 0.$$

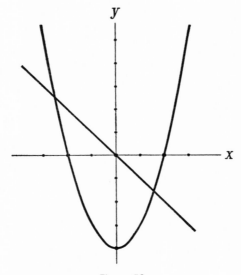

Figure 50

Solution: Since a product of real numbers is zero if and only if one of the factors is zero, the points (x, y) which satisfy this equation are the points which satisfy the equation $y + x = 0$, together with those points which satisfy the equation $y - x^2 + 4 = 0$.   Hence the graph (Figure 50) consists of the line with equation

$$x + y = 0,$$

and the parabola with equation

$$y - x^2 + 4 = 0,$$

already discussed in Example 2.

26. SYMMETRY

Let l be a given line and P a given point.   The point P' which is so located that l is the perpendicular bisector of the segment PP' is called the **image**

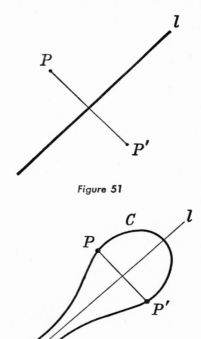

Figure 51

Figure 52

of the point P in the line l (Figure 51).   It is clear that if P' is the image of P in the line l, then P is the image of P' in the line l.

Now let C be a given curve and l a line in the plane of the curve. The curve C is said to be **symmetric** *with respect to the line l* if the image P' in the line l of *every* point P on C is also a point on C (Figure 52).

We are particularly interested in determining when the graph of a given equation is symmetric with respect to a coordinate axis.   Observe, first of all, that if $P(x, y)$ is a point in the coordinate plane, the *image of P in the y-axis* is the point P' $(-x, y)$, and the *image of P in the x-axis* is the point P'' $(x, -y)$. (See Figure 53.)

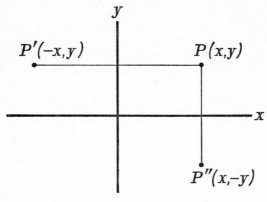

Figure 53

In Example 2, we saw that if $(a, a^2 - 4)$ is any point on the curve, then the point $(-a, a^2 - 4)$ also is on the curve. Since these points are images of each other in the y-axis, we conclude that the curve is symmetric with respect to the y-axis.

The graph of a given equation is symmetric with respect to the y-axis if whenever the point (x, y) is on the graph, the point $(-x, y)$ is also on the graph. Stated in another way, whenever (x, y) satisfies the given equation, $(-x, y)$ must also satisfy it. Thus, if in the given equation we replace x by $-x$ and if the resulting equation is the same as the given one (that is, if the new equation has the same graph as the given one), then the graph of the given equation is symmetric with respect to the y-axis. Similar observations can be made regarding symmetry relative to the x-axis. The symmetry tests are summarized below.

3·2 Symmetry Test (*x*-axis)

A curve is symmetric with respect to the x-axis if the equation of the curve is unchanged when y is replaced by $-y$.

3·3 Symmetry Test (*y*-axis)

A curve is symmetric with respect to the y-axis if the equation of the curve is unchanged when x is replaced by $-x$.

A curve will be *symmetric with respect to the y-axis if its equation involves x to even powers only*, since then the equation is obviously unchanged if x is replaced by $-x$. Similarly, a curve will be *symmetric with respect to the x-axis if its equation involves y to even powers only.*

In Example 2 of this chapter, x occurs to even powers only. For this reason, the graph is symmetric with respect to the y-axis.

In Example 3 both x and y occur to even powers only, and therefore the graph is symmetric with respect to both axes.

So far we have considered symmetry only with respect to a line, but there is another kind of symmetry which we shall mention briefly. If Q is the midpoint of the segment PP', then P' may be called the **image**

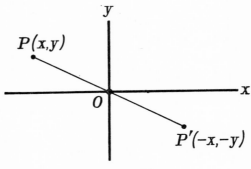

Figure 54

of P in the point Q; likewise, P is the image of P' in the point Q. A curve is said to be **symmetric** *with respect to the point Q* if the image in the point Q of *every* point on the curve is also on the curve. The case of most interest to us is that in which Q is the origin of coordinates. If P has coordinates (x, y), then the image of P in the origin clearly has coordinates $(-x, -y)$. (See Figure 54.) Hence the test for symmetry of a curve with respect to the origin is that $(-x, -y)$ must satisfy the equation of the curve whenever (x, y) does. Thus we arrive at the following conclusion.

3·4 Symmetry Test (Origin)

A curve is symmetric with respect to the origin if the equation of the curve is unchanged when x is replaced by $-x$ and y is replaced by $-y$.

As a simple example, consider the graph of the equation $xy = 1$ (Example 4 above). If in this equation we replace x by $-x$ and y by $-y$, we obtain $(-x)(-y) = 1$ or $xy = 1$, and hence the graph of $xy = 1$ is symmetric with respect to the origin. Thus any line l on the origin O which intersects the curve, intersects it in two points P and P', and

$$|OP| = |OP'|.$$

If a curve is symmetric with respect to both the x-axis and the y-axis, one may readily see that it is symmetric with respect to the origin. However, the converse need not be true, as is illustrated by Example 4.

In sketching the graph of an equation, one may often lessen the work by considering symmetry.

Example 6

Sketch the graph of the equation

$$4x^2 + 9y^2 = 36.$$

Solution: We can apply 3·2 and 3·3 to see that the graph is symmetric with respect to both coordinate axes. Thus the curve can be drawn completely if it can be drawn in the first quadrant. The points given in the following table are on the graph. We plot these points, and make a

x	0	1	2	$\dfrac{3\sqrt{3}}{2}$	3
y	2	$\dfrac{4\sqrt{2}}{3}$	$\dfrac{2\sqrt{5}}{3}$	1	0

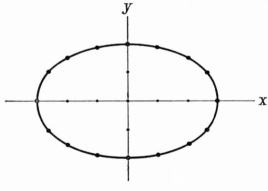

Figure 55

plausible sketch of the curve in the first quadrant. Then, by symmetry, we sketch the curve in the other quadrants, as in Figure 55. This curve is called an *ellipse*. It is easy to verify that this curve is bounded, since it lies entirely within the rectangle $x = \pm 3$, $y = \pm 2$.

EXERCISES

In each of Exercises 1–6, determine which of the given points are on the curve with the given equation.

1. $(0, 1)$, $(-2, -11)$, $(4, 48)$, $(-1, 4)$; $y - 3x^2 - 1 = 0$.

2. $(1, 1)$, $(-3, 1/3)$, $(0, 1/2)$, $(9, 5/9)$; $2xy - 1 = x$.

3. $(1, 2)$, $(0, \sqrt{2})$, $(\sqrt{2}, 0)$, $(-7, -1)$; $5x - x^2 = 3xy - y^2 + 2$.

4. $(1, -2)$, $(-1, 1)$, $(-1.8, 3)$, $(1/8, -1/2)$; $y^2 + 2xy - x = 0$.

5. $(0, 1)$, $(-2, 3)$, $(2\sqrt{14}/3, 8)$, $(2, 5)$; $x^2 + x^2 y + y = y^2$.

6. $(\sqrt[3]{3}, 0)$, $(2, -1)$, $(1, 1)$, $(-2, -3)$; $y^3 + 3 = x^3 + 3xy$.

7. Determine k so that the point $(1, 4)$ shall lie on the curve with equation $2y = x^2 + k$.

8. Determine k so that the point $(2, -3)$ shall lie on the curve with equation $3x^2 + ky^2 = 30$.

9. Determine A and B so that both the points $(-1, 4)$ and $(2, -7)$ shall lie on the curve with equation $Ax^2 + By^2 = 1$.

10. Determine A and B so that both the points $(1, -1)$ and $(-2, 3)$ shall lie on the curve with equation $x^3 + Axy = By^2 + 5$.

11. Find the image of each of the following points in the x-axis; in the y-axis; in the origin: $(-1, 4)$, $(-3, -7)$, $(2, 4)$, $(1, -3)$.

12. Find the image of the point $(1, 5)$ in each of the following lines: $x = 0$, $y = 0$, $x = 3$, $y = 2$, $x = y$.

13. Find the image of the point $(-3, 9)$ in each of the following lines: $x = 0$, $y = 0$, $x = -5$, $y = 8$, $y = -x$.

14. Find the image of the point $(4, 7)$ in each of the following points: $(0, 0)$, $(4, 2)$, $(3, 7)$, $(-1, 1)$, $(7, -1)$.

15. Find the image of the point $(-2, 5)$ in each of the following points: $(0, 0)$, $(1, 5)$, $(-2, 1)$, $(1, -7)$, $(-3, -1)$.

16. Find the image of the point $(-1, -2)$ in each of the following points: $(0, 0)$, $(2, -2)$, $(-1, 3)$, $(1, 4)$, $(5, -1)$.

In each of Exercises 17–30, discuss the symmetry of the curve with the given equation.

17. $4x^2 + 9y = 0$.

18. $y = (x - 1)^2$.

19. $y = 7x^3$.

20. $3x^2 + 4y^2 = 1$.

21. $x^2 - xy^2 = 1 - x$.

22. $3x^2 - y^2 = y - x^4$.

23. $y^2 = 3 - xy + x^2$.

24. $xy - x^3 = 4xy^2$.

25. $3 - x^2 + y^2 = x^2 y^2$.

26. $2x^2 + 4y^2 + xy = 4$.

27. $x^3 - x = y^3 - y + 1$.

28. $x^2 + 2xy + 3y^2 = 4 + x^2 y^2$.

29. $x^2 + y^2 + x^2 y^2 = 16x^4$.

30. $x + y = 3x^2 y$.

In each of Exercises 31–50, discuss the intercepts, extent, and symmetry of the curve with the given equation, and sketch its graph.

31. $y = x^2$.

32. $y = 1 - x^2$.

33. $x^2 + y^2 = 9$.

34. $xy = 4$.

35. $y = x^3$.

36. $y = 4 - x^3$.

37. $y = 1/(x - 1)$.

38. $y^2 - x^2 = 0$.

39. $xy - x^3 = 0$.

40. $x^2y + y^3 - 9y = 0$.

41. $x^2 + 4y^2 = 36$.

42. $y = -4x^2$.

43. $xy + 2x^3 = 0$.

44. $y = x^3 - x$.

45. $xy + 2 = 0$.

46. $3y^2 - 4x^2 = 0$.

47. $y = 4x - x^3$.

48. $y = x^2 - 4x + 3$.

49. $y^2 = x^3 - x$.

50. $y^2 = x^2 + 1$.

51. Prove that the curve with equation $y = 2x - x^2$ is symmetric with respect to the line $x = 1$.

52. Prove that the curve with equation $y^2 - 4y - x + 3 = 0$ is symmetric with respect to the line $y = 2$.

53. Prove that the curve with equation $xy = 1$ is symmetric with respect to the line $y = x$.

54. Prove that the curve with equation $y = x^3 - 3x^2 + 2x$ is symmetric with respect to the point $(1, 0)$.

27. INTERSECTION OF CURVES

If the equations of two curves are given, the points of intersection of the curves are simply the points with coordinates which satisfy both of the equations. Finding the points of intersection is thus reduced to the process of solving the equations simultaneously.

Example 7

Find the points of intersection of the hyperbola having the equation $xy = 4$ and the line having the equation $x - y - 3 = 0$.

Solution: From the equation of the line we have $y = x - 3$; therefore we substitute $x - 3$ for y in the equation of the hyperbola and solve for x as follows:

$$x(x - 3) = 4,$$
$$x^2 - 3x - 4 = 0,$$
$$(x + 1)(x - 4) = 0.$$

Thus the x-coordinates of the points of intersection are -1 and 4. Substituting these, in turn, in the equation of the line we find the corresponding values of y to be respectively -4 and 1. Thus the points of intersection are $(-1, -4)$ and $(4, 1)$. As a final check, it may be verified that these points satisfy both the given equations.

Frequently the points of intersection of two curves will have irrational coordinates, as illustrated in the next example. It may also be remarked that if imaginary solutions are found in the solving of two simultaneous equations, they correspond to no points on the graph and are therefore to be discarded.

Example 8

Find the points of intersection of the circle with equation $x^2 + y^2 = 4$ and the line with equation $y = 2x - 1$.

Solution: Substituting $y = 2x - 1$ in the equation of the circle, and simplifying, we obtain the equation

$$5x^2 - 4x - 3 = 0.$$

The solutions of this equation are found, by use of the quadratic formula, to be

$$x = \frac{2 \pm \sqrt{19}}{5}.$$

Substitution of these solutions in the equation of the line yields the corresponding values of y, and the points of intersection are found to be

$$\left(\frac{2 + \sqrt{19}}{5}, \frac{-1 + 2\sqrt{19}}{5} \right) \quad \text{and} \quad \left(\frac{2 - \sqrt{19}}{5}, \frac{-1 - 2\sqrt{19}}{5} \right).$$

EXERCISES

Find the points of intersection of the curves with the following pairs of equations.

1. $y^2 = 4x$,
   $x - 2y + 3 = 0$.

2. $x^2 + 2y^2 = 4$,
   $x - y - 1 = 0$.

3. $4x^2 - 3y^2 = 1$,
   $x - y = 0$.

4. $x^2 + y^2 = 11$,
   $x^2 + y^2 - 2x - 8 = 0$.

5. $x^2 + y^2 = 5$,
   $3x - y = 5$.

6. $x^2 + y^2 = 2$,
   $x + 2y = 3$.

7. $xy + 6 = 0$,
   $3x + 2y = 5$.

8. $x^2 + 3y^2 = 1$,
   $y = 2x^2$.

9. $y^2 = 4x$,
   $y = x + 2$.

10. $x^2 + y^2 = 15$,
    $2x^2 + y^2 = 24$.

11. $4y = x^2 + 6x - 3$,
    $y = 1 + x$.

12. $x + xy = 7$,
    $3xy + y = 16$.

13. $x^2 + y^2 = 34$,
    $xy = 1$.

14. $x^2 + y^2 = 1$,
    $y = x^2$.

28. EQUATION OF A LOCUS

So far we have considered the problem of determining the graph of a given equation. Sometimes we need to consider the reverse problem, namely, that of finding the equation which has as its graph a given locus. The term *locus* refers here to any geometrically described collection of points in the plane. By the equation of a locus, we mean the equation which has the given locus as its graph.

From the discussion of Example 3 in this chapter, it is clear that the equation of the locus of all points at a distance of 2 units from the origin is $x^2 + y^2 = 4$. This locus is, of course, a circle.

We now illustrate the general method of finding the equation of a locus.

Example 9

Find the equation of the locus of all points that are equidistant from the point $A(0, 2)$ and the point $B(3, 1)$.

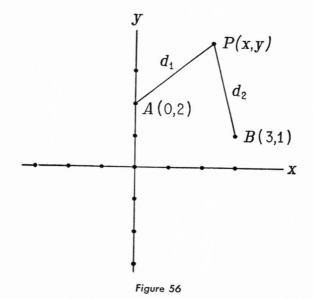

Figure 56

Solution: Let $P(x, y)$ be any point on the locus, that is, any point which is equidistant from the two given points. Using the notation of Figure 56, we have

$$d_1 = \sqrt{x^2 + (y - 2)^2}, \qquad d_2 = \sqrt{(x - 3)^2 + (y - 1)^2};$$

hence the required condition is $d_1 = d_2$ or

$$\sqrt{x^2 + (y-2)^2} = \sqrt{(x-3)^2 + (y-1)^2}.$$

On squaring both sides of this equation, we obtain

$$x^2 + (y-2)^2 = (x-3)^2 + (y-1)^2,$$

or, simplifying,

$$3x - y - 3 = 0.$$

This is the *equation of the given locus*, since the graph of this equation is precisely the given locus. That any point $P(x, y)$ satisfying this linear equation is on the given locus can be verified by retracing the steps above. The reader already knows from Euclidean geometry that the given locus is the perpendicular bisector of the segment AB. That the perpendicular bisector of AB has the equation

$$3x - y - 3 = 0$$

can be verified by methods of the previous chapter.

Example 10

Find the equation of the locus of all points P such that the slope of the line on P and the point $A(2, 0)$ is twice the slope of the line on P and the point $B(-2, 0)$.

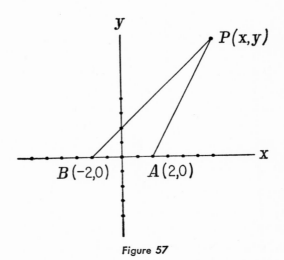

Figure 57

Solution: Let $P(x, y)$ be any point satisfying the stated condition (Figure 57). Now the slope of the line on P and A is $y/(x-2)$, and the slope of the line on P and B is $y/(x+2)$. Hence we must have

$$\frac{y}{x-2} = 2\left(\frac{y}{x+2}\right)$$

as the *equation of the given locus.* Note that x cannot equal $+2$ or -2 in this equation, since division by zero is impossible. Remembering that $x \neq \pm 2$, we can simplify this equation in the usual way to obtain

$$yx + 2y = 2yx - 4y,$$

or

$$y(x - 6) = 0.$$

By the principle illustrated in Example 5, the graph of the equation $y(x - 6) = 0$ consists of the line $y = 0$ and the line $x = 6$. Hence the given locus consists of these lines with the two points $A(2, 0)$ and $B(-2, 0)$ excluded.

In trying to find the equation of a given locus, we always proceed as indicated in the above examples. That is, we let $P(x, y)$ be *any* point on the given locus. We then convert the geometric description of the locus into an equation in x and y. The resulting equation is the desired equation of the locus.

EXERCISES

1. Find the equation of the locus of points that are at a distance of 3 units from the point $(-1, 2)$.

2. Find the equation of the locus of points that are equidistant from the points $(-5, 1)$ and $(5, -3)$.

3. Find the equation of the locus of points that are equidistant from the point $(4, 2)$ and the y-axis.

4. Find the equation of the locus of points that are twice as far from the point $(-1, 0)$ as from the point $(2, 0)$.

5. Find the equation of the locus of points that are equidistant from the point $(0, 2)$ and the x-axis.

6. Find the equation of the locus of points that are equidistant from the two parallel lines $3x - 2y + 4 = 0$ and $3x - 2y - 8 = 0$.

7. Find the equation of the locus of points that are twice as far from the point $(0, 4)$ as from the line $y = 2$.

8. Find the equation of the locus of points that are four times as far from the x-axis as from the point $(0, -2)$.

9. Consider all triangles AOB of area 8 where A is a point on the x-axis, B is a point on the y-axis, and O is the origin. Find the equation of the locus of all midpoints of side AB.

10. Find the equation of the locus of points P such that the slope of the line on P and the origin is equal to one half the slope of the line on P and the point $(1, -2)$.

11. Find the equation of the locus of points that are equidistant from the point $(2, 0)$ and the line $x = -2$.

12. Find the equation of the locus of points that are equidistant from the point $(0, 3)$ and the line $y = -3$.

13. Find the equation of the locus of points P such that the slope of the line on P and the point $(0, 1)$ is three times the slope of the line on P and the point $(0, 3)$.

14. Find the equation of the locus of points P such that the product of the slopes of the lines on P and $(2, 0)$ and on P and $(4, 2)$ is two.

15. Find the equation of the locus of points that are equidistant from the line $y = x$ and the point $(-2, 2)$.

16. Find the equation of the locus of points that are equidistant from the point $(1, -1)$ and from the line $x + y - 2 = 0$.

17. Let A be the point $(0, 1)$ and B the point $(6, 1)$. Find the equation of the locus of points P such that the sum of the distance between P and A and the distance between P and B is equal to 10.

18. Let A be the point $(-4, 1)$ and B the point $(6, 1)$. Find the equation of the locus of points P such that the absolute value of the difference of the distances $|PA|$ and $|PB|$ is 6.

19. Find the equation of the locus of points P such that P is the third vertex of a right triangle, the ends of the hypotenuse of which are $A(-2, 3)$ and $B(1, -7)$.

20. Points $A(-2, 1)$ and $B(1, 5)$ are two vertices of a triangle the area of which is 30. Find the equation of the locus of the third vertex of the triangle.

29. THE BISECTOR OF AN ANGLE (OPTIONAL)

In this section we shall discuss briefly the problem of finding the equations of the bisectors of the angles formed by two intersecting lines with known equations. Although the equations of the two bisectors can be found quite easily by using the results of Sections 18 and 20, the use of the normal form (Section 21) simplifies the problem of determining which equation is the equation of a particular one of the bisectors. The method will be sufficiently illustrated by the following example.

Example 11

Find the equations of the bisectors of the angles formed by the intersecting lines l_1 and l_2 with respective equations $x + 4y - 9 = 0$ and $2x - y + 4 = 0$.

Solution: Let us denote by l the line bisecting the angle from l_1 to l_2, and by l' the line bisecting the angle from l_2 to l_1 (Figure 58). We know from Euclidean geometry that the points which are equidistant from l_1 and l_2 are precisely the points on l and l'. Accordingly, we can obtain the equations of l and l' by finding the equation of the locus of all points that are equidistant from l_1 and l_2.

We now observe from the figure that each point on l (except the point of intersection of the two given lines) is above one of the given

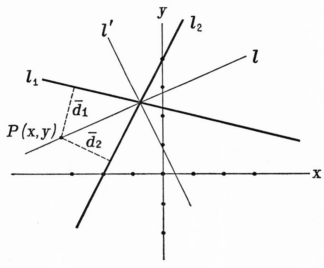

Figure 58

lines and below the other, whereas each point on l' is either above both given lines or below both of them. Let $P(x, y)$ be any point on the bisector l, and let $\bar{d}_1$ and $\bar{d}_2$ be the respective directed distances from l_1 and l_2 to the point $P(x, y)$. By the results of Section 21, it follows that $\bar{d}_1$ and $\bar{d}_2$ have opposite signs. Since they are equal in absolute value, the points on l are characterized by the equation

$$\bar{d}_1 = -\bar{d}_2.$$

But, by 2·26, we have

$$\bar{d}_1 = \frac{x + 4y - 9}{\sqrt{17}};$$

and

$$\bar{d}_2 = \frac{2x - y + 4}{-\sqrt{5}};$$

thus the equation of l is

$$\frac{x + 4y - 9}{\sqrt{17}} = -\frac{2x - y + 4}{-\sqrt{5}}.$$

Similarly, the equation of l' is $\bar{d}_1 = \bar{d}_2$, or,

$$\frac{x + 4y - 9}{\sqrt{17}} = \frac{2x - y + 4}{-\sqrt{5}}.$$

EXERCISES

In each of the following exercises, find the equations of the bisectors of the angles formed by the given pair of lines.

1. $2x + y - 7 = 0,$
   $2x - 4y + 2 = 0.$

2. $x - 7y + 4 = 0,$
   $x + y - 3 = 0.$

3. $3x - 2y + 3 = 0,$
   $x + y - 4 = 0.$

4. $x - 4 = 0,$
   $x + 2y - 3 = 0.$

5. $8x + 6y - 3 = 0,$
   $3x - 4y + 2 = 0.$

6. $2x + y + 4 = 0,$
   $x + 3y - 5 = 0.$

For each of the triangles with the given vertices, find the equation of the bisector of angle A.

7. $A(-2, -1), B(-1, 4), C(3, 1).$

8. $A(-1, 3), B(5, 1), C(2, -6).$

9. $A(4, 1), B(4, 4), C(7, 5).$

10. $A(-2, 2), B(3, 2), C(1, 4).$

11. The equations of the three sides of a triangle are as follows:

$$3x - 4y + 4 = 0, \qquad 12x + 5y - 18 = 0, \qquad 3x + 4y - 1 = 0.$$

Find the equations of the bisectors of the angles of the triangle and show that they meet on a point. This point is the center of what circle?

12. Show that the equation of the line parallel to the lines $Ax + By + C = 0$ and $Ax + By + C' = 0$, and which is halfway between them is

$$Ax + By + \frac{C + C'}{2} = 0.$$

chapter 4

The Circle

30. EQUATION OF A CIRCLE

It is easy to write the equation of a circle by making use of the familiar definition of a circle as the locus of all points at a given distance (the **radius**) from a fixed point (the **center**). Thus let us consider the equation of the circle with the point (h, k) as center and with radius r (Figure 59). A point $P(x, y)$ is on this circle if and only if the distance between

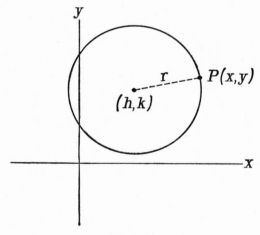

Figure 59

P and the center is r; that is, the points $P(x, y)$ on the circle are those and only those whose coordinates satisfy the equation

$$\sqrt{(x - h)^2 + (y - k)^2} = r.$$

This equation is, of course, equivalent to the equation

4·1
$$(x - h)^2 + (y - k)^2 = r^2,$$

which is, therefore, *the equation of the circle with center (h, k) and with radius r.*

An important special case is that in which the center is the origin. In this case, $h = 0$ and $k = 0$, and the equation takes the simpler form

4·2 $$x^2 + y^2 = r^2.$$

One should observe that any equation which can be put in the form 4·1 is the equation of a circle.

Example 1

Discuss the graph of the equation

$$x^2 + y^2 - 6x + 4y - 3 = 0.$$

Solution: Let us attempt to write this equation in the form 4·1 by completing the squares as follows:

$$(x^2 - 6x + 9) + (y^2 + 4y + 4) = 3 + 9 + 4,$$

or

$$(x - 3)^2 + (y + 2)^2 = 16.$$

This is now in the form 4·1 with $h = 3$, $k = -2$, and $r = 4$; we therefore know that it is the equation of a circle with center $(3, -2)$ and with radius 4.

As indicated by this example, the equation of a circle may appear in a form other than 4·1, but can always be written in the form 4·1. However, it is desirable to be able to recognize at once equations that can be written in this form. We shall accordingly prove the following theorem.

4·3   Theorem

The equation of any circle can be written in the form

4·4 $$x^2 + y^2 + Dx + Ey + F = 0.$$

Conversely, if the graph of 4·4 consists of more than one point, the graph is a circle with center $(-D/2, -E/2)$ and radius

$$\frac{1}{2} \sqrt{D^2 + E^2 - 4F}.$$

Proof: The first sentence of the theorem follows at once by squaring out 4·1 and setting $D = -2h$, $E = -2k$, and $F = h^2 + k^2 - r^2$.

To prove the converse, let us write 4·4 in the form 4·1 by completing the squares. If we transpose F to the right side and then add $D^2/4$ and $E^2/4$ to both sides, we obtain

$$\left(x^2 + Dx + \frac{D^2}{4}\right) + \left(y^2 + Ey + \frac{E^2}{4}\right) = \frac{D^2 + E^2 - 4F}{4},$$

which can be written in the form

4·5 $$\left(x + \frac{D}{2}\right)^2 + \left(y + \frac{E}{2}\right)^2 = \frac{D^2 + E^2 - 4F}{4}.$$

If $D^2 + E^2 - 4F < 0$, the equation has no graph, since the left side, being the sum of two squares, can never be negative. If $D^2 + E^2 - 4F = 0$, the point $(-D/2, -E/2)$ is the only point on the graph of 4·5. Finally, if $D^2 + E^2 - 4F > 0$, a positive real number r exists such that

$$r^2 = \frac{D^2 + E^2 - 4F}{4}.$$

A comparison with 4·1 shows that 4·5 (and hence 4·4) is the equation of a circle with center $(-D/2, -E/2)$ and radius

$$\frac{1}{2}\sqrt{D^2 + E^2 - 4F}.$$

This completes the proof.

In 4·4, the coefficients of x and y are unity. However, any equation of the form

$$ax^2 + ay^2 + dx + ey + f = 0,$$

with $a \neq 0$, can be put in the form 4·4 by dividing through by a. Thus, again, the graph of any such equation is a circle if it has a graph consisting of more than one point.

Example 2

Determine the graph of the equation

$$2x^2 + 2y^2 + 8x - 4y + 9 = 0.$$

Solution: First we divide each member of this equation by 2 and obtain the equation

$$x^2 + y^2 + 4x - 2y + \frac{9}{2} = 0.$$

This equation is now in the form 4·4, and we can either complete the squares and write it in the form 4·1, or apply 4·3 directly to obtain the center and radius. We do the latter and observe that in this case we have $D = 4$, $E = -2$, and $F = 9/2$. Hence $D^2 + E^2 - 4F = 2$, and thus the graph is a circle with center $(-2, 1)$ and radius $\sqrt{2}/2$.

EXERCISES

In each of Exercises 1–9, find the equation of the circle satisfying the given conditions.

1. Center $(2, -1)$, radius 3.

2. Center $(-3, 5)$, radius 4.

3. Center $(0, -5)$, radius 5.

4. Center $(10, 7)$, radius 6.

5. Center $(3, -2)$ and passing through $(0, 2)$.

6. Center $(-5, -3)$ and passing through the origin.

7. Center $(0, 4)$ and passing through $(4, 0)$.

8. Center $(4, 5)$ and passing through $(-3, 7)$.

9. Center $(-2, -2)$ and passing through the origin.

In each of Exercises 10–21, find the center and radius of the circle with the given equation.

10. $x^2 + y^2 + 6x - 2y + 6 = 0$.   11. $4x^2 + 4y^2 - 12x + 1 = 0$.

12. $9x^2 + 9y^2 - 6x - 17 = 0$.   13. $x^2 + y^2 + 2x + 2y - 2 = 0$.

14. $x^2 + y^2 + x - y = 0$.   15. $x^2 + y^2 - 10x + 10y = 0$.

16. $x^2 + y^2 + 6x - 10y + 26 = 0$.   17. $4x^2 + 4y^2 + 4x - 20y + 22 = 0$.

18. $3x^2 + 3y^2 + 2x - 4y - 4 = 0$.   19. $5x^2 + 5y^2 - 8y - 9 = 0$.

20. $2x^2 + 2y^2 - 3x - 5y - 2 = 0$.   21. $x^2 + y^2 + x + 2y = 0$.

22. Find the equation of the locus of all points P such that the line on P and the point $(2, 0)$ is perpendicular to the line on P and the point $(0, 2)$. Use the equation to discuss the locus.

23. Find the equation of the locus of all points P such that the distance between P and the point $(0, 1)$ is twice the distance between P and the point $(3, 5)$. Use the equation to discuss the locus.

24. Find the equation of the locus of all points P such that P is the midpoint of a line segment of fixed length $2a$ with one end of the segment on the x-axis and the other end on the y-axis. What is the locus?

31.   CIRCLES DETERMINED BY GIVEN CONDITIONS

One is sometimes required to find the equation of a circle satisfying given conditions. In such a problem one may consider the desired equation to be of the form 4·1 or 4·4, whichever is more convenient. Thus form 4·1 is used if the given conditions are concerned with the center or radius of the circle, whereas form 4·4 is used otherwise. In making use of 4·4 it is assumed that the desired equation is of this form, and the appropriate values of D, E, and F are computed algebraically. In this latter case the equation is obtained in the form 4·4 without one's ever finding the center or radius of the circle.

Example 3

Find the equation of the circle passing through the points $(1, 2)$, $(-2, 1)$, and $(3, -1)$.

Solution: It is convenient to use the form 4·4, and hence we assume that the desired equation is

$$x^2 + y^2 + Dx + Ey + F = 0.$$

The problem is then that of finding the values of D, E, and F. Since the point $(1, 2)$ is on the circle, the equation must be satisfied when $x = 1$ and $y = 2$; thus we have

4·6 $$5 + D + 2E + F = 0.$$

In like manner, we use each of the other two points and find

4·7 $$5 - 2D + E + F = 0,$$
4·8 $$10 + 3D - E + F = 0.$$

We now have three equations to solve for the unknowns D, E, and F. Various methods may be used to solve these equations, but a rather simple one is the following. If we subtract the members of 4·7 from those of 4·6, and also subtract the members of 4·8 from those of 4·7, we get the two equations

$$3D + E = 0,$$
$$-5 - 5D + 2E = 0.$$

From these it is easy to find that $D = -5/11$ and $E = 15/11$. If we substitute these values in 4·6, for example, we obtain $F = -80/11$. The desired equation is therefore

$$x^2 + y^2 - \frac{5}{11}x + \frac{15}{11}y - \frac{80}{11} = 0,$$

or

$$11x^2 + 11y^2 - 5x + 15y - 80 = 0.$$

Any three points in the plane not on a line determine a unique circle, as is shown in Euclidean geometry. The fact that the three points are noncollinear allows us to solve the three equations 4·6, 4·7, and 4·8 simultaneously.

There also is a unique circle passing through a given point and tangent to a given line at a given point on the line (if both given points are not on the given line). The following example shows how to find the equation of a circle determined by these conditions.

Example 4

Find the equation of the circle which passes through the point $(0, 1)$ and is tangent to the line $x + 2y + 2 = 0$ at the point $(4, -3)$.

Solution: In this problem we shall seek the center and radius of the desired circle and then use 4·1 to find its equation. Let us denote the unknown center by (h, k) (Figure 60). Since the points $(0, 1)$ and $(4, -3)$

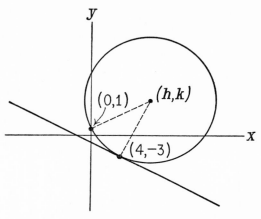

Figure 60

are on the circle, they must be equidistant from the center (h, k). Thus we must have

$$h^2 + (k - 1)^2 = (h - 4)^2 + (k + 3)^2.$$

This equation easily simplifies to

4·9 $$h - k - 3 = 0.$$

Now from Euclidean geometry we know that a tangent to a circle is perpendicular to the radius to the point of contact. Hence the radius to $(4, -3)$ is perpendicular to the given tangent $x + 2y + 2 = 0$, a line of slope $-1/2$. Thus the slope of the radius to the point $(4, -3)$ must be 2, and therefore, by 2·4, we must have

$$\frac{k + 3}{h - 4} = 2.$$

This can be put in the simpler form

4·10 $$2h - k - 11 = 0.$$

Solving 4·9 and 4·10 simultaneously, we find $h = 8$ and $k = 5$; hence the center is $(8, 5)$. The radius is then the distance between $(8, 5)$ and one of the known points, say $(0, 1)$, on the circle.   The radius is found to be $\sqrt{80}$, and the desired equation is therefore

$$(x - 8)^2 + (y - 5)^2 = 80.$$

Example 5

Find the equation of the circle which is tangent to the line with equation $3x + 4y + 4 = 0$ and which passes through the points $(0, 0)$ and $(4, 0)$.

Solution: As in the preceding example, we first seek the center of the required circle.   If (h, k) is the center (Figure 61), then (h, k) must be

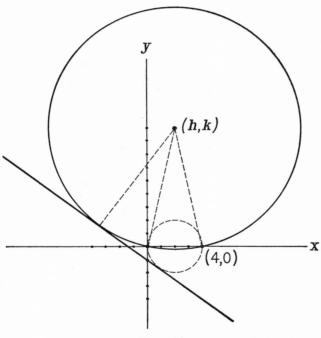

Figure 61

equidistant from $(0, 0)$ and $(4, 0)$.   This leads to the equation

$$h^2 + k^2 = (h - 4)^2 + k^2,$$

which easily reduces to $h = 2$.   Now since the required circle is tangent to the line $3x + 4y + 4 = 0$, the distance of the center $(2, k)$ from this line must be equal to the radius of the circle, and therefore equal to the distance between $(0, 0)$ and the center $(2, k)$.   Thus, by 2·18, we see that

$$\frac{|3\cdot 2 + 4\cdot k + 4|}{5} = \sqrt{4 + k^2},$$

or

$$|10 + 4k| = 5\sqrt{4 + k^2}.$$

If we square and simplify, this reduces to

$$9k^2 - 80k = 0,$$

which has the two solutions $k = 0$ and $k = 80/9$. It thus appears that there are *two* circles which satisfy the given conditions, one with center $(2, 0)$ and the other with center $(2, 80/9)$. An easy calculation shows that the radius of the first is 2, and that of the second is $82/9$. The respective equations are therefore

$$(x - 2)^2 + y^2 = 4,$$

and

$$(x - 2)^2 + \left(y - \frac{80}{9}\right)^2 = \frac{6724}{81}.$$

These circles are drawn in Figure 61.

This last example illustrates the power of the algebraic method of solving problems in geometry. It may not have been obvious at first that there was more than one solution, but both solutions appeared in the process of solving the problem algebraically. In other words, one's geometric intuition (or lack of it) is not so important in analytic geometry as in ordinary Euclidean geometry.

EXERCISES

In each of Exercises 1–16, find the equations of all circles satisfying the given conditions.

1. Passing through the points $(-1, 3)$, $(2, 0)$, and $(3, 5)$.
2. Passing through the points $(4, 0)$, $(-1, 3)$, and $(-2, -4)$.
3. Passing through the points $(0, 4)$, $(2, 0)$, and $(-3, 1)$.
4. Passing through the points $(6, 8)$, $(0, 0)$, and $(2, 6)$.
5. Passing through the points $(5, 2)$, $(4, 4)$, and $(9, 1)$.
6. Passing through the points $(4, 2)$, $(6, 0)$, and $(7, 1)$.
7. Passing through the points $(5, 3)$ and $(-2, 2)$, and of radius 5.
8. Tangent to both axes and of radius 3.
9. Passing through the point $(-7, 3)$ and tangent to the line $x - 2y + 3 = 0$ at the point $(-1, 1)$.
10. Passing through the point $(6, 0)$ and tangent to the line $y = x$ at the point $(4, 4)$.

11. Passing through the points $(-1, -1)$ and $(3, 1)$, and with center on the line $x - y + 10 = 0$.

12. Passing through the point $(6, 5)$ and tangent to the line $2x + y - 8 = 0$ at $(3, 2)$.

13. Passing through the points $(-1, -2)$ and $(6, -1)$ and tangent to the x-axis.

14. With center $(2, 3)$ and tangent to the line $x + 3y - 4 = 0$.

15. Passing through the point $(2, 1)$ and tangent to both axes.

16. Concentric with the circle $x^2 + y^2 + 6x - 10y + 33 = 0$ and tangent to the x-axis.

17. Find the equations of the circles with centers at $(4, -7)$ which are tangent to the circle with equation $x^2 + y^2 + 4x - 2y + 1 = 0$.

In each of Exercises 18–23, find the equation of the tangent to the given circle at the point indicated.

18. $x^2 + y^2 - 6x - 8y = 0$, at $(7, 1)$.

19. $x^2 + y^2 - 9x - 8y + 5 = 0$, at $(-1, 3)$.

20. $11x^2 + 11y^2 - 5x + 15y - 80 = 0$, at $(1, 2)$.

21. $x^2 + y^2 - 3x + 2y - 7 = 0$, at $(4, 1)$.

22. $2x^2 + 2y^2 + 9x - 8y + 16 = 0$, at $(-3, 2)$.

23. $x^2 + y^2 + 4x - y - 5 = 0$, at $(-5, 0)$.

24. Find the points of intersection of the circles having the equations $x^2 + y^2 - 2x = 0$ and $x^2 + y^2 - 4x + 3 = 0$. What is the angle of intersection of their radii at each of these points?

25. Show that the equation of the tangent to the circle $x^2 + y^2 = r^2$ at any point (a, b) on the circle is $ax + by = r^2$.

26. Find the equation of each of the lines of slope $-3/4$ which is tangent to the circle with equation $x^2 + y^2 - 6x - 2y + 6 = 0$.

27. If the length of the tangent from an external point (a, b) to the circle with Equation 4·4 is denoted by t, show that

$$t^2 = a^2 + b^2 + Da + Eb + F.$$

28. Verify that the points $A(-5, 0)$, $B(0, 5)$, and $C(3, 4)$ are on the circle with equation $x^2 + y^2 = 25$. If P is any other point on the circle, show that the respective projections of P on the three sides of the triangle ABC (extended if necessary) are collinear. (A similar result holds for any four points on any circle.)

32. CIRCLES THROUGH THE INTERSECTIONS OF TWO CIRCLES (OPTIONAL)

Let C_1 and C_2 be two intersecting circles whose equations are, respectively,

4·11
$$x^2 + y^2 + D_1x + E_1y + F_1 = 0,$$

and

4·12 $x^2 + y^2 + D_2x + E_2y + F_2 = 0.$

Let k be a real number, and let us consider the equation

4·13 $x^2 + y^2 + D_1x + E_1y + F_1 + k(x^2 + y^2 + D_2x + E_2y + F_2) = 0.$

First, we observe that if $P(x_1, y_1)$ is a point of intersection of the circles C_1 and C_2, then $P(x_1, y_1)$ is on the graph of Equation 4·13. This is so since the substitution of x_1 for x and y_1 for y in 4·13 yields $0 + k \cdot 0 = 0$.

Next, we rewrite Equation 4·13 in the form

$$(1 + k)(x^2 + y^2) + (D_1 + kD_2)x + (E_1 + kE_2)y + F_1 + kF_2 = 0.$$

If $k \neq -1$, we may divide through by $1 + k$ and write the result in the form

$$x^2 + y^2 + \frac{D_1 + kD_2}{1 + k}\,x + \frac{E_1 + kE_2}{1 + k}\,y + \frac{F_1 + kF_2}{1 + k} = 0.$$

We now observe that this (and therefore also 4·13) is the equation of a circle and, by the remarks above, this circle must pass through the points of intersection of the two given circles C_1 and C_2.

If $k = -1$, Equation 4·13 reduces to the equation

4·14 $(D_1 - D_2)x + (E_1 - E_2)y + F_1 - F_2 = 0.$

We have assumed that the circles C_1 and C_2 intersect; hence they are not concentric and we cannot have both $D_1 = D_2$ and $E_1 = E_2$. (Why?) Therefore 4·14 is an equation of the first degree and its graph is a line. Moreover, this line must pass through the points of intersection of C_1 and C_2, so that *if these circles intersect in two distinct points, the line* 4·14 *is the line of their common chord.*

Equation 4·13 is sometimes referred to as the equation of a *family* of circles, since we obtain different circles by different choices of the real number k.

The results of this section greatly simplify the solutions of problems of a certain type. This fact will be illustrated by the following example.

Example 6

Find the equation of the circle which passes through the points of intersection of the circles with equations

$$x^2 + y^2 + 2x - 4y - 11 = 0$$

and

$$x^2 + y^2 - 2x - 3 = 0,$$

and which also passes through the point $(3, -2)$.

Solution: For these particular circles, Equation 4·13 becomes

4·15 $\quad x^2 + y^2 + 2x - 4y - 11 + k(x^2 + y^2 - 2x - 3) = 0.$

We now seek a value of k such that the point $(3, -2)$ will satisfy this equation. Substituting $x = 3$ and $y = -2$ in 4·15, we obtain $16 + k \cdot 4 = 0$, or $k = -4$. Thus we know that the equation

4·16 $\quad x^2 + y^2 + 2x - 4y - 11 - 4(x^2 + y^2 - 2x - 3) = 0$

is the equation of a circle through the points of intersection of the two given circles and, by the choice of k, we know that the point $(3, -2)$ is also on the circle. Hence 4·16 is the desired equation. By multiplying out and simplifying, this equation can be written in the form

$$3x^2 + 3y^2 - 10x + 4y - 1 = 0.$$

EXERCISES

In each of Exercises 1–6, find the equation of the circle which passes through the points of intersection of the given circles and also through the given point.

1. $x^2 + y^2 + 2x - 1 = 0,\ x^2 + y^2 + x - y - 4 = 0;\ (1, 1).$

2. $x^2 + y^2 - 3x + 2y = 0,\ x^2 + y^2 + 5x - 2y = 0;\ (-2, 3).$

3. $x^2 + y^2 + 6x - 4y - 4 = 0,\ x^2 + y^2 - 4x - 2y = 0;\ (0, 6).$

4. $x^2 + y^2 + x + 6y - 7 = 0,\ x^2 + y^2 + 6x - y - 2 = 0;\ (1, -5).$

5. $3x^2 + 3y^2 + 4x - 10y + 2 = 0,\ 3x^2 + 3y^2 - 8x - 2y = 0;\ (2, 1).$

6. $x^2 + y^2 + 2x - 8y - 13 = 0,\ x^2 + y^2 - 6x - 2y + 1 = 0;\ (0, 0).$

7. Find the equation of the circle which passes through the points of intersection of the circles of Exercise 1 and has its center on the line $x - 2y - 3 = 0$.

8. Find the equation of the circle which passes through the points of intersection of the circles of Exercise 2 and has its center on the line $y - 3x - 2 = 0$.

9. If the circles with Equations 4·11 and 4·12 are tangent, show that 4·14 is the equation of their common tangent. [*Hint:* Show that the line 4·14 is always perpendicular to the line of centers.]

10. If P is a point on the line passing through the two points of intersection of two given circles and is outside these two circles, prove that the lengths of the tangents from P to the two circles are equal. [*Hint:* Use Exercise 27, p. 91 and 4·14.]

chapter 5

The Conic Sections

In this chapter, we shall make a rather detailed study of parabolas, ellipses, and hyperbolas. Each of these curves will be described geometrically, and each will then be shown to be the graph of some quadratic equation in x and y. Many properties of these curves will be derived from their equations. Incidentally, it will be found that a circle may be considered to be a special case of an ellipse.

The parabola, ellipse, and hyperbola are called *conic sections* (or simply *conics*) because each of them can be described as the curve of intersection of a plane with a cone. We shall indicate in a later section of this chapter how the various conic sections are obtained in this way.

33. THE PARABOLA

The first of the curves to be studied in this chapter is defined as follows.

5·1 Definition

*A **parabola** is the locus of all points equidistant from a fixed point and a fixed line not on the fixed point.*

The fixed point is called the **focus,** and the fixed line the **directrix,** of the parabola. In Figure 62, Let F be the focus and l the directrix of a parabola. The line k on F perpendicular to l is called the **axis** of the parabola. Let the axis of the parabola intersect the directrix at A. Now the midpoint V of the segment AF is a point on the parabola since $|AV| = |VF|$. This point V is called the **vertex** of the parabola. If P is a point in the plane and Q its projection on l, then P is on the parabola provided that $|PF| = |PQ|$. If P is on the parabola and P' is the image of P in the line k, evidently P' is also on the parabola; that is, the axis k of the parabola is an axis of symmetry.

We now seek the equation of a parabola, and the first step is that of choosing coordinate axes. Let us choose the x-axis to be the axis of the parabola, and the origin to be the vertex of the parabola. Let the focus have coordinates $(p, 0)$, so that p is positive or negative according as the focus is to the right or left of the directrix. In either case, the distance between the focus and directrix is $|2p|$, and the equation of the directrix is $x = -p$. Figure 63 illustrates the case in which $p > 0$, and reference may be made to this figure in the succeeding paragraph.

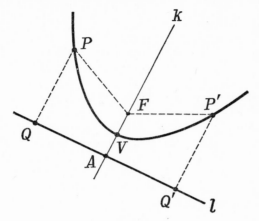

Figure 62

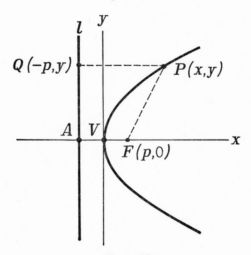

Figure 63

It is now a simple task to obtain the equation of the parabola. If $P(x, y)$ is a point in the plane, and Q the projection of P on l, then P is on the parabola if and only if

$$|PF| = |PQ|.$$

Now, Q has coordinates $(-p, y)$; hence

$$|PQ| = |x + p|.$$

Since

$$|PF| = \sqrt{(x - p)^2 + y^2},$$

the point $P(x, y)$ is on the parabola if and only if

$$\sqrt{(x - p)^2 + y^2} = |x + p|.$$

By squaring and simplifying, we may reduce this equation to

5·2 $$y^2 = 4px,$$

which is the desired form of the *equation of a parabola* when the coordinate axes are located as described above.

From 5·2, certain observations can be made about the parabola. The symmetry of the parabola with respect to its axis, the x-axis, follows

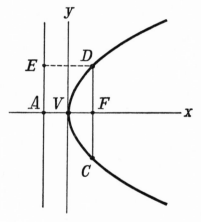

Figure 64

at once, since y appears to an even power.   Since $y^2 \geq 0$ for *all* real numbers y, we must have $4px \geq 0$.   This in turn means that $x \geq 0$ if $p > 0$, and $x \leq 0$ if $p < 0$.   Thus if $p > 0$, the parabola is to the right of the y-axis, whereas if $p < 0$, the parabola is to the left of the y-axis.   In either case, for large values of $|x|$, y^2 is large and the parabola is far from the x-axis.   We may thus conveniently say that the parabola opens to the right if $p > 0$, and opens to the left if $p < 0$.

The chord through the focus of a paragola which is perpendicular to the axis of the parabola is called the **latus rectum** of the parabola.   In Figure 64 the latus rectum is CD.   Let E and A be the respective projections of D and F on the directrix.   Then $|ED| = |DF|$ by the very definition of the parabola.   However, $|ED| = |AF| = |2p|$; therefore $|DF| = |2p|$.   It follows that the total length $|CD|$ of the latus rectum is

$|4p|$. It may be helpful to note that the length of the latus rectum of the parabola 5·2 is just the absolute value of the coefficient of x in its equation.

An approximate idea of the shape of a parabola may be obtained from a knowledge of the vertex and the points at the ends of the latus rectum. To draw a more accurate graph, one should plot additional points.

Example 1

Discuss the parabola with equation $y^2 = -6x$.

Solution: This equation is of the form 5·2 with $4p = -6$ or $p = -3/2$. Hence the focus is $(-3/2, 0)$ and the equation of the directrix is $x = 3/2$. The length of the latus rectum is 6; so the ends of the latus rectum are $(-3/2, 3)$ and $(-3/2, -3)$. Knowing that the vertex is the origin and that the parabola opens to the left (since $p < 0$), we may sketch an appropriate graph, as indicated in Figure 65.

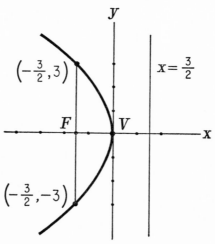

Figure 65

In the derivation of the equation of a parabola, if we had chosen the axis of the parabola to be the y-axis and the vertex to be the origin, the effect would have been simply to interchange the roles of x and y. Thus the equation of a parabola with the origin as its vertex and with the y-axis as its axis is

5·3
$$x^2 = 4py.$$

The focus of this parabola is $(0, p)$ and the equation of its directrix is $y = -p$. Clearly the parabola opens upward if $p > 0$ and downward if $p < 0$. The length of the latus rectum is still $|4p|$.

We emphasize that the equation of a parabola has the simple form 5·2 or 5·3 only if the vertex of the parabola is the origin and the axis of the parabola is a coordinate axis. It will appear later that the equation of a parabola may be much more complicated if the parabola is not in such a special position relative to the coordinate axes.

EXERCISES

In each of Exercises 1–12, find the focus, directrix, and latus rectum of the given parabola, and sketch.

1. $x^2 = -12y.$
2. $x^2 = 2y.$
3. $y^2 = 8x.$
4. $y^2 = -3x.$
5. $2x^2 + 3y = 0.$
6. $y^2 = 3x.$
7. $x^2 = 14y.$
8. $3y^2 - 2x = 0.$
9. $y^2 - x = 0.$
10. $4x^2 - y = 0.$
11. $x^2 + 6y = 0.$
12. $3y^2 + 4x = 0.$

In each of Exercises 13–20, find the equation of the parabola with the given focus and directrix.

13. $(4, 0); x = -4.$
14. $(0, 2); y = -2.$
15. $(0, -3); y = 3.$
16. $(-7, 0); x = 7.$
17. $(-1/2, 0); x = 1/2.$
18. $(4/3, 0); x = -4/3.$
19. $(0, \sqrt{2}); y = -\sqrt{2}.$
20. $(0, -1/4); y = 1/4.$

In each of Exercises 21–28, use the *definition* of the parabola to find the equation of the parabola with given focus and directrix.

21. $(0, 4); y = 0.$
22. $(0, 0); y = -4.$
23. $(0, 0); x = -2.$
24. $(-5, 4); x = -9.$
25. $(4, 6); x = 2.$
26. $(1, 5); y = 4.$
27. $(1, 1); x + y = 0.$
28. $(0, 0); x + y + 1 = 0.$

29. Find the equation of the circle which has as a diameter the latus rectum of the parabola with equation $x^2 = -16y.$

30. Find the points of intersection of the parabola $y^2 = 4x$ and the line $x - 2y + 3 = 0.$

31. Find the points of intersection of the parabola $y + x^2 = 0$ and the line $y + 2x + 3 = 0.$

32. Find the points of intersection of the two parabolas $y^2 = 3x$ and $x^2 = 24y.$

33. Show that the midpoints of all chords of the parabola $y^2 = 4px$ having the given slope m lie on the line with equation $y = 2p/m.$

34. The distance between a point on a parabola and the focus of the parabola is called a *focal radius* of the parabola. Prove that the focal radius of the point (a, b) on the parabola $x^2 = 4py$ equals $|b + p|.$

35. Prove that the line $y = mx + b$ intersects the parabola $y^2 = 4px$ in two points if and only if $p^2 > mbp$; in one point if and only if $p = mb$; in no points if and only if $p^2 < mbp$.

36. Find the equation of the locus of the midpoints of all chords passing through the vertex of the parabola $y^2 = 4px$.

34. THE ELLIPSE

We now make the following definition.

5·4 Definition

Let F and F' be two fixed points, let $2c$ denote the distance between them, and let a be a real number such that $a > c$. Then the locus of all points P such that

$$|FP| + |F'P| = 2a$$

is called an **ellipse**.

Each of the two fixed points, F and F', is called a **focus**; together they are called the **foci** of the ellipse. The midpoint O of the segment FF' is called the **center** of the ellipse. Since $|FF'| = 2c$, evidently $|OF| = |OF'| = c$.

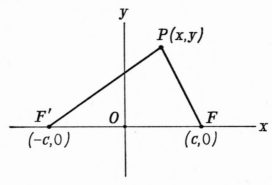

Figure 66

We now select coordinate axes in the plane and derive the equation of an ellipse. It seems sensible to choose one of the axes, say the x-axis, on the foci; and the other, say the y-axis, on the center of the ellipse. Then the foci have coordinates $(-c, 0)$ and $(c, 0)$, as indicated in Figure 66, and the point $P(x, y)$ is on the ellipse if and only if

$$|FP| + |F'P| = 2a;$$

that is, if and only if

$$\sqrt{(x - c)^2 + y^2} + \sqrt{(x + c)^2 + y^2} = 2a.$$

If we transpose one of the radicals, say the first, to the other side of the equation and square both sides of the resulting equation, we obtain

$$(x + c)^2 + y^2 = 4a^2 - 4a \sqrt{(x - c)^2 + y^2} + (x - c)^2 + y^2.$$

This equation can be simplified to give

$$a \sqrt{(x - c)^2 + y^2} = a^2 - cx.$$

If we again square and simplify, this reduces to

$$(a^2 - c^2)x^2 + a^2y^2 = a^2(a^2 - c^2).$$

If we divide both sides of this equation by the quantity appearing on the right side, this equation becomes

$$\frac{x^2}{a^2} + \frac{y^2}{a^2 - c^2} = 1.$$

Now $a > c$ so that $a^2 - c^2 > 0$, and hence $a^2 - c^2$ has a positive square root b. In other words, we propose to *define* the positive number b by

5·5 $$b^2 = a^2 - c^2,$$

and thus write the above equation in the form

5·6 $$\frac{x^2}{a^2} + \frac{y^2}{b^2} = 1.$$

Our calculations show that for any point $P(x, y)$ on the ellipse, the coordinates x and y of P satisfy 5·6. The converse is also true, although we omit the details; that is, if x and y satisfy 5·6, then the point $P(x, y)$ is on the ellipse. The proof is obtained by reversing the steps by which we derived 5·6. Thus 5·6 is the *equation of the ellipse*.

From Equation 5·6 it is easy to establish several important properties of the ellipse (Figure 67). First of all, we observe that the graph is symmetric with respect to both the x-axis and the y-axis (why?), and is therefore also symmetric with respect to the origin. Thus an ellipse is symmetric with respect to its center. The x-intercepts are the points $V(a, 0)$ and $V'(-a, 0)$, and the y-intercepts are the points $B(0, b)$ and $B'(0, -b)$. Since, by 5·5,

$$a^2 = b^2 + c^2,$$

it follows that $a > b$. The points V and V' are called the **vertices** of the ellipse, and the segment VV' is called the **major axis** of the ellipse. The segment BB' is called the **minor axis** of the ellipse. The *length* of the major axis is $2a$, and the *length* of the minor axis is $2b$.

If we solve Equation 5·6 for y, we obtain

5·7
$$y = \pm \frac{b}{a} \sqrt{a^2 - x^2}.$$

From this it follows that if $|x| > a$, there is no corresponding real value of y, and hence the ellipse lies between the lines $x = a$ and $x = -a$. A similar calculation also shows that the ellipse lies between the lines $y = b$ and $y = -b$. Thus the ellipse lies in the rectangle determined by these four lines.

It may be pointed out that we have found it convenient to define

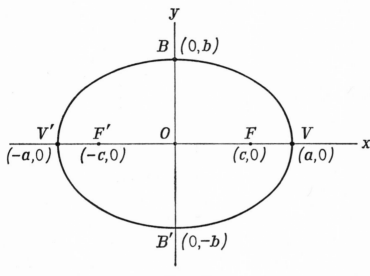

Figure 67

the vertices, and the major and minor axes, of an ellipse after coordinates have been introduced. However, it is clear that these could be defined without reference to coordinate axes. Thus the vertices are the points of intersection of the ellipse and the line on the foci. The segment joining the vertices is the major axis, and the minor axis is the segment cut by the ellipse from the line on the center perpendicular to the major axis.

The line on a focus F of an ellipse perpendicular to the major axis cuts the ellipse in two points, say C and D (Figure 68). The segment CD is called a **latus rectum** of the ellipse. If GH is the corresponding segment on the other focus F', then $|GH| = |CD|$, and GH is also a latus rectum. To find the y-coordinates of the points C and D, we substitute $x = c$ in 5·7 and find that

$$y = \pm \frac{b}{a} \sqrt{a^2 - c^2}.$$

However, by 5·5, $\sqrt{a^2 - c^2} = b$, and hence

$$y = \pm \frac{b^2}{a}.$$

Thus D is the point $(c, b^2/a)$, and C is the point $(c, -b^2/a)$. Similarly, H and G have coordinates $(-c, b^2/a)$ and $(-c, -b^2/a)$, respectively. It is clear that the *length* $|CD|$ (*or* $|GH|$) *of a latus rectum is* $2b^2/a$.

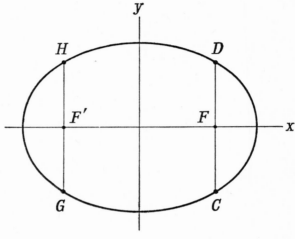

Figure 68

To obtain the approximate shape of an ellipse with given equation, it is frequently sufficient to locate the vertices, the ends of the minor axis, and the ends of the latera recta.

If we had chosen the line on the foci of the ellipse to be the y-axis, and the center to be the origin, the effect would have been simply that of interchanging the roles of x and y. Thus the equation of an ellipse with its center the origin and with its foci on the y-axis is

5·8
$$\frac{y^2}{a^2} + \frac{x^2}{b^2} = 1.$$

As before, the major axis (along the y-axis now) has length $2a$, the minor axis has length $2b$, the distance between the foci is $2c$, and the length of each latus rectum is $2b^2/a$. Thus, for example, the foci are now $(0, c)$ and $(0, -c)$, whereas $(0, a)$ and $(0, -a)$ are the vertices.

Example 2

Discuss the graph of the equation

$$16x^2 + 9y^2 = 36.$$

Solution: Upon dividing by 36, we obtain the equation

$$\frac{4x^2}{9} + \frac{y^2}{4} = 1,$$

which may be written in the form

$$\frac{x^2}{9/4} + \frac{y^2}{4} = 1.$$

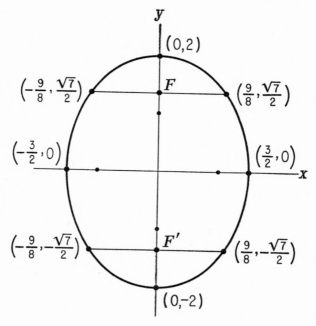

Figure 69

Since $4 > 9/4$, this equation has the form 5·8 with $a^2 = 4$ and $b^2 = 9/4$. By 5·5,

$$c^2 = a^2 - b^2 = \frac{7}{4};$$

hence we have $a = 2$, $b = 3/2$, $c = \sqrt{7}/2$. The major axis of this ellipse is along the y-axis, and hence the vertices are $(0, 2)$ and $(0, -2)$. The ends of the minor axis are $(3/2, 0)$ and $(-3/2, 0)$, and the foci are $(0, \sqrt{7}/2)$ and $(0, -\sqrt{7}/2)$. Since the total length of each latus rectum is $2b^2/a$, it is easy to find that the ends of the latera recta are $(\pm 9/8, \pm \sqrt{7}/2)$. The graph is sketched in Figure 69.

Throughout our discussion of the ellipse we have tacitly assumed that the two fixed points (foci) mentioned in the definition of an ellipse are distinct points, and hence that $c > 0$. If, as a special case, the two points happen to coincide, then $c = 0$ and 5·5 shows that $a = b$; hence both 5·6 and 5·8 reduce to the equation of a circle with the origin as center. Thus we can think of a circle as a special case of an ellipse.

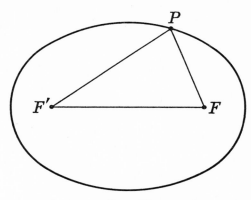

Figure 70

We conclude this section with a brief description of a simple way to draw an ellipse. Let thumbtacks be placed at points F and F' which are $2c$ units apart on a drawing board. Take a piece of string and tie the ends together so as to make a loop of length $2c + 2a$. Now slip the loop over the thumbtacks and hold the string taut by means of a pencil point P (Figure 70). If the pencil is moved, always keeping the string taut, the point will trace out an ellipse, since for every position of P we must have

$$|FP| + |F'P| = 2a.$$

EXERCISES

In each of Exercises 1–12, discuss and sketch the graph of the given equation.

1. $4x^2 + 9y^2 = 36$.
2. $x^2 + 2y^2 = 2$.
3. $25x^2 + 9y^2 = 225$.
4. $16x^2 + y^2 = 16$.
5. $25x^2 + 9y^2 - 25 = 0$.
6. $16x^2 + 36y^2 = 576$.
7. $x^2 + 25y^2 - 25 = 0$.
8. $2y^2 + 3x^2 = 8$.
9. $4x^2 + y^2 = 1$.
10. $9x^2 + 4y^2 = 1$.
11. $4x^2 + 4y^2 = 25$.
12. $2x^2 + 3y^2 = 5$.

In each of Exercises 13–20, find the equation of the ellipse having the properties given.

13. Foci $(\pm 4, 0)$, vertices $(\pm 5, 0)$.

14. Foci $(0, \pm 2)$, vertices $(0, \pm 4)$.

15. Vertices $(\pm 4, 0)$, latus rectum of length 2.

16. Vertices $(\pm 5, 0)$, ends of minor axis $(\pm 1, 0)$.

17. Ends of minor axis $(\pm 2, 0)$, foci $(0, \pm 2)$.

18. Ends of minor axis $(0, \pm 3)$, latus rectum of length 3.

19. Foci $(0, \pm 4)$, latus rectum of length 12.

20. Vertices $(0, \pm 5)$, passing through the point $(4/5, 3)$.

21. Use the definition of the ellipse to find the equation of the ellipse having foci $(3, 5)$ and $(9, 5)$, and having $a = 5$.

22. Use the definition of the ellipse to find the equation of the ellipse having foci $(-1, -2)$ and $(-1, 0)$, and having one vertex $(-1, 1)$.

23. Find the equation of the circle passing through the focus of the parabola $x^2 + 8y = 0$ and the foci of the ellipse $16x^2 + 25y^2 - 400 = 0$.

24. Find the equation of each parabola having the origin as its vertex and such that the focus of the parabola coincides with a focus of the ellipse $169x^2 + 25y^2 = 4225$.

25. A chord through the center of an ellipse is called a *diameter*. If (x, y) is an endpoint of a diameter of an ellipse with Equation 5·6, show that the length of the diameter can be expressed in the form

$$\frac{2}{b} \sqrt{a^2 b^2 - (a^2 - b^2)y^2},$$

and also in the form

$$\frac{2}{a} \sqrt{(a^2 - b^2)x^2 + a^2 b^2}.$$

Prove from this that the length of the longest diameter is $2a$ and that of the shortest diameter is $2b$.

26. Prove that the line $y = mx + d$ and the ellipse 5·6 have precisely one point in common if and only if

$$d^2 = a^2 m^2 + b^2.$$

35. A FOCUS-DIRECTRIX PROPERTY OF THE ELLIPSE

Using the notation of the preceding section, the ratio c/a may be called the **eccentricity** of the ellipse. It is customary to denote the eccentricity by e, and thus we have

5·9
$$\frac{c}{a} = e \qquad \text{or} \qquad c = ae.$$

Since $c < a$, we must have $e < 1$. From the relation 5·5, it follows that $a^2 = b^2 + a^2 e^2$, or

5·10
$$a^2(1 - e^2) = b^2.$$

From 5·10 it is apparent that if $e = 0$, then $a = b$ and the ellipse is a circle. *Henceforth we shall assume that $e > 0$.*

If e is very small, then a and b will be almost equal and the ellipse will be nearly circular. On the other hand, if e is almost equal to 1, so that $1 - e^2$ is very small, b will be small in comparison with a and the ellipse will be long and narrow. We see, therefore, that the shape of an ellipse depends upon the value of its eccentricity.

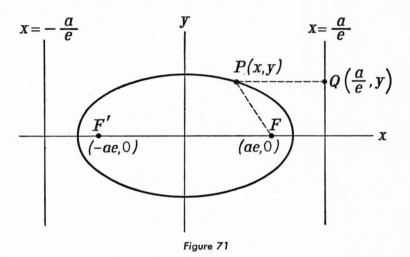

Figure 71

We now define the **directrices** of an ellipse to be the lines perpendicular to the major axis at a distance of a/e from the center of the ellipse. Since $e < 1$, clearly $a/e > a$, and so the directrices do not intersect the ellipse.

If an ellipse has its center at the origin and its major axis along the x-axis, so that its equation is

5·11
$$\frac{x^2}{a^2} + \frac{y^2}{b^2} = 1,$$

the directrices have equations $x = a/e$ and $x = -a/e$, and the foci have coordinates $(ae, 0)$ and $(-ae, 0)$ (Figure 71).

We shall now prove the following theorem.

5·12   Theorem

The ellipse with Equation 5·11 is the locus of all points P such that the ratio of the distance of P from the focus $F(ae, 0)$ to its distance from the directrix $x = a/e$ is equal to the eccentricity e.

Proof: We shall prove this theorem by finding the equation of the stated locus and showing that it simplifies to Equation 5·11. If $P(x, y)$ is any point in the plane, let Q be the projection of P on the line $x = a/e$ (Figure 71). Evidently Q has coordinates $(a/e, y)$, and P will be on the locus if and only if

5·13
$$\frac{|PF|}{|PQ|} = e.$$

Expressing this equation in terms of coordinates, we find that

$$\frac{\sqrt{(x - ae)^2 + y^2}}{\left| \dfrac{a}{e} - x \right|} = e,$$

and this leads to the equation

$$(x - ae)^2 + y^2 = e^2 \left(\frac{a}{e} - x \right)^2.$$

Squaring out and collecting terms, we obtain

$$x^2(1 - e^2) + y^2 = a^2(1 - e^2),$$

or

5·14
$$\frac{x^2}{a^2} + \frac{y^2}{a^2(1 - e^2)} = 1.$$

Since, by 5·10, for the ellipse 5·11 we have $b^2 = a^2(1 - e^2)$, it follows that 5·14 coincides with 5·11, and the proof is completed.

This result shows that the points P on the ellipse 5·11 are characterized by the ratio property stated in 5·13. In view of symmetry, it is clear also that in place of the focus $(ae, 0)$ and the directrix $x = a/e$, we could just as well have used the focus $(-ae, 0)$ and the corresponding directrix $x = -a/e$.

Example 3

Find the equation of the ellipse having the origin as its center if one focus is the point $(4, 0)$ and the corresponding directrix is the line $x = 6$.

Solution: Since $c = 4$ for this ellipse, we see by 5·9 that $ae = 4$. Also, by definition of the directrices, it follows that $a/e = 6$. Multiplying corresponding members of these two equations, we find $a^2 = 24$. Then $b^2 = 24 - 16 = 8$, and since the major axis is along the x-axis, the desired equation is

$$\frac{x^2}{24} + \frac{y^2}{8} = 1.$$

Example 4

Find the eccentricity, the coordinates of the foci, and the equations of the directrices of the ellipse with the equation

$$\frac{y^2}{25} + \frac{x^2}{9} = 1.$$

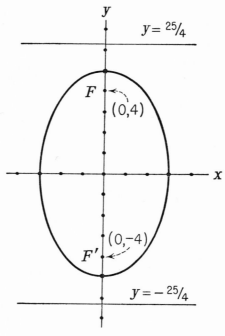

Figure 72

Solution: For this ellipse we have $a = 5$, $b = 3$; and it follows readily that $c = 4$. Thus $ae = 4$ and $e = 4/5$. Since the major axis is along the y-axis, the coordinates of the foci are $(0, 4)$ and $(0, -4)$. Now $a/e = 25/4$, so the equations of the directrices are $y = 25/4$ and $y = -25/4$. The graph is shown in Figure 72.

EXERCISES

In each of Exercises 1–8, find the eccentricity, foci, and directrices of the ellipse with given equation.

1. $16x^2 + 25y^2 = 400$.

2. $7x^2 + 16y^2 = 112$.

3. $4x^2 + 3y^2 = 12$.

4. $4x^2 + 3y^2 = 108$.

5. $20x^2 + 36y^2 = 5$.

6. $12x^2 + 9y^2 = 4$.

7. $9x^2 + y^2 = 1$.   8. $x^2 + 2y^2 = 1$.

In each of Exercises 9–18, find the equation of the ellipse with center at the origin that satisfies the given conditions.

9. Focus $(2, 0)$, directrix $x = 8$.

10. Focus $(0, 4)$, directrix $y = 9$.

11. Focus $(0, -3)$, directrix $y = -4$.

12. Eccentricity $1/2$, focus $(-2, 0)$.

13. Eccentricity $1/3$, directrix $x = 12$.

14. Vertex $(5, 0)$, directrix $x = 25/3$.

15. Eccentricity $3/5$, end of minor axis $(0, -8)$.

16. Eccentricity $2/3$, length of latus rectum $20/3$, major axis along the y-axis.

17. Directrix $x = 16$, length of latus rectum 12.

18. Eccentricity $1/2$, major axis along x-axis, distance between foci 1.

19. On the line segment AB of length $a + b$ mark off the point P so that $|AP| = a$. Keeping the point A on the y-axis and the point B on the x-axis, prove that the locus of all such points P is the ellipse 5·6. How could this fact be used to construct an ellipse?

20. A square with sides parallel to the axes may be inscribed in an ellipse. Find the area of the square so inscribed in the ellipse 5·6.

36. THE HYPERBOLA

We next introduce and discuss the remaining one of the conic sections, and we therefore make the following definition.

5·15 Definition

Let F and F' be two distinct fixed points, let $2c$ be the distance between them, and let a be a real number such that $0 < a < c$. Then the locus of all points P such that

$$|FP| - |F'P| = \pm 2a$$

is called a **hyperbola.**

The two fixed points, F and F', are called the **foci** of the hyperbola, and the midpoint O of the segment FF' is called the **center** of the hyperbola. Since $|FF'| = 2c$, evidently $|OF| = |OF'| = c$.

It is clear that the ellipse and hyperbola have similar definitions. A fundamental difference is that $a < c$ for the hyperbola, whereas $a > c$ in the case of the ellipse. Also, it is necessary to assume specifically that the foci of a hyperbola are distinct (hence that $c > 0$). For an ellipse, we found that the foci could coincide as a special case, and that in such a case the ellipse was actually a circle.

The derivation of the equation of a hyperbola is quite analogous to that for the equation of an ellipse, and we shall therefore omit some of the algebraic details. Let us choose the x-axis as the line on the foci, and the origin as the center of the hyperbola (Figure 73). Then the

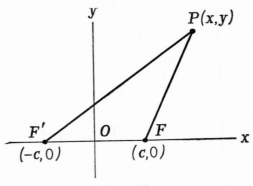

Figure 73

foci have coordinates $(-c, 0)$ and $(c, 0)$, and the point $P(x, y)$ is on the hyperbola if and only if

$$|FP| - |F'P| = \pm 2a;$$

that is, if and only if

$$\sqrt{(x - c)^2 + y^2} - \sqrt{(x + c)^2 + y^2} = \pm 2a.$$

Precisely the same operations as were used in simplifying the equation of an ellipse will give the same equation as obtained previously, namely,

$$\frac{x^2}{a^2} + \frac{y^2}{a^2 - c^2} = 1.$$

However, we now have $a < c$ so that $a^2 - c^2$ is negative. Accordingly, we *define* the positive real number b by the equation

5·16
$$b^2 = c^2 - a^2.$$

The equation of the hyperbola can then be written in the form

5·17
$$\frac{x^2}{a^2} - \frac{y^2}{b^2} = 1.$$

It follows from this equation that the hyperbola is symmetric with respect to both coordinate axes, and therefore also with respect to the origin. The points $V(a, 0)$ and $V'(-a, 0)$ on the hyperbola are called the **vertices,** and the segment VV' is called the **transverse axis** of the hyperbola. Clearly, there are no y-intercepts (why?), so the curve does not cross the y-axis. If we solve 5·17 for y, we obtain

$$y = \pm \frac{b}{a} \sqrt{x^2 - a^2},$$

and real values of y occur if and only if $x^2 \geqq a^2$; that is, if and only if $x \geqq a$ or $x \leqq -a$. Accordingly, the hyperbola consists of two branches, one in the region where $x \geqq a$ and the other in the region where $x \leqq -a$. The curve is clearly not bounded. The general shape is indicated in Figure 74.

A **latus rectum** of a hyperbola is a chord of the hyperbola which

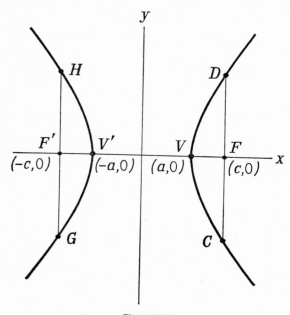

Figure 74

passes through a focus and is perpendicular to the line on the foci. Thus, for example, the hyperbola of Figure 74 has CD and GH as its latera recta. As in the case of the ellipse, it is easy to show that the length of a latus rectum is $2b^2/a$.

If the y-axis, instead of the x-axis, is chosen as the line on the foci, and the origin as the center of the hyperbola, the equation of the hyperbola becomes

5·18
$$\frac{y^2}{a^2} - \frac{x^2}{b^2} = 1.$$

In this case, $(0, a)$ and $(0, -a)$ are the vertices, and $(0, c)$ and $(0, -c)$ are the foci of the hyperbola. Clearly there are no x-intercepts in this case.

37.   THE ASYMPTOTES OF A HYPERBOLA

Let us consider that part of the hyperbola

$$\frac{x^2}{a^2} - \frac{y^2}{b^2} = 1$$

which is in the first quadrant.   For any $x \geqq a$, the corresponding value of y is given by

$$y = \frac{b}{a} \sqrt{x^2 - a^2}.$$

Since $x^2 - a^2 < x^2$ and therefore $\sqrt{x^2 - a^2} < x$, we see that $y < (b/a)x$. In Figure 75 we have drawn the line whose equation is $y = (b/a)x$, and

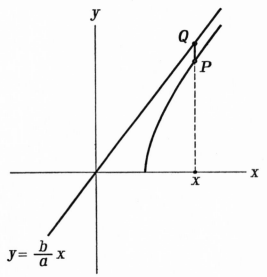

Figure 75

the observation which we have just made is that everywhere in the first quadrant the hyperbola lies *below* the line.   We shall now show that as we go to the right on the hyperbola, the hyperbola approaches nearer and nearer to the line.   Let P and Q denote the respective points on the hyperbola and the line with the same x-coordinate x.   Then $|PQ|$ is equal to the y-coordinate of Q minus the y-coordinate of P, that is,

$$|PQ| = \frac{b}{a} x - \frac{b}{a} \sqrt{x^2 - a^2}$$

$$= \frac{b}{a} (x - \sqrt{x^2 - a^2}).$$

If we now multiply and divide the right side of this equation by $x + \sqrt{x^2 - a^2}$, we obtain

$$|PQ| = \frac{ab}{x + \sqrt{x^2 - a^2}}.$$

From this we can draw the desired conclusion; that is, if x is large, the denominator is large $(>x)$ so that the fraction is correspondingly small. It is clear that as x increases, $|PQ|$ decreases and can be made arbitrarily small if x is chosen sufficiently large. Geometrically, this means that as we go to the right on that branch of the hyperbola in the first quadrant, the hyperbola approaches nearer and nearer to the line $y = (b/a)x$.

By symmetry we can extend the result to the other quadrants and state that the hyperbola approaches the lines

$$y = \frac{b}{a}x \qquad \text{and} \qquad y = -\frac{b}{a}x$$

as $|x|$ becomes large. These lines are called the **asymptotes** of the hyperbola. For the hyperbola under consideration, the asymptotes are therefore the lines on the origin with slopes b/a and $-b/a$.

Before we sketch a hyperbola we will find it helpful to draw the asymptotes, since they quickly give an indication of the position of the curve at large distances from the center. An easy way to draw the asymptotes of a hyperbola will now be shown. Construct the rectangle with sides parallel to the coordinate axes and of lengths $2a$ and $2b$, with the vertices of the hyperbola at the midpoints of the sides of length $2b$. The lines on the diagonals of this rectangle have slopes b/a and $-b/a$, and each is on the origin (the center of the rectangle). Thus the asymptotes of the hyperbola are the lines on the diagonals of this rectangle. In Figure 76, the rectangle has vertices A, B, C, and D. Incidentally, we may observe that $|OV| = a$, $|VA| = b$, and hence $|OA| = \sqrt{a^2 + b^2} = c$; thus the length of a diagonal of this rectangle is just the distance between the foci. The right triangle OVA gives a convenient way of remembering 5·16, that is, that $b^2 = c^2 - a^2$.

For the hyperbola having its foci on the y-axis (Equation 5·18), the asymptotes are the lines $y = \pm(a/b)x$. They are the diagonals of the rectangle constructed as described above. The sides of length $2b$ are now parallel to the x-axis, and the sides of length $2a$ are parallel to the y-axis.

If the two asymptotes of a hyperbola are perpendicular, the hyperbola is called a **rectangular hyperbola.** A hyperbola with Equation 5·17 is therefore a rectangular hyperbola if and only if

$$\left(\frac{b}{a}\right)\left(-\frac{b}{a}\right) = -1;$$

that is, if and only if $a = b$.   The same conclusion holds in case the equation is of the form 5·18.

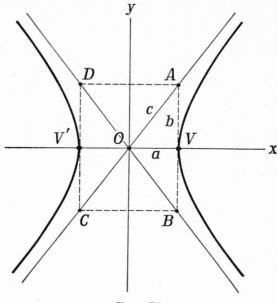

Figure 76

Example 5

Discuss and sketch the graph of the hyperbola with equation

$$\frac{x^2}{4} - \frac{y^2}{9} = 1.$$

Solution: For this hyperbola, $a = 2$ and $b = 3$; hence $c = \sqrt{13}$.   The vertices are therefore $(2, 0)$ and $(-2, 0)$, and the foci are $(\sqrt{13}, 0)$ and $(-\sqrt{13}, 0)$.   Now $b^2/a = 9/2$, so the ends of the latera recta have coordinates $(\pm \sqrt{13}, \pm 9/2)$.   The asymptotes are the lines $y = 3x/2$ and $y = -3x/2$.   The graph is sketched in Figure 77.

Example 6

Discuss and sketch the graph of the hyperbola with equation

$$16y^2 - 9x^2 = 144.$$

Solution: If we divide each member of this equation by 144, the equation takes on the form

$$\frac{y^2}{9} - \frac{x^2}{16} = 1.$$

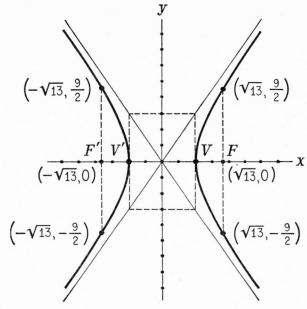

Figure 77

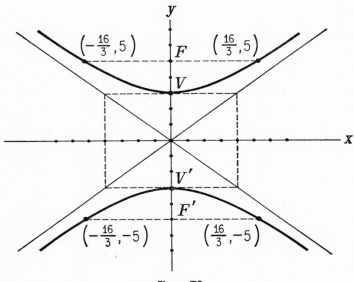

Figure 78

It is clear from this form of the equation that $a = 3$, $b = 4$, and $c = 5$. Since this equation is of the form 5·18, the foci are on the y-axis and therefore have coordinates $(0, \pm 5)$. The vertices are $(0, 3)$ and $(0, -3)$, and the ends of the latera recta have coordinates $(\pm 16/3, \pm 5)$. The equations of the asymptotes are

$$y = \pm \frac{3}{4} x.$$

The graph is shown in Figure 78.

EXERCISES

1. Show that the length of each latus rectum of a hyperbola is $2b^2/a$.

2. Derive Equation 5·17 of a hyperbola.

In each of Exercises 3–14, discuss and sketch the graph of the given equation.

3. $y^2 - x^2 = 4$.   4. $2x^2 - y^2 = 2$.

5. $25y^2 - 144x^2 = 3600$.   6. $9x^2 - 16y^2 = 144$.

7. $4x^2 - 9y^2 = 36$.   8. $x^2 - y^2 - 16 = 0$.

9. $4x^2 - 3y^2 - 12 = 0$.   10. $5y^2 - 12x^2 - 60 = 0$.

11. $x^2 - 4y^2 + 4 = 0$.   12. $y^2 = 9x^2 + 9$.

13. $x^2 - y^2 - 1 = 0$.   14. $3y^2 - 5 = 2x^2$.

In each of Exercises 15–22, find the equation of the hyperbola having the given properties.

15. Foci $(\pm 5, 0)$, vertices $(\pm 3, 0)$.

16. Foci $(0, \pm 3)$, vertices $(0, \pm 2)$.

17. Vertices $(\pm 4, 0)$, latus rectum of length 2.

18. Vertices $(0, \pm 3)$, rectangular hyperbola.

19. Foci $(\pm \sqrt{13}, 0)$, asymptotes $y = \pm 2x/3$.

20. Vertices $(0, \pm 4)$, asymptotes $y = \pm 3x$.

21. Asymptotes $y = \pm x$, latus rectum of length 10.

22. Vertices $(\pm 1, 0)$, passing through the point $(-3, 8)$.

23. Use the definition of the hyperbola to find the equation of the hyperbola having foci $(-1, 2)$ and $(9, 2)$, and one vertex $(7, 2)$.

24. Use the definition of the hyperbola to find the equation of the hyperbola having foci $(3, \pm 4)$ and vertices $(3, \pm 3)$.

25. Prove that a line parallel to an asymptote intersects the hyperbola in precisely one point.

26. Prove that the line $y = mx + d$, not parallel to an asymptote, intersects the hyperbola 5·17 in precisely one point if and only if $d^2 = m^2a^2 - b^2$.

27. Prove that the product of the distances of any point on a hyperbola from its asymptotes is a constant.

38.   A FOCUS-DIRECTRIX PROPERTY OF THE HYPERBOLA

In this section we obtain results for the hyperbola that are analogous to those of Section 35 for the ellipse.

The ratio c/a is called the **eccentricity** of a hyperbola.   If the eccentricity is denoted by e, we therefore have

5·19
$$\frac{c}{a} = e \qquad \text{or} \qquad c = ae,$$

just as for the ellipse.

The **directrices** of a hyperbola are the lines perpendicular to the transverse axis at a distance of a/e from the center of the hyperbola. This definition coincides with the corresponding definition for the ellipse, with the transverse axis of the hyperbola taking the place of the major axis of the ellipse.

Now for a hyperbola we have $c > a$, and hence $e > 1$ (for the ellipse we had $e < 1$).   It follows that $a/e < a$; therefore the directrices of a hyperbola do not intersect the hyperbola.   For a hyperbola, the relation $b^2 = c^2 - a^2$ and 5·19 show that

5·20
$$b^2 = a^2(e^2 - 1).$$

If the hyperbola has its center at the origin and its transverse axis along the x-axis, its equation is known to be of the form

5·21
$$\frac{x^2}{a^2} - \frac{y^2}{b^2} = 1.$$

In this case the foci are the points $(ae, 0)$ and $(-ae, 0)$, and the directrices are the lines $x = a/e$ and $x = -a/e$ (Figure 79).

The following theorem for the hyperbola is seen to be identical in statement to Theorem 5·12 for the ellipse.

5·22   Theorem

The hyperbola with Equation 5·21 is the locus of all points P such that the ratio of the distance of P from the focus $F(ae, 0)$ to its distance from the directrix $x = a/e$ is equal to the eccentricity e.

The proof of this coincides with the proof of Theorem 5·12 down to Equation 5·14; therefore we omit the details.   Then, by 5·20, we see that $a^2(1 - e^2) = -b^2$, so for the hyperbola Equation 5·14 reduces to the desired Equation 5·21.   Of course, the same result would have been obtained had we used the focus $(-ae, 0)$ and the corresponding directrix $x = -a/e$.

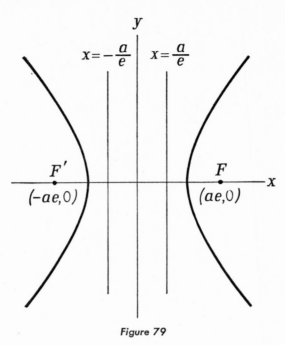

Figure 79

Example 7

Find the eccentricity, the coordinates of the foci, and the equations of the directrices of the hyperbola with the equation

$$\frac{x^2}{4} - \frac{y^2}{16} = 1.$$

Solution: Clearly $a = 2$, $b = 4$, and it is easy to find that $c = 2\sqrt{5}$. Since the transverse axis is along the x-axis, the foci have coordinates $(2\sqrt{5}, 0)$ and $(-2\sqrt{5}, 0)$.   Using 5·19, we see that $e = \sqrt{5}$.   The equations of the directrices are therefore $x = 2/\sqrt{5}$ and $x = -2/\sqrt{5}$.

EXERCISES

In each of Exercises 1–8, find the eccentricity, foci, and directrices of the hyperbola with the given equation.

1. $16x^2 - 9y^2 = 144$.   2. $11x^2 - 25y^2 = 275$.

3. $x^2 - y^2 + 4 = 0$.

4. $4x^2 - 3y^2 = 108$.

5. $9x^2 - y^2 - 9 = 0$.

6. $x^2 - 2y^2 + 1 = 0$.

7. $9x^2 - y^2 + 1 = 0$.

8. $x^2 - 5y^2 + 30 = 0$.

In each of Exercises 9–16, find the equation of the hyperbola with center at the origin that satisfies the given conditions.

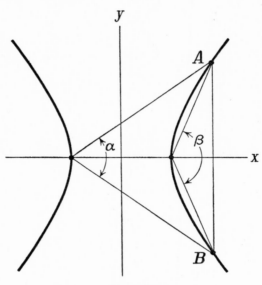

Figure 80

9. Focus $(8, 0)$, directrix $x = 2$.

10. Focus $(0, 2)$, directrix $y = 1/18$.

11. Focus $(0, -36)$, directrix $y = -4$.

12. Eccentricity 2, focus $(6, 0)$.

13. Eccentricity $3/2$, directrix $x = 3$.

14. Vertex $(0, 5)$, eccentricity 3.

15. Eccentricity $5/3$, length of latus rectum $64/3$, transverse axis along y-axis.

16. Eccentricity $3/2$, length of latus rectum 15, transverse axis along x-axis.

17. Prove that the eccentricity of any rectangular hyperbola is equal to $\sqrt{2}$.

18. Find the equations of the asymptotes of the hyperbola having its center at the origin and eccentricity 3, if the transverse axis is along the x-axis; if the transverse axis is along the y-axis.

19. Let two given hyperbolas have their centers at the origin with one transverse axis along the x-axis and the other along the y-axis. If e and f are the

respective eccentricities of these hyperbolas, prove that the given hyperbolas have the same asymptotes if and only if

$$\frac{1}{e^2} + \frac{1}{f^2} = 1.$$

20. Let AB be any chord of a rectangular hyperbola perpendicular to the transverse axis (Figure 80).   Prove that the angles α and β subtended by AB at the vertices of the hyperbola are supplementary.

39.   AN ALTERNATE DEFINITION OF THE CONIC SECTIONS

The results of Sections 35 and 38 make it possible to give a unified definition of the three different conic sections as follows.

5·23   Definition

Let F be a fixed point and l a fixed line not on the point F.   The locus of all points P such that the ratio of the distance of P from the point F to its distance from the line l is equal to the positive constant e is

an ellipse if $e < 1$,
a parabola if $e = 1$,
a hyperbola if $e > 1$.

In each case, F is called a *focus*, l a *directrix*, and e the *eccentricity* of the particular conic.   Thus, although we have not previously spoken of the eccentricity of a parabola, it may be said to have eccentricity 1.

Clearly, for the parabola, Definition 5·23 coincides with our earlier Definition 5·1.   Moreover, Theorems 5·12 and 5·22 show that an ellipse or hyperbola according to our previous definitions (5·4 and 5·15) is an ellipse or hyperbola, respectively, according to 5·23.   Of course, the converse is also true or we would not be justified in calling 5·23 another *definition*.   We omit further details, but in the interest of accuracy we may point out the following one trivial exception for the ellipse.   Using Definition 5·4, a circle may be considered as a special case of an ellipse for which the foci coincide and hence for which $e = 0$.   However, in Definition 5·23, it is necessary that we have $e > 0$, and the foci must be distinct.   In saying that the two definitions are equivalent we must therefore consider the word "ellipse" to mean "ellipse that is not a circle."

40.   SECTIONS OF A CONE

As mentioned in the introduction to this chapter, the parabola, the ellipse, and the hyperbola have in common the property that they may be obtained as the intersection of a plane with a right circular cone.   We shall not give any proofs, since the methods of solid geometry would be involved, but we shall indicate briefly how these different curves may be obtained.

Consider a circle with center O and a point A such that the line l on O and A is perpendicular to the plane in which the circle lies (Figure 81). Let B be a point on the circle. The surface generated by the line k on A

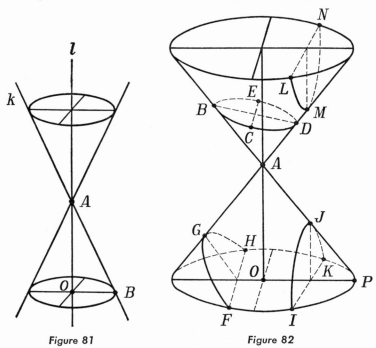

Figure 81   Figure 82

and B as B moves around the circle (that is, the locus of all lines k on A and any point B on the circle) is called a *right circular cone* with vertex A and *axis* l. A line such as k is called an *element* of the cone. The word *right* refers to the fact that l is perpendicular to the plane of the circle. The cone as defined will consist of two parts or *nappes*, one on each side of the vertex.

Now let us consider a right circular cone, a part of which is indicated in Figure 82. A plane which does not pass through the vertex A and which cuts all elements of the cone in the same nappe intersects the cone in an ellipse such as $BCDE$. Of course, the ellipse reduces to a circle if the cutting plane is perpendicular to the axis of the cone. A plane which cuts both nappes of the cone and does not pass through the vertex of the cone intersects the cone in a hyperbola, illustrated in the figure by IJK and LMN. Finally, a plane which is parallel to, but does not coincide with, an element of the cone cuts the cone in a parabola. This is illustrated by FGH which lies in a plane parallel to the element on A and P.

Historically, the parabola, ellipse, and hyperbola were first *defined* by the Greeks as sections of a cone, as we have just portrayed them, and a great many of their properties were established by the methods of solid geometry long before the invention of analytic geometry.

41. SOME APPLICATIONS OF THE CONICS

We shall mention briefly a few of the many applications of the conics to physical problems.

The path of each of the planets, including the earth, is an ellipse with the sun at a focus.   The path of a comet may be an ellipse or a parabola, again with the sun at a focus.

When a baseball, or any other projectile, is thrown through the air, the path approximates a portion of a parabola. The path would actually be along a parabola if the friction of the air were not involved, that is, if the projectile were thrown in a vacuum.

Arches of bridges are frequently made in the form of a semiellipse or of an arc of a parabola.   If the weight of a suspension bridge is distributed uniformly along the bridge itself, the cables from which the bridge is suspended hang in the shape of a parabola.

Parabolic surfaces are often used in the construction of search-lights, reflecting telescopes, and other optical instruments.   These and other related applications are based on certain "reflection properties" of the conics.   A precise statement involves the concept of tangent to a conic and will therefore be postponed to Chapter 11.

chapter 6

Transformation of Coordinates

The solution of a problem in analytic geometry can often be simplified by a proper choice of coordinate axes. However, in some cases it is necessary to start with given coordinate axes and then during the process of solution to change to new coordinate axes. For example, this procedure is frequently helpful when one is seeking to determine the graph of a given equation.

A change to new coordinate axes may consist of a *translation* of axes, a *rotation* of axes, or a combination of both. These will be discussed in this chapter, and a number of applications made to the equations of the conics. In the following chapter we shall use the results of this chapter to determine the graph of any equation of the second degree.

42. TRANSLATION OF AXES

We start with a coordinate plane with x- and y-axes as usual, and some fixed point O' with coordinates (h, k) (Figure 83). On O' let us construct lines parallel to the x- and y-axes. We think of these lines as new coordinate axes and label them accordingly the x'- and y'-axes, respectively. Moreover, we assume that these axes are directed as are the original axes, that is, the x'-axis is directed to the right and the y'-axis is directed upward. Let H and K denote the projections of O' on the x- and y-axes, respectively, so that H has coordinate h on the x-axis and K has coordinate k on the y-axis. Now any point P in the plane has two sets of coordinates: coordinates (x, y) relative to the x- and y-axes, and coordinates (x', y') relative to the x'- and y'-axes. Let M and N be the projections of P on the x- and y-axes, respectively; M' and N' on the x'- and y'-axes, respectively. Then

$$x' = \overline{O'M'} = \overline{HM} = x - h; \qquad y' = \overline{O'N'} = \overline{KN} = y - k.$$

These equations follow from the fact that the directed distance from point H with coordinate h to the point M with coordinate x is $x - h$ (on the x-axis), whereas the directed distance from the point O' to the point M' (on the x'-axis) is just the coordinate of M', namely x'; and so on.

These calculations show that if, starting with x- and y-axes, we take the point (h, k) as a new origin with x'- and y'-axes respectively parallel to the x- and y-axes, and if a point P has coordinates (x, y) relative to the original axes and coordinates (x', y') relative to the new axes, then

6·1
$$
\begin{array}{ll}
x' = x - h, & \qquad x = x' + h, \\
y' = y - k, & \text{or} \qquad y = y' + k.
\end{array}
$$

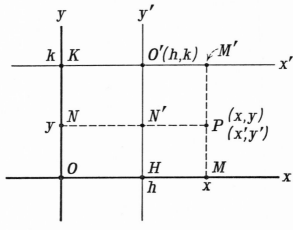

Figure 83

The process of choosing new axes parallel to a given set of axes is called **translation of axes** or *translation of the origin*.

Example 1

A parabola has equation $x^2 = 4y$ relative to the usual x- and y-axes. Find the equation of this parabola if the origin is translated to the point $(1, -3)$.

Solution: The parabola is sketched in Figure 84. We are given that $h = 1$, $k = -3$; hence from 6·1 we have

$$x = x' + 1, \qquad y = y' - 3.$$

The equation of this parabola relative to the x'- and y'-axes is therefore

$$(x' + 1)^2 = 4(y' - 3),$$

which can be written in the form

$$x'^2 + 2x' - 4y' + 13 = 0.$$

In this example, the equation was made more complicated by translation of axes. Naturally, one usually wants to do the reverse of this, as will be illustrated in the next example.

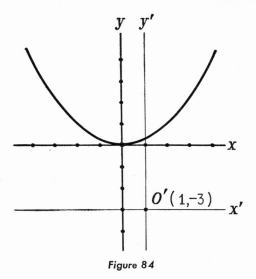

Figure 84

Example 2

Discuss the graph of the equation

$$4x^2 + 9y^2 + 8x - 36y + 4 = 0.$$

Solution: We shall try to translate the axes to a new origin (h, k) in such a way that the given curve (the graph of the given equation) has a simpler equation relative to the new axes. Not knowing offhand what the best choices of h and k might be, we start by translating the origin to (h, k) and later determine specific values for h and k. The equation of the curve relative to the new x'- and y'-axes is

$$4(x' + h)^2 + 9(y' + k)^2 + 8(x' + h) - 36(y' + k) + 4 = 0,$$

which is obtained by replacing x by $x' + h$ and y by $y' + k$ in the given equation. Expanding and collecting terms, we obtain the equation

$$4x'^2 + 9y'^2 + (8h + 8)x' + (18k - 36)y' + 4h^2 + 9k^2 + 8h - 36k + 4 = 0.$$

Now we observe that we can make the coefficient of x' zero if we choose h so that $8h + 8 = 0$, that is, if we choose $h = -1$. Likewise the coefficient of y' will be zero if $18k - 36 = 0$, that is, if $k = 2$. Accordingly, we choose $h = -1$ and $k = 2$, and the equation simplifies to

$$4x'^2 + 9y'^2 = 36.$$

This we can write in the form

$$\frac{x'^2}{9} + \frac{y'^2}{4} = 1,$$

which is of the form 5·6.   Thus, relative to the x'- and y'-axes, the graph of this equation is an ellipse with center at the origin O', and major axis along the x'-axis (Figure 85).   For this ellipse, $a = 3$, $b = 2$, and $c = \sqrt{5}$; and we can easily write the coordinates of the vertices, foci, and so on, rela-

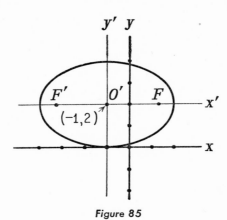

Figure 85

tive to the x'- and y'-axes, and then determine their coordinates relative to the x- and y-axes.   For example, we observe that $(\sqrt{5}, 0)$ and $(-\sqrt{5}, 0)$ are the coordinates of the foci relative to the x'- and y'-axes.   Since $x = x' - 1$ and $y = y' + 2$, we have $x = \sqrt{5} - 1$ when $x' = \sqrt{5}$, $y = 2$ when $y' = 0$, and so on.   We conclude therefore that the points $(\sqrt{5} - 1, 2)$ and $(-\sqrt{5} - 1, 2)$ are the coordinates of the foci relative to the x- and y-axes.

   In the next section we shall use the method of the present section to prove some rather general results about the equations of the conics.

43.   STANDARD FORMS OF EQUATIONS OF CONICS

We shall first show, by the results of the preceding section, that

6·2 $$(y - k)^2 = 4p(x - h)$$

is the equation of a parabola with vertex (h, k), with its axis parallel to the x-axis, and with $2p$ the directed distance from the directrix to the focus.   In other words, we may think of the graph of 6·2 as the same parabola as the graph of $y^2 = 4px$ except that the latter is moved, with its axis remaining parallel to the x-axis, until the vertex is the point (h, k).   It still opens to the right or left according as $p > 0$ or $p < 0$.

The proof of these statements is almost immediate. If we start with the graph of Equation 6.2 and translate the origin to the point (h,k), the equation of the given curve becomes

$$y'^2 = 4px'$$

relative to the x'- and y'-axes. This is the equation of a parabola having exactly the same relations to the x'- and y'-axes as the graph of $y^2 = 4px$ does to the x- and y-axes.

In like manner, the equation

6·3
$$(x - h)^2 = 4p(y - k)$$

is the equation of a parabola with vertex (h,k) and with its axis parallel to the y-axis. It opens upward if $p > 0$ and downward if $p < 0$.

Example 3

Find the equation of the parabola whose focus is $(-1, 3)$ and directrix is the line $y = -1$.

Solution: The focus is 4 units above the directrix; so $2p = 4$, $p = 2$. Now the vertex is halfway between the focus and directrix; hence it is the point $(-1, 1)$ (Figure 86). If x'- and y'-axes are chosen so that this

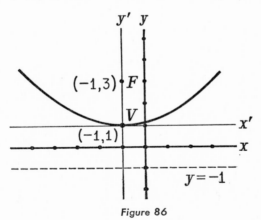

Figure 86

point is the origin, the equation of the parabola is

$$x'^2 = 8y'.$$

By 6.3, since $h = -1$, $k = 1$, and $p = 2$, its equation relative to the x- and y-axes is

$$(x + 1)^2 = 8(y - 1),$$

or

$$x^2 + 2x - 8y + 9 = 0.$$

Example 4

Discuss the graph of the equation

$$y^2 + 2y - 8x + 25 = 0.$$

Solution: Since y^2 (but not x^2) appears in this equation, the form 6.2 is suggested.   It is quite possible to go through the work of translating the

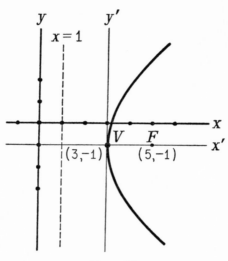

Figure 87

axes, as in the preceding section, but it is frequently more convenient to write the equation in the form 6·2 by completing the square as follows:

$$y^2 + 2y = 8x - 25,$$
$$y^2 + 2y + 1 = 8x - 25 + 1,$$
$$(y + 1)^2 = 8x - 24,$$
$$(y + 1)^2 = 8(x - 3).$$

This is now in the form 6.2 with $h = 3$, $k = -1$, and $p = 2$.   The graph is therefore a parabola with vertex $(3, -1)$, with its axis parallel to the x-axis, and opening to the right (Figure 87).   Since the distance from the vertex to the focus is p, it follows that the focus is $(5, -1)$. The directrix has equation $x = 1$.

The Equations 6·2 and 6·3 are frequently called the *standard forms* of the equation of a parabola.   Clearly, 5·2 and 5·3 are special cases in which $h = k = 0$.

We now pass to the ellipse and hyperbola, and omit the proofs since they follow easily by the method used to prove the statements about 6·2.

The equation

6·4
$$\frac{(x-h)^2}{a^2} + \frac{(y-k)^2}{b^2} = 1$$

is the equation of an ellipse with center (h, k). Its major axis is parallel to the x-axis, the length of the major axis is $2a$ and that of the minor axis is $2b$. We may consider this ellipse to be the same ellipse as the one with Equation 5·6, except that here the center is (h, k) rather than the origin.

In like manner, the equation of an ellipse with center (h, k) and with major axis parallel to the y-axis is

6·5
$$\frac{(y-k)^2}{a^2} + \frac{(x-h)^2}{b^2} = 1.$$

Entirely analogous results hold for the hyperbola. Thus

6·6
$$\frac{(x-h)^2}{a^2} - \frac{(y-k)^2}{b^2} = 1$$

is the equation of a hyperbola with transverse axis parallel to the x-axis, and with center (h, k). Likewise, the equation

6·7
$$\frac{(y-k)^2}{a^2} - \frac{(x-h)^2}{b^2} = 1$$

is the equation of a hyperbola with center (h, k) and with transverse axis parallel to the y-axis.

The equations 6·4 and 6·5 are called the *standard forms* of the equations of an ellipse, and 6·6 and 6·7 are the *standard forms* of the equation of a hyperbola.

Example 5

Find the equation of the ellipse with foci $(1, 2)$ and $(5, 2)$ if the major axis is known to be 6 units long.

Solution: The center of this ellipse (Figure 88) is the point $(3, 2)$ halfway between $(1, 2)$ and $(5, 2)$. Since $2a = 6$, $a = 3$; and since the distance between the foci is 4, $c = 2$. Now, by 5·5,

$$b^2 = a^2 - c^2 = 9 - 4 = 5.$$

Thus, by 6·4, the desired equation is

$$\frac{(x-3)^2}{9} + \frac{(y-2)^2}{5} = 1.$$

To aid in sketching the ellipse, we find the vertices to be $(0, 2)$ and $(6, 2)$, and the ends of the minor axis to be $(3, 2 + \sqrt{5})$ and $(3, 2 - \sqrt{5})$. The length of a latus rectum is $10/3$ (the value of $2b^2/a$); hence the ends of the latera recta may be determined by moving up and down a distance of $5/3$ units from each focus.

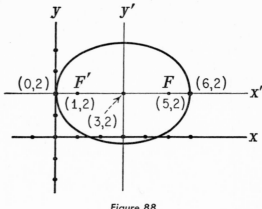

Figure 88

Example 6

Discuss the graph of the equation

$$16x^2 - 9y^2 - 64x + 18y - 89 = 0.$$

Solution: In order to write this in a standard form of an equation of one of the conics, we begin by completing the squares on the terms in x and also on the terms in y.   As a first step it is well to factor the coefficient 16 of x^2 out of the terms involving x; and similarly, -9 from the terms involving y:

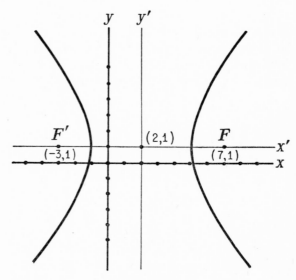

Figure 89

$$16(x^2 - 4x) - 9(y^2 - 2y) = 89,$$
$$16(x^2 - 4x + 4) - 9(y^2 - 2y + 1) = 89 + 64 - 9,$$
$$16(x - 2)^2 - 9(y - 1)^2 = 144.$$

If we divide each member of this equation by 144, it assumes the form

$$\frac{(x - 2)^2}{9} - \frac{(y - 1)^2}{16} = 1.$$

This equation is of the type 6·6 with $a = 3$, $b = 4$, $h = 2$, and $k = 1$. Thus the graph is a hyperbola with center $(2, 1)$ and with transverse axis parallel to the x-axis (Figure 89). The vertices are 3 units from the center; hence the vertices are $(-1, 1)$ and $(5,1)$. For a hyperbola, $c^2 = a^2 + b^2$, so in this case $c = 5$ and the foci are $(-3, 1)$ and $(7, 1)$. The asymptotes have slopes $\pm b/a = \pm 4/3$. Since the asymptotes are on the center $(2, 1)$ they have equations

$$y - 1 = \pm \frac{4}{3}(x - 2).$$

EXERCISES

1. Find the equation of the parabola with vertex $(3, 2)$ and focus $(3, 4)$.

2. Find the equation of the hyperbola with vertices $(-2, 1)$ and $(-2, 3)$, and with one focus $(-2, 4)$.

3. Find the equation of the hyperbola with transverse axis parallel to the x-axis if the length of a latus rectum is 4 and the asymptotes are the lines $x - y - 1 = 0$ and $x + y - 3 = 0$.

4. Find the equation of the ellipse with center $(1, 2)$ and which passes through the points $(0, 7)$ and $(3, 5)$, assuming that the axes of the ellipse are parallel to the coordinate axes.

5. Find the equation of the ellipse with foci $(4, 2)$ and $(8, 2)$, and with eccentricity $1/2$.

6. Find the equation of the hyperbola with foci $(5, 1)$ and $(-11, 1)$, and with one directrix $x = -1$.

7. Find the equation of the parabola with directrix $y = 7$ and focus $(-5, 3)$.

8. Find the equation of the hyperbola with eccentricity $3/2$ and vertices $(1, 1)$ and $(1, 9)$.

9. Find the equation of the ellipse with directrices $y = 0$ and $y = 8$, and with one focus $(2, 5)$.

10. Find the equation of the parabola with directrix $x = 0$ and vertex $(2, 5)$.

11. Find the equation of the locus of points P such that the distance of P from the x-axis is twice the distance between P and the point $(-1, 2)$. Verify that the locus is an ellipse and find the coordinates of the foci.

12. Find the equation of the locus of points P such that the distance between P and the origin is equal to twice the distance of P from the line $x = 4$. Verify that the locus is a hyperbola and find the coordinates of the foci.

13. Find the equation of the circle passing through the vertex and the ends of the latus rectum of the parabola with equation $y^2 + 6y - 4x + 13 = 0$.

14. Find the equation of the hyperbola, the foci and vertices of which are, respectively, the vertices and foci of the ellipse with the equation

$$9x^2 + 25y^2 - 36x + 150y + 36 = 0.$$

In each of Exercises 15–28, discuss and sketch the graph of the given equation.

15. $x^2 - 4y^2 - 4x + 16y - 8 = 0$.   16. $x^2 + x + y + 1 = 0$.

17. $2x^2 + y^2 + 2y - 1 = 0$.   18. $x^2 + y^2 + 6x + 4y = 0$.

19. $4y^2 - x^2 + 8y + 6x - 9 = 0$.   20. $2x^2 + 3y^2 - 16x + 29 = 0$.

21. $16x^2 - 9y^2 - 32x + 16 = 0$.   22. $y^2 + 2y - 4x + 13 = 0$.

23. $x^2 - 2x - 2y + 9 = 0$.   24. $4x^2 - 9y^2 - 24x - 18y - 9 = 0$.

25. $3x^2 + 4y^2 - 6x + 8y - 5 = 0$.   26. $4x^2 + 9y^2 + 4x - 6y - 34 = 0$.

27. $9y^2 - 9x - 6y - 5 = 0$.   28. $x^2 - 4y^2 + 12y - 5 = 0$.

44. ROTATION OF AXES

We now discuss another method of changing coordinate axes. Let us start with given x- and y-axes, and then choose new axes, which we shall call x'- and y'-axes, having the same origin O as the given axes. More precisely, let us assume that Ox and Ox' are the positive halves of the x- and x'-axes respectively, and that Ox' is obtained by rotating Ox through angle θ, as indicated in Figure 90.

Let P be any point in the plane, other than the origin, with coordinates (x, y) relative to the x- and y-axes, and coordinates (x', y') relative to the x'- and y'-axes. Also, let ϕ be the angle in standard position relative to the x'- and y'-axes having P on its terminal side. If $p = |OP|$, then, since P has coordinates (x', y') relative to the x'- and y'-axes, $\sin \phi = y'/p$ and $\cos \phi = x'/p$. Thus we have

6·8
$$\begin{aligned} x' &= p \cos \phi, \\ y' &= p \sin \phi. \end{aligned}$$

Clearly, P is on the terminal side of angle $(\theta + \phi)$ which is in standard position relative to the x- and y-axes, and since P has coordinates (x, y) relative to these axes, we have $\sin (\theta + \phi) = y/p$ and $\cos (\theta + \phi) = x/p$. These give the following equations:

$$\begin{aligned} x &= p \cos (\theta + \phi), \\ y &= p \sin (\theta + \phi). \end{aligned}$$

Using the formulas for the cosine and the sine of the sum of two angles, these take on the form

6·9
$$x = p \cos \theta \cos \phi - p \sin \theta \sin \phi,$$
$$y = p \sin \theta \cos \phi + p \cos \theta \sin \phi.$$

Substituting 6·8 in 6·9, we obtain

6·10
$$x = x' \cos \theta - y' \sin \theta,$$
$$y = x' \sin \theta + y' \cos \theta.$$

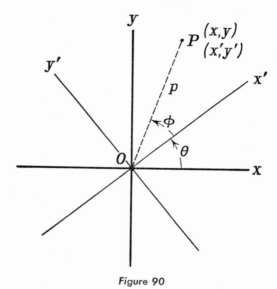

Figure 90

It is not difficult to solve these equations for x' and y' in terms of x and y, to obtain

6·11
$$x' = x \cos \theta + y \sin \theta,$$
$$y' = -x \sin \theta + y \cos \theta.$$

The process of choosing new axes having the same origin as the original axes is called a **rotation of axes**; the angle θ described above is called the **angle of rotation.** What we have shown above is that a point P with coordinates (x, y) relative to the x- and y-axes has coordinates (x', y') given by 6·11 relative to the x'- and y'-axes if the x'- and y'-axes are obtained by a rotation of the x- and y-axes through the angle θ.

We shall now illustrate the use of 6·10 and 6·11.

Example 7

Discuss the graph of the equation $xy = 2$ by using a rotation of axes through an angle of 45°.

Solution: We are here given that $\theta = 45°$. Since

$$\sin 45° = \cos 45° = 1/\sqrt{2},$$

6·10 and 6·11, become, respectively,

$$x = \frac{x' - y'}{\sqrt{2}},$$

6·12

$$y = \frac{x' + y'}{\sqrt{2}},$$

and

$$x' = \frac{x + y}{\sqrt{2}},$$

6·13

$$y' = \frac{-x + y}{\sqrt{2}}.$$

To find the equation of the given curve relative to the new x'- and y'-axes, we replace x and y by their values in 6·12 and find that the equation $xy = 2$ becomes

$$\frac{x'^2 - y'^2}{2} = 2,$$

or

$$\frac{x'^2}{4} - \frac{y'^2}{4} = 1.$$

This we now recognize to be of the form 5·17, which is the equation of a hyperbola with vertices on the x'-axis (Figure 91). Relative to the new coordinate axes, the vertices are $(2, 0)$ and $(-2, 0)$, the foci are $(\sqrt{8}, 0)$ and $(-\sqrt{8}, 0)$, and the equations of the asymptotes are $y' = x'$ and $y' = -x'$. We use 6·12 to find these quantities relative to the original coordinate axes. Thus when $x' = 2$ and $y' = 0$, 6·12 gives $x = 2/\sqrt{2} = \sqrt{2}$ and $y = 2/\sqrt{2} = \sqrt{2}$. Continuing in this manner, we find the vertices to be $(\sqrt{2}, \sqrt{2})$ and $(-\sqrt{2}, -\sqrt{2})$, the foci $(2, 2)$ and $(-2, -2)$, and the equations of the asymptotes $x = 0$ and $y = 0$, all relative to the original axes.

We can now state the final results without mention of the x'- and y'-axes, as follows. The graph of the equation $xy = 2$ is the rectangular hyperbola with the origin as center, vertices $(\sqrt{2}, \sqrt{2})$ and $(-\sqrt{2}, -\sqrt{2})$, foci $(2, 2)$ and $(-2, -2)$, and asymptotes the coordinate axes.

By a simple modification of this example, it is easy to show that if c is any real number other than 0, the equation $xy = c$ is the equation of a rectangular hyperbola with the x- and y-axes as asymptotes. The curve lies in the first and the third quadrants if $c > 0$, and in the second and fourth quadrants if $c < 0$.

Example 7 illustrates a very common use of the formulas for rotation of axes. First, a rotation is performed which changes the equation into one with a known graph, and then the results are expressed relative to the given axes.

In the above example we were *given* the angle of rotation, but fre-

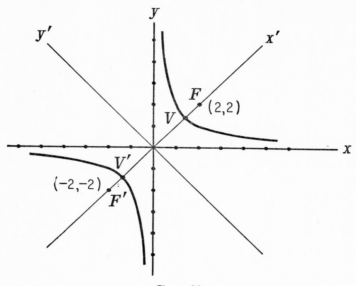

Figure 91

quently one must determine an angle of rotation which will simplify a given equation. This will be illustrated in the next chapter.

EXERCISES

In each of Exercises 1–8, discuss the graph of the given equation by using a rotation of axes through the angle indicated.

1. $x^2 + 4xy + y^2 = 12$; $45°$.

2. $x^2 - 2xy + y^2 - 4\sqrt{2}(x + y) + 8 = 0$; $45°$.

3. $13x^2 - 6\sqrt{3}\,xy + 7y^2 = 16$; $60°$.

4. $4x^2 + 6xy - 4y^2 = 20$; acute angle θ such that $\tan \theta = 1/3$.

5. $5x^2 + 6xy + 5y^2 - 28\sqrt{2}\,x - 20\sqrt{2}\,y + 48 = 0$; $45°$.

6. $x^2 + 6xy + y^2 - 12\sqrt{2}\,x - 20\sqrt{2}\,y + 20 = 0$; $45°$.

7. $x^2 - 4xy + 4y^2 + 2\sqrt{5}\,x + \sqrt{5}\,y = 0$; acute angle θ such that $\tan \theta = 1/2$.

8. $3x^2 + 26\sqrt{3}\,xy - 23y^2 - 144 = 0$; $30°$.

9. Prove 6·11 by solving 6·10 for x' and y'.

chapter 7

Graphs of Equations
of the Second Degree

An equation of the *second degree* is an equation of the form

7·1 $$Ax^2 + Bxy + Cy^2 + Dx + Ey + F = 0,$$

where A, B, C, D, E, and F are real numbers with A, B, and C not all zero. It was shown in Chapter 5 that each of the conics has an equation of the second degree. In this chapter we shall be concerned with the reverse problem of determining the graph of any given equation of the second degree. In particular, we shall prove that, with some rather trivial exceptions, the graph of any second-degree equation is one of the conic sections.

45. SPECIAL EQUATIONS OF THE SECOND DEGREE

We begin with a few almost obvious, but important, remarks about the graphs of equations of some particular types. First, we may point out that not all equations of the second degree *have* graphs, as is easily seen by examples. Thus there are no real numbers x and y which satisfy the equation

$$x^2 + y^2 + 2 = 0,$$

and hence the equation has no graph. Other equations may have graphs consisting of only one point, as illustrated by the equation

$$x^2 + y^2 = 0,$$

the graph of which consists of the single point $(0, 0)$.

Another special case is the following. Let us say that an equation of the second degree is *factorable* if it can be written in the form

7·2 $$(ax + by + c)(dx + ey + f) = 0,$$

where a, b, c, d, e, and f are real numbers. As illustrated in Example 5 of Chapter 3, it is easy to see that the graph of 7·2 consists of the line with equation

$$ax + by + c = 0,$$

and the line with equation

$$dx + ey + f = 0.$$

Thus, for example, the graph of the equation

$$x^2 - y^2 = 0$$

consists of the lines with equations $x + y = 0$ and $x - y = 0$. Also, the graph of the equation

$$x^2 + 2xy + y^2 = 0$$

consists of the *one* line with equation $x + y = 0$, since the left side of the given equation is $(x + y)^2$.

It may be rather difficult to decide whether or not a given equation is factorable, but if it *is* factorable the graph consists of one or two lines. Henceforth, we shall generally restrict our attention to equations that are not factorable and have graphs consisting of more than one point.

46. SECOND-DEGREE EQUATIONS WITH xy-TERM MISSING

We have now reached a point where we can make some preliminary conclusions regarding the graphs of equations of the second degree. In each of the standard forms of the equations of the conics there has been no term involving xy. As a matter of fact, this is because in our previous studies an axis of the conic has always been parallel to one of the coordinate axes. The treatment of conics in an entirely arbitrary position relative to the coordinate axes will be discussed in the following sections. However, the results which we have already obtained in Section 43 will enable us to prove the following theorem.

7·3 Theorem

> *Let*

7·4
$$Ax^2 + Cy^2 + Dx + Ey + F = 0$$

be an equation of the second degree which is not factorable and with a graph consisting of more than one point. Then the graph is always one of the conic sections. More precisely, its graph is an ellipse if A and C have the same sign (that is, if $A \cdot C > 0$), a hyperbola if A and C have opposite signs (that is, if $A \cdot C < 0$), a parabola if either A or C is zero (that is, if $A \cdot C = 0$).

Proof: We observe that A and C are *not both* zero, since 7·4 is an equation of the second degree.

Let us first consider the case in which neither A nor C is zero.   We may then complete the square on the terms involving x, and on the terms involving y, and write 7·4 in the form

7·5
$$A(x - h)^2 + C(y - k)^2 = M,$$

where h, k, and M are real numbers depending on the coefficients of 7·4. We will show, in view of our hypotheses about the graph of 7·4, and therefore of 7·5, that M cannot be zero; for, suppose that $M = 0$ in 7·5.   Then, if A and C have the same sign, the graph would consist of the single point (h, k); whereas if A and C have opposite signs, the left side of 7·5 could be factored, since it is the difference of two squares.   For example, the equation $2(x - 1)^2 - 3(y + 2)^2 = 0$ could be written in the form

$$[\sqrt{2}\,(x - 1) - \sqrt{3}\,(y + 2)][\sqrt{2}\,(x - 1) + \sqrt{3}\,(y + 2)] = 0.$$

Since we have assumed that our given equation (and therefore 7·5) is not factorable and has a graph consisting of more than one point, we conclude that $M \neq 0$.   Thus 7·5 can be written in the form

7·6
$$\frac{(x - h)^2}{M/A} + \frac{(y - k)^2}{M/C} = 1.$$

We now consider two cases according to the signs of A and C.   If A and C have the *same* sign, then M must also have this same sign since otherwise 7·5 would have no graph.   (Why?)   In this case, therefore, M/A and M/C are both positive and 7·6 is the equation of an ellipse in standard form 6·4 or 6·5 depending on the relative magnitudes of M/A and M/C.

If A and C have *opposite* signs, then M/A and M/C have opposite signs and 7·6 is the equation of a hyperbola of the form 6·6 or 6·7.

We now return to 7·4 and consider the case in which either A or C is zero; for definiteness, let us assume that $A \neq 0$ and $C = 0$.   In this case, we can complete the square on the terms in x and write 7·4 in the form

7·7
$$A(x - h)^2 = -Ey + N,$$

where h and N are real numbers depending on the coefficients in 7·4. Now we can conclude that $E \neq 0$; for, if $E = 0$, then 7·7 can be put in the form

$$(x - h)^2 - \frac{N}{A} = 0,$$

and clearly this equation has no graph if A and N have opposite signs, and the equation is factorable if they have the same sign or if $N = 0$.   In view of our hypotheses, we therefore conclude that $E \neq 0$.   Hence we can write 7·7 in the form

7·8
$$(x - h)^2 = -\frac{E}{A}\left(y - \frac{N}{E}\right),$$

and recognize this as being in the form 6·3, which is the equation of a parabola.

If $A = 0$ and $C \neq 0$, similar considerations clearly lead to an equation of a parabola in the form 6·2. This completes the proof of the theorem.

47. ELIMINATION OF *xy*-TERM

In Theorem 7·3 of the preceding section we determined the graph of any equation of the second degree in which there is no term involving xy. The proof of this theorem was based on the standard forms of the equations of the conics. These were obtained as an application of the use of *translation* of axes. In this section we will consider equations of the second degree in which there is a term involving xy, and will show that by a suitable *rotation* to new x'- and y'-axes it is always possible to change the equation into one in which the coefficient of $x'y'$ is zero. The graph can then be determined by the methods previously developed.

Let

7·9
$$Ax^2 + Bxy + Cy^2 + Dx + Ey + F = 0$$

be an equation of the second degree with $B \neq 0$. If we rotate the axes through an angle θ by means of 6·10, this equation takes the form

7·10
$$A'x'^2 + B'x'y' + C'y'^2 + D'x' + E'y' + F' = 0,$$

and a straightforward but detailed calculation shows that

7·11
$$
\begin{aligned}
A' &= A\cos^2\theta + B\sin\theta\cos\theta + C\sin^2\theta, \\
B' &= 2(C - A)\sin\theta\cos\theta + B(\cos^2\theta - \sin^2\theta), \\
C' &= A\sin^2\theta - B\sin\theta\cos\theta + C\cos^2\theta, \\
D' &= D\cos\theta + E\sin\theta, \\
E' &= E\cos\theta - D\sin\theta, \\
F' &= F.
\end{aligned}
$$

Evidently B' will be zero provided that

$$2(C - A)\sin\theta\cos\theta + B(\cos^2\theta - \sin^2\theta) = 0.$$

Dividing through by $\cos^2\theta$ and replacing $\sin\theta/\cos\theta$ by $\tan\theta$, we may write this equation in the form

$$B\tan^2\theta - 2(C - A)\tan\theta - B = 0.$$

Solving this as a quadratic equation in $\tan\theta$, we obtain

7·12
$$\tan\theta = \frac{C - A \pm \sqrt{(C - A)^2 + B^2}}{B}.$$

Thus $\tan \theta$ equals one of two real numbers given by the right side of 7·12. Since there always exists an angle whose tangent is a given real number, there always exists an angle θ satisfying 7·12. Furthermore, our calculations show that a rotation of axes through *any* angle θ satisfying 7·12 will transform 7·9 into 7·10 with $B' = 0$, and the method of the preceding section can then be used to discuss the graph.

As a matter of fact, we can always limit ourselves to a rotation through an angle θ such that $0° < \theta < 90°$ if we wish. To see this, we observe that $B \neq 0$ implies that

$$\sqrt{(C - A)^2 + B^2} > |C - A|,$$

and hence one of the values of $\tan \theta$ in 7·12 is positive and the other is negative. The desired result then follows from the observation that there exists an *acute* angle θ such that $\tan \theta$ is any given positive real number.

Example 1

Discuss the graph of the equation

$$29x^2 - 24xy + 36y^2 + 118x - 24y - 55 = 0$$

by a suitable rotation of axes.

Solution: For this equation, $A = 29$, $B = -24$, and $C = 36$; therefore 7·12 becomes

$$\tan \theta = \frac{7 \pm \sqrt{49 + 576}}{-24} = \frac{7 \pm 25}{-24},$$

from which we get $\tan \theta = 3/4$ or $\tan \theta = -4/3$. Let us choose θ to be the *acute* angle such that $\tan \theta = 3/4$. It follows easily that $\sin \theta = 3/5$ and $\cos \theta = 4/5$; hence Equations 6·10 for a rotation of axes through angle θ become

7·13
$$x = \frac{4x' - 3y'}{5},$$
$$y = \frac{3x' + 4y'}{5}.$$

If we substitute these expressions for x and y in the given equation, and simplify, we obtain

$$4x'^2 + 9y'^2 + 16x' - 18y' - 11 = 0.$$

By completion of the squares, this can be put in the form

$$\frac{(x' + 2)^2}{9} + \frac{(y' - 1)^2}{4} = 1.$$

We now recognize this as the standard form 6·4 of the equation of an ellipse with center $(-2, 1)$ in the x'- and y'-coordinates, and with major axis parallel to the x'-axis. For this ellipse, $a = 3$ and $b = 2$, so the vertices are $V(1, 1)$ and $V'(-5, 1)$, and the ends of the minor axis are $B(-2, 3)$ and $B'(-2, -1)$ in x'- and y'-coordinates (Figure 92). To find

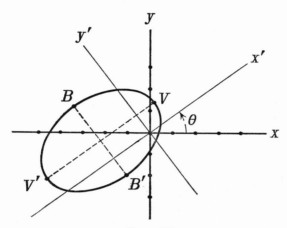

Figure 92

the coordinates of V and V' relative to the x- and y-axes, we use Equations 7·13 above. Thus when $x' = 1$ and $y' = 1$, $x = (4 - 3)/5$ and $y = (3 + 4)/5$; and the coordinates of V relative to the x- and y-axes are $(1/5, 7/5)$. Similarly, V' has coordinates $(-23/5, -11/5)$, B has coordinates $(-17/5, 6/5)$, and B' has coordinates $(-1, -2)$, all relative to the x- and y-axes. The center of the ellipse is $(-11/5, -2/5)$, relative to the x- and y-axes. Of course, the coordinates of the foci and of the ends of the latera recta can be found by the same method.

EXERCISES

In each of Exercises 1–16, discuss and sketch the graph by first performing a suitable rotation of axes.

1. $2x^2 + 4xy + 5y^2 = 6$.

2. $x^2 + 3xy + 5y^2 = 22$.

3. $9x^2 + 24xy + 16y^2 - 125y = 0$.

4. $2x^2 - 4xy - y^2 = 6$.

5. $x^2 - 2xy + y^2 - 2\sqrt{2}\,x - 2\sqrt{2}\,y + 2 = 0$.

6. $17x^2 - 12xy + 8y^2 + 2\sqrt{5}\,x + 4\sqrt{5}\,y - 15 = 0$.

7. $2x^2 + 6xy + 10y^2 - 11 = 0$.

8. $9x^2 - 12xy + 4y^2 + 30x - 20y + 24 = 0$.

9. $xy + x + y = 0$.

10. $16x^2 + 24xy + 9y^2 + 60x - 80y - 100 = 0$.

11. $4x^2 + 3xy + 45 = 0$.

12. $44y^2 + 600xy - 551x^2 - 676 = 0$.

13. $73x^2 + 72xy + 52y^2 - 220x - 40y + 100 = 0$.

14. $64x^2 - 240xy + 225y^2 - 1020x - 544y = 0$.

15. $119x^2 + 240xy - 119y^2 + 130x - 312y - 338 = 0$.

16. $36x^2 - 24xy + 29y^2 - 24x - 32y - 160 = 0$.

17. Show that $\cot 2\theta = (A - C)/B$, where θ is the angle of rotation in 7·12.

18. Show that the two values of $\tan \theta$ given in 7·12 are negative reciprocals.

48. GRAPH OF ANY SECOND-DEGREE EQUATION

The methods which we have so far developed show how to determine the graph of any equation of the second degree; for, if $B \neq 0$, Equation 7·1 can be transformed by a suitable rotation of axes into Equation 7·10 with $B' = 0$. Then we can attempt to write the equation in a standard form of the equation of one of the conic sections by completing the squares. If the equation cannot be put in any such form, the proof of 7·3 implies that the equation is factorable (in which case the graph is one or two lines), or has no graph, or has a graph of only one point. At any rate, the nature of the graph will then be apparent from the form of the equation.

Although the above process can be carried out with any given second-degree equation, the following theorem is of considerable theoretical importance. It is clearly a generalization of 7·3.

7·14   Theorem

Let

7·15 $$Ax^2 + Bxy + Cy^2 + Dx + Ey + F = 0$$

be an equation of the second degree which is not factorable and with a graph consisting of more than one point.   Then its graph is always one of the conics. Its graph is a parabola if $B^2 - 4AC = 0$, an ellipse (or a circle as a special case) if $B^2 - 4AC < 0$, a hyperbola if $B^2 - 4AC > 0$.

Proof: First we consider a rotation of axes through *any* angle θ, and under this rotation Formulas 6·10 transform 7·15 into

7·16 $$A'x'^2 + B'x'y' + C'y'^2 + D'x' + E'y' + F' = 0,$$

where the coefficients are given by Formulas 7·11.   Using the fact that $\sin^2 \theta + \cos^2 \theta = 1$, it follows easily from 7·11 that

7·17 $$A' + C' = A + C.$$

Also, by straightforward algebraic calculation and use of appropriate trigonometric identities, it is possible to show that

7·18 $$B'^2 - 4A'C' = B^2 - 4AC.$$

Now we can easily show that 7·16 is actually an equation of the second degree, that is, that we cannot have A', B', and C' all zero. For suppose that $A' = B' = C' = 0$. Then, from 7·17, $A = -C$, and thus we see from 7·18 that $B^2 + 4C^2 = 0$. Hence we must have $B = C = 0$, and also $A = -C = 0$. However, it is given that 7·15 is an equation of the second degree, which means that A, B, and C are not all zero. Since the assumption that $A' = B' = C' = 0$ leads to the false conclusion that $A = B = C = 0$, the assumption itself must be false; therefore not all of A', B', and C' are zero. Thus by rotation of axes an equation of the second degree is always transformed into an equation of the second degree.

The graph of 7·15 consists of more than one point and therefore the same certainly holds for 7·16, since these are two different equations with the same graph. If 7·16 were factorable, say

$$(ax' + by' + c)(dx' + ey' + f) = 0,$$

then, on replacing x' and y' in this factored form by their values given in 6·11, we would obtain a factorization of 7·15, contrary to assumption. Thus we conclude that 7·16 is never factorable for any angle θ.

We now choose the angle of rotation θ in such a way that $B' = 0$ in 7·16. That this is always possible was shown in the preceding section. Thus under this rotation of axes, 7·15 becomes

7·19 $$A'x'^2 + C'y'^2 + D'x' + E'y' + F' = 0,$$

and by our hypotheses on 7·15 we know that this is a second-degree equation which is not factorable and with a graph consisting of more than one point. Since now $B' = 0$, 7·18 becomes

7·20 $$-4A'C' = B^2 - 4AC.$$

We may now complete our proof by applying Theorem 7·3 to Equation 7·19. If $B^2 - 4AC = 0$, then 7·20 shows that $-4A'C' = 0$ and hence $A' = 0$ or $C' = 0$. Thus 7·3 states that the graph is a parabola. If $B^2 - 4AC < 0$, 7·20 shows that $A'C' > 0$, so that by 7·3 the graph is an ellipse. Finally, if $B^2 - 4AC > 0$, then $A'C' < 0$ and, again by 7·3, the graph is a hyperbola. This concludes the proof of the theorem.

EXERCISES

1. Prove Equation 7·18.

On the assumption that each of the following equations is not factorable and has a graph consisting of more than one point, identify its graph.

2. $3x^2 + 12xy + 12y^2 + 10x + 10y + 7 = 0.$

3. $x^2 - 3xy + 2y^2 + 2x - y + 6 = 0.$

4. $3x^2 - 4xy + 2y^2 - 3y = 0.$

5. $2x^2 + 12xy + 18y^2 - x + 3y + 6 = 0.$

6. $3x^2 - xy - 2y^2 + 1 = 0.$

7. $-x^2 + xy - y^2 + 1 = 0.$

8. $x^2 - 4xy + y^2 + 4x - 3y + 7 = 0.$

9. $3x^2 - 2xy + 4y^2 - 8 = 0.$

10. $x^2 + 3xy - x + y = 0.$

11. $x^2 - 6xy + 9y^2 + x - y - 1 = 0.$

12. $xy - 3x + 2y + 4 = 0.$

Algebraic and Transcendental Curves

Up to this point we have studied in detail the graphs of linear and quadratic equations. In this chapter we shall discuss briefly the graphs of a number of other types of equations and, in so doing, we shall use freely the ideas and results of Chapter 3 having to do with intercepts, symmetry, and extent of a curve.

An **algebraic curve** is the graph of an equation of the form

$$P(x, y) = 0,$$

where $P(x, y)$ represents a polynomial in x and y. Thus the lines and the conic sections are examples of algebraic curves, as are the graphs of such equations as the following:

$$xy^2 - 2y - x = 0,$$
$$xy - x^3 - 1 = 0,$$
$$y - 3x^4 + 4x^3 + 12x^2 - 15 = 0.$$

Those curves which are not algebraic curves are called **transcendental curves.** Simple examples of transcendental curves are the graphs of the following equations:

$$y = \log_{10} x,$$
$$\sin x + y - \cos x = 0,$$
$$y = 2^x.$$

In a brief account such as this it will be impossible to illustrate and discuss all the different types of algebraic and transcendental curves, but we shall consider some of the simpler and more common types. We begin with a discussion of an important special class of algebraic curves.

49. POLYNOMIAL CURVES

A **polynomial curve** is the graph of an equation of the form $y = P(x)$, where $P(x)$ is a polynomial in x. Thus the equation of a polynomial curve has the form

8·1$$y = a_0x^n + a_1x^{n-1} + \cdots + a_n,$$

where the coefficients $a_0, a_1, \cdots, a_n$ are real numbers with $a_0 \neq 0$, and n is a positive integer or zero. The polynomial on the right side of 8·1, as well as the equation itself, is said to have *degree n*. If $n = 0$ or 1, we already know that the graph of Equation 8·1 is a line, and if $n = 2$, that it is a parabola. Accordingly, we shall here limit ourselves to a consideration of equations of degree 3 or higher.

Before proceeding to a number of illustrative examples, we may state, without proof, the following facts from algebra, which may be helpful in drawing the graph of an equation 8·1 of degree n. In the first place, the graph cannot cut the x-axis (or any other line) in more than n points. The number may, of course, be smaller than n. Another useful observation is that if $|x|$ is sufficiently large, the term a_0x^n is numerically larger than the sum of all the other terms. It follows that for sufficiently large $|x|$, the sign of y is determined by the sign of a_0x^n. As an illustration, if $|x|$ is sufficiently large, the values of y determined from the equation

$$y = 2x^3 - 3x^2 - 20x + 250$$

must have the sign of $2x^3$; that is, they are positive for large positive x and negative for large negative x. Thus we know that for large positive values of x the graph of the equation is *above* the x-axis, and for large negative values of x it is *below* the x-axis.

Example 1

Sketch the graph of the equation $y = x^3$.

Solution: Clearly the only intercept on either axis is the origin. Also, by 3·4, the curve is symmetric with respect to the origin. Since x and y have the same sign, the curve lies in the first and third quadrants. Accordingly, we only need to determine the graph in the first quadrant, and then draw the rest of it by symmetry. Since x^3 may be arbitrarily large if x is taken sufficiently large, the curve is not bounded in any way. Listed below is a table of corresponding values of x and y, from which we can make a satisfactory sketch of the graph in the first quadrant.

x	0	.1	.5	.75	1	1.5	2	2.5	3
y	0	.001	.12	.42	1	3.4	8	15.6	27

We have taken several values of x between 0 and 1 to bring out the fact that for small values of x the corresponding values of y are very small, and the curve is quite close to the x-axis. The graph is indicated in Figure 93. It will be noted that we have made the scale along the y-axis different from that along the x-axis.*

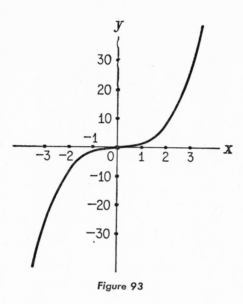

Figure 93

Example 2

Sketch the graph of the equation $y = x^4$.

Solution: In this case, the curve is symmetric with respect to the y-axis and lies in the first and second quadrants. The graph is shown in Figure 94 and has been drawn using symmetry and the following table of values.

x	0	.1	.5	1	1.5	2	2.5
y	0	.0001	.06	1	5.06	16	39.1

It will be observed that for x between 0 and 1, the curve lies under the curve of Figure 93, but for $x > 1$, the curve is above the curve of Figure 93. Although this graph somewhat resembles a parabola it is *not* a parabola since the equation of a parabola is an equation of the second degree.

---

* It is frequently convenient to do this when we are concerned only with showing the general shape of the graph. Of course, if we were interested in areas in the plane or in distances along lines not parallel to either coordinate axis, it would be desirable to use the same unit on both axes.

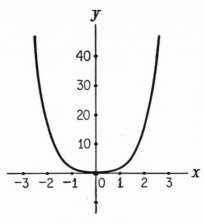

Figure 94

Example 3

Sketch the graph of the equation

$$y = x(x - 2)(x + 4).$$

Solution: Setting $y = 0$, we find that the x-intercepts are $x = 0, 2$, and -4. There is no symmetry with respect to either axis or to the origin; therefore we simply construct the following table of values.

x	-4.5	-4	-3.5	-3	-2.5	-2	-1.5	-1
y	-14.6	0	9.6	15	16.9	16	13.1	9

x	$-.5$	0	$.5$	1	1.5	2	2.5	3
y	4.4	0	-3.4	-5	-4.1	0	8.1	21

The graph is sketched in Figure 95.   Since the equation of this curve can be written in the form

$$y = x^3 + 2x^2 - 8x,$$

it is an equation of degree 3, and, from the remarks made above, the curve can not cross the x-axis more than three times.   Hence we know that for $x > 2$, y will have to remain positive, as is indeed obvious from the factored form of the equation.   Similarly, for $x < -4$, y will always be negative.

It appears from our graph that the curve has a "minimum point" near $x = 1$, and a "maximum point" somewhere between -3 and -2. The exact determination of these points is a problem of the calculus and cannot be treated here. It may be of interest to state without proof that these points occur, respectively, at the following two values of x:

$$x = \frac{-2 + 2\sqrt{7}}{3} \qquad \text{and} \qquad x = \frac{-2 - 2\sqrt{7}}{3}.$$

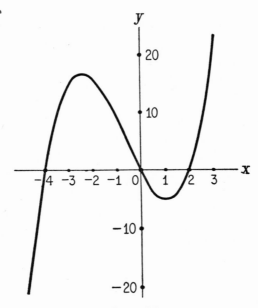

Figure 95

These are approximately equal to 1.097 and -2.431, respectively.

Example 4

Sketch the graph of the equation

$$y = 3x^4 - 4x^3 - 12x^2 + 15.$$

Solution: In the preceding examples, the right side of the equation has been given in factored form, and it was very easy to compute the value of y corresponding to a given value of x. In this case, considerably more work is involved, and it is therefore convenient to use the process of "synthetic division" which is explained in algebra courses. For example, to find the value of y corresponding to $x = 2$, we may substitute directly into the given equation, or, better, we may carry out the following calculations.

$$\begin{array}{rrrrr|r}
3 & -4 & -12 & 0 & 15 & \underline{2} \\
 & 6 & 4 & -16 & -32 & \\
\hline
3 & 2 & -8 & -16 & -17 &
\end{array}$$

The desired value of y is therefore -17.

To illustrate synthetic division with one more case, let us find the

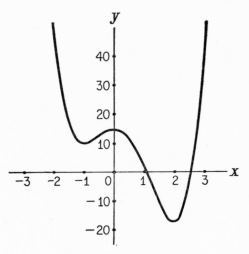

Figure 96

value of y corresponding to $x = -3$.   The calculations are as follows.

$$\begin{array}{rrrrr|r}
3 & -4 & -12 & 0 & 15 & \underline{-3} \\
 & -9 & 39 & -81 & 243 & \\
\hline
3 & -13 & 27 & -81 & 258 &
\end{array}$$

Thus the value of y is 258.   The table below has been constructed by this process.   The graph is sketched in Figure 96.

x	-2	-1.5	-1	$-.5$	0	.5	1	1.5	2	2.5	3
y	47	16.7	10	12.7	15	11.7	2	-10.3	-17	-5.3	42

EXERCISES

In each of Exercises 1–22, sketch the graph of the given equation.

1. $y = x^3 + 2.$ 2. $y = 2x^3 + 1.$

3. $y = x - x^3.$ 4. $y = x^3 - 4x.$

5. $y = x^3 - 2x^2 + x.$

6. $y = x(x + 1)(2 - x).$

7. $y = x^4 + 3.$

8. $y = x^2 - x^4.$

9. $y = x^3 - x^4 + 1.$

10. $y = (x - 1)^4 + 1.$

11. $y = x^4 + 4x^3 - 2x^2 + 12x - 10.$

12. $y = x^4 + x^3 - x^2 - 5.$

13. $y = x^5.$

14. $y = x^6.$

15. $y = x(1 - x^2)^2.$

16. $y = (1 - x^2)^2.$

17. $y = x^2(1 - x)^3.$

18. $y = x^5 - x.$

19. $y = 2x^3 - x^2 + x - 4.$

20. $y = x^4 - x^3 + x^2 + x + 1.$

21. $y = x^4 + 3x^2 - 2.$

22. $y = 2x^3 + 2x^2 - 3x - 1.$

23. Show that the graph of the equation $y = x^3 + ax + b$ is symmetric with respect to the point $(0, b)$. [*Hint:* Translate the origin to this point.]

24. Show that the graph of the equation $y = x^3 + 3ax^2 + bx + c$ is symmetric with respect to the point $(-a, 2a^3 - ba + c)$. [*Hint:* Translate the origin to this point.]

50.   RATIONAL CURVES

We next consider another special class of algebraic curves. A **rational curve** is the graph of an equation of the form

$$y = \frac{P(x)}{Q(x)},$$

where $P(x)$ and $Q(x)$ are polynomials in x. In more explicit form, a rational curve has an equation of the form

8·2
$$y = \frac{a_0 x^n + a_1 x^{n-1} + \cdots + a_n}{b_0 x^m + b_1 x^{m-1} + \cdots + b_m},$$

where the coefficients of the different powers of x are real numbers with $a_0 \neq 0$ and $b_0 \neq 0$. If the degree m of the denominator is zero, the right side of 8·2 is a polynomial in x. Since polynomial equations have been considered in the preceding section, in the discussion which follows we shall assume that m is a *positive* integer. The degree n of the numerator may be zero or a positive integer.

Before proceeding to some illustrative examples, we make one definition as follows. If a point on a curve approaches arbitrarily near to a fixed line l as the point recedes indefinitely along the curve, the line l is called an **asymptote** of the curve. Of course, this agrees with our previous use of the term for the hyperbola.

It happens frequently that a rational curve has one or more asymptotes. For example, the rational curve with equation $xy = 2$ (or $y = 2/x$), which was discussed in Example 7 of Chapter 6, was found to be a hyperbola with the x- and y-axes as asymptotes.   Methods of finding the asymptotes of a rational curve will be indicated in the following examples.

Example 5

Sketch the graph of the equation

$$y = x^2 + \frac{1}{x}.$$

Solution: A fundamental way in which the graph of this equation differs from the previous graphs of this chapter is that there is one value of x,

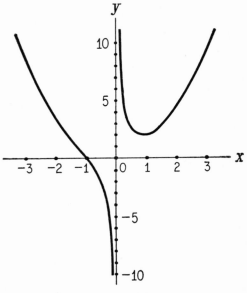

Figure 97

namely 0, that has no corresponding value of y.   Furthermore, if x is very near to zero, x^2 will be small, but $|1/x|$ will be very large.   Hence $|y|$ will be very large, with the sign of y depending on the sign of x.   It is therefore clear that the curve approaches arbitrarily near to the y-axis as x approaches zero, that is, that the y-axis is an asymptote of the curve.

If $|x|$ is large, $|1/x|$ will be small but x^2 will be large, so that y will be a large positive number.   There is no symmetry; therefore we have to consider both positive and negative values of x.   By setting $y = 0$, we find that the only x-intercept is $x = -1$.   In the accompanying table of values, some of the values are carried out to a large number of decimal places, although such precision cannot be shown on the graph.   This has been done merely to indicate how y varies if $|x|$ is small.   The graph is shown in Figure 97.

x	-3	-2	-1	$-.5$	$-.1$	$-.01$
y	8.7	3.5	0	-1.7	-9.99	-99.9999

x	.01	.1	.5	1	1.5	2	3
y	100.00001	10.01	2.2	2	2.9	4.5	9.3

The following observations furnish a partial check on our work. If $|x|$ is large, $x^2 + 1/x$ is approximately equal to x^2, and hence for large values of x (either positive or negative) the graph should closely resemble that of the parabola $y = x^2$. Also, if $|x|$ is small, $x^2 + 1/x$ is approximately equal to $1/x$, and thus for small values of $|x|$ the graph should resemble that of the hyperbola $y = 1/x$. It will be observed that this is indeed the case.

Example 6

Discuss the graph of the equation

$$y = \frac{x - 1}{x^2 - 2x - 3}.$$

Solution: Since $x^2 - 2x - 3 = (x - 3)(x + 1)$, we see that the denominator is zero for $x = 3$ or $x = -1$, and hence for these values of x there are no corresponding values of y. As in the preceding example, the lines $x = 3$ and $x = -1$ are asymptotes of this curve. These asymptotes are indicated by dotted lines in Figure 98.

By setting $x = 0$, we see that the y-intercept is $1/3$; and by setting $y = 0$, we find that the only x-intercept is 1. The graph, shown in Figure 98, has been drawn using the facts just mentioned and the accompanying table of values. From the figure it seems apparent that the curve

x	-4	-3	-2	-1.5	-1.25	-1.1	$-.9$	$-.5$	0
y	$-.23$	$-.33$	$-.60$	-1.11	-3.13	-5.1	4.9	.85	.33

x	.5	1	2	2.5	2.9	3.1	3.5	4	5
y	.13	0	$-.33$	$-.85$	-4.9	5.1	1.1	.60	.33

approaches arbitrarily close to the x-axis as one moves far to the right or left, or, in other words, that the x-axis also is an asymptote of the curve. That this is the case can be shown as follows. In the given equation divide the numerator and the denominator of the right side by x^2, and write the equation in the form

$$y = \frac{\dfrac{1}{x} - \dfrac{1}{x^2}}{1 - \dfrac{2}{x} - \dfrac{3}{x^2}}.$$

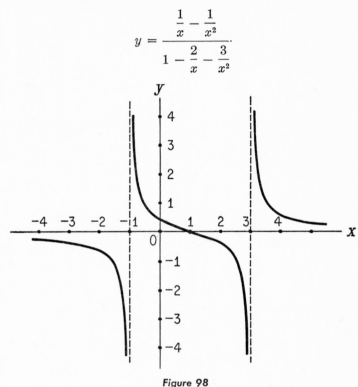

Figure 98

If $|x|$ is sufficiently large, the numerator is arbitrarily small in absolute value, whereas the denominator is close to 1. Thus y approaches zero as x increases indefinitely in absolute value. This fact shows that the x-axis is an asymptote.

Example 7

Sketch the graph of the equation

$$y = \frac{x^2 + x - 2}{2x^2 + 1}.$$

Solution: First we find the x-intercepts by setting $y = 0$. This leads to the equation $x^2 + x - 2 = 0$, or $(x + 2)(x - 1) = 0$. The x-intercepts are therefore $x = 1$ and $x = -2$. The y-intercept is $y = -2$.

Since the equation $2x^2 + 1 = 0$ has no real solution, there is no vertical asymptote. However, we find, by the following steps, that there is a horizontal asymptote. If we divide $x^2 + x - 2$ by $2x^2 + 1$ by use of long division, we find that the quotient is $1/2$ and the remainder is $x - 5/2$. Hence the given equation can be written in the form

$$y = \frac{1}{2} + \frac{x - \dfrac{5}{2}}{2x^2 + 1}.$$

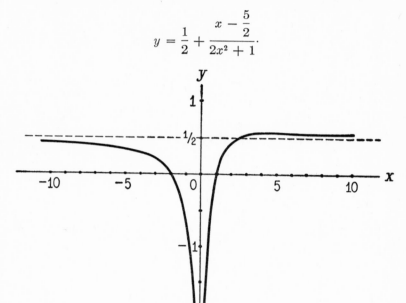

Figure 99

By the argument used in the preceding example, it follows that

$$\frac{x - \dfrac{5}{2}}{2x^2 + 1}.$$

approaches zero as $|x|$ increases indefinitely, and hence y approaches $1/2$. It follows that the line $y = 1/2$ is a horizontal asymptote of the curve.

Using the information so far obtained, along with the table of values given below, we may sketch the graph as shown in Figure 99. In the table we have inserted two entries which do not show on the graph, namely, $x = -100$ and $x = 100$, to verify that y has a value nearly $1/2$ for large $|x|$. Since y changes so little between various entries in the neighborhood of $x = -6$, we have carried these out to two decimal places; and to show how y changes with x in the neighborhood of $x = 5$ we have had to carry these out to three decimal places.

x	-100	-8	-7	-6	-5	-4	-3	-2	-1	0
y	.495	.42	.40	.38	.35	.30	.21	0	$-.67$	-2

x	.5	1	2	3	4	5	6	7	8	100
y	$-.83$	0	.44	.53	.545	.549	.548	.545	.543	.505

The preceding examples suggest a few general facts about the asymptotes of a rational curve. The vertical asymptotes are always obtained by finding those values of x, if any, for which the denominator is equal to zero. If a rational curve has an equation 8·2 in which the degree m of the denominator is greater than the degree n of the numerator, the x-axis is an asymptote of the curve (Example 6). If $m = n$, as in Example 7, there will be a horizontal asymptote which is not the x-axis. If $m < n$, there will be no horizontal asymptote (Example 5). However, in the special case in which the degree of the numerator exceeds the degree of the denominator by exactly 1, there will be an asymptote which is neither horizontal nor vertical. As an example, consider the equation

$$y = \frac{3x^3 + 2x^2 - x + 4}{x^2 - 5}.$$

By use of long division, we can write this equation in the form

$$y = 3x + 2 + \frac{14x + 14}{x^2 - 5}.$$

Since the last term approaches zero as x increases indefinitely, it is clear that y approaches $3x + 2$. Thus the line $y = 3x + 2$ will be an asymptote of the graph.

EXERCISES

Sketch the graph of each of the following equations.

1. $y = x - \dfrac{1}{x}.$ 2. $y = 2x + \dfrac{3}{x}.$

3. $y = \dfrac{x + 1}{x - 1}.$ 4. $y = \dfrac{x^2 + 2}{x + 2}.$

5. $y = \dfrac{x + 2}{x^2 - 1}.$ 6. $y = \dfrac{x}{x^2 - 3x + 2}.$

7. $y = \dfrac{x^2 + 1}{x^2}.$ 8. $2xy + 1 = x^2(1 - y).$

9. $x^3 - x^2y - xy + 6y = 0.$

10. $x^2(y - x) = 1 - y.$

11. $y = \dfrac{x}{x^2 + 1}.$

12. $y = \dfrac{x^2}{4x^2 - 1}.$

13. $y = \dfrac{2x^2 + 5x - 3}{x^2 - 3x}.$

14. $y = \dfrac{(x + 1)(x - 2)^2}{(x - 1)^2}.$

15. $x^4 - 4y = x^2(1 - y).$

16. $y = \dfrac{(x^2 - 9)(x - 2)}{x^2 - 1}.$

17. $y = \dfrac{1}{x(x^2 - 1)}.$

18. $y = \dfrac{x - 1}{x^3 + x^2}.$

19. $xy^2 - 4x - y = 0.$

20. $y^2(1 - x) = 4.$

51. OTHER ALGEBRAIC CURVES

In this section we shall give a few simple examples of algebraic curves that are not rational curves.

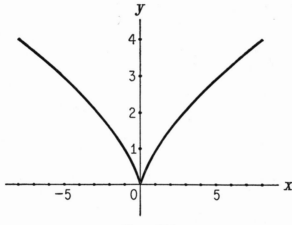

Figure 100

Example 8

Sketch the graph of the equation $y^3 = x^2$.

Solution: In this case there is symmetry with respect to the y-axis. Since x^2 can never be negative, and the real cube root of a positive number is always positive, no part of the graph is in the third or fourth quadrants. Accordingly, we need only sketch the graph in the first quadrant, and the part in the second quadrant can be drawn by symmetry. Since $y = x^{2/3}$, the values of y corresponding to most values of x have to be computed by using a table of cube roots or by use of logarithms. The following table of values gives sufficient information to enable us to indicate the shape of the graph as shown in Figure 100.

x	0	.1	.5	1	1.5	2	3	4	5	6	7	8
y	0	.21	.63	1	1.31	1.59	2.08	2.51	2.92	3.30	3.66	4

Example 9

Sketch the graph of the equation

$$y^2 = x(x - 2)(x - 3).$$

Solution: It is easily verified that the product $x(x - 2)(x - 3)$ is negative for $x < 0$ or for $2 < x < 3$. Since $y^2 \geqq 0$ for every real number y, no portion of the curve can be to the left of the y-axis or between the lines $x = 2$ and $x = 3$. In computing a table of values we therefore consider only values of x such that $0 \leq x \leq 2$ or $x \geq 3$. Furthermore, the curve is symmetric with respect to the x-axis; so we can limit our table to positive values of y.

x	0	.2	.5	.8	1	1.5	2	3	3.5	4	4.5	5
y	0	1	1.37	1.45	1.41	1.06	0	0	1.62	2.83	4.11	5.48

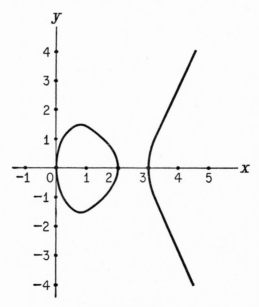

Figure 101

The graph is indicated in Figure 101. Note that the graph consists of an oval and another distinct branch.

Example 10

Sketch the graph of the equation

$$xy^2 - 2y - x = 0.$$

Solution: In this case, we can easily solve for x and write the equation in the form

$$x = \frac{2y}{y^2 - 1}.$$

Accordingly, we can use the methods of Section 50, provided we interchange the roles of x and y. Since $y^2 - 1 = 0$ has the solutions $y = \pm 1$, we see that the lines $y = 1$ and $y = -1$ are asymptotes of the curve. Also, as $|y|$ increases indefinitely, x approaches zero; hence $x = 0$ is an asymptote. Clearly the only intercept on either axis is the origin. The curve is symmetric with respect to the origin; so we may limit ourselves to positive values of y and draw the rest of the graph by use of this sym-

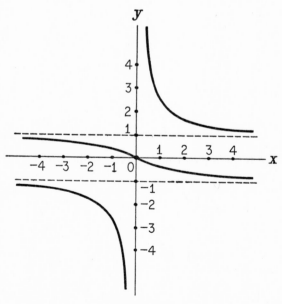

Figure 102

metry.   In the table below, we have assigned values to y and computed the corresponding values of x.   The graph is shown in Figure 102.

x	$-.42$	$-.96$	-1.87	-4.45	5.45	2.92	2.05	1.61	1.33	$.95$	$.75$	$.53$	$.42$
y	$.2$	$.4$	$.6$	$.8$	1.2	1.4	1.6	1.8	2	2.5	3	4	5

Example 11

Sketch the graph of the equation

$$x^2 y^2 - y^2 = 1.$$

Solution: This curve is symmetric with respect to both coordinate axes,

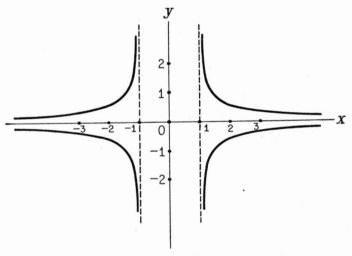

Figure 103

and there are no intercepts on either axis.   The equation can be written in the form

$$y^2 = \frac{1}{x^2 - 1},$$

from which it is apparent that the lines $x = 1$ and $x = -1$ are asymptotes.   Also, for increasingly large $|x|$, the right side approaches zero, and hence $y = 0$ also is an asymptote.   The graph in Figure 103 is drawn in the first quadrant from the table of values, and the rest is then drawn by use of symmetry.   Since $x^2 - 1 < 0$ for $-1 < x < 1$, no point on the curve is between the vertical asymptotes.

x	1.1	1.2	1.4	1.6	1.8	2	3	4	5
y	2.18	1.51	1.02	.80	.67	.58	.35	.26	.20

EXERCISES

Sketch the graph of each of the following equations.

1. $y^2 = 4x^3$.
2. $y^3 + 1 = x^2$.
3. $y^2 = x^3 - x$.
4. $y^2 = x^3 - 4x^2$.
5. $y^2 = (x - 2)(x^2 - 1)$.
6. $y^2 = x - x^3$.
7. $y^2 = \dfrac{1}{x^2 + 1}$.
8. $x^2y^2 = 4$.
9. $y^2x^3 = x^2 + 2x + 1$.
10. $x + y^2 + xy^2 = 0$.
11. $y^2 = x^2(1 - x^2)$.
12. $y^2 = x^2(x^2 - 1)$.
13. $x + y^2 - x^2y^2 = 0$.
14. $y^2 = \dfrac{x(x + 1)}{x - 1}$.
15. $y^2 = \dfrac{x^3}{x - 1}$.
16. $y^2 = \dfrac{x^2 - 1}{x + 2}$.
17. $y^2 + xy^2 + 1 = x$.
18. $y^2x^2 - x^2 = x + 1$.
19. $xy + x - y^3 = 1$.
20. $xy^2 = 4x + y^2$.

52. TRIGONOMETRIC CURVES

We now discuss briefly a few transcendental curves, and begin with a consideration of the graphs of simple trigonometric equations. In drawing the graphs of equations involving the trigonometric functions we shall conform with the usual procedure of advanced mathematics and consider the angles to be measured in radians rather than in degrees. The student will find a brief explanation of radian measure and some other facts from trigonometry in the appendix to this book.

Values of certain of the trigonometric functions are given in Table I of the appendix. This table also has entries which make it possible to change from degree measure to radian measure, and vice versa.

Example 12

Discuss and sketch the graph of the equation $y = \sin x$.

Solution: First, let us find the intercepts. If we set $x = 0$, we obtain $y = \sin 0 = 0$; hence the only y-intercept is the origin of coordinates. However, if we set $y = 0$, the equation $\sin x = 0$ is satisfied for $x = n\pi$, where *n* is *any* integer, and hence there is an unlimited number of *x*-intercepts.

Since *x* can take on any value, it is evident that the graph is not bounded. On the other hand, since for all values of *x*, $|\sin x| \leqq 1$, the graph does lie between the lines $y = 1$ and $y = -1$.

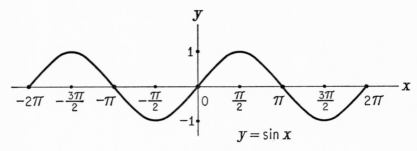

$$y = \sin x$$

Figure 104

Now, $\sin(-x) = -\sin x$, and hence if in the given equation we replace *x* by $-x$ and *y* by $-y$, the equation becomes

$$-y = -\sin x,$$

which is equivalent to the given equation. It follows from 3·4 that the graph is symmetric with respect to the origin.

By use of the accompanying table, the graph (Figure 104) can be sketched from $x = 0$ to $x = \pi$. The graph from $x = \pi$ to $x = 2\pi$ can

x	0	$\pi/6$	$\pi/3$	$\pi/2$	$2\pi/3$	$5\pi/6$	π
$y = \sin x$	0	.50	.85	1	.85	.50	0

then be drawn by using the fact that $\sin (x + \pi) = -\sin x$. Thus, for example, $\sin (7\pi/6) = -\sin (\pi/6) = -.50$.

In view of our particular choice of values of *x* in the above table, the values of *y* can be obtained without use of trigonometric tables. Of course, other points on the graph can be obtained from Table I. For example, if $x = .5$ radians (approximately equal to 28° 40′), $\sin x$ is approximately equal to .48. Hence the point (.5, .48) is on the curve. Since angle *x* is given in radians, we have found it convenient to mark off the *x*-axis in terms of fractions of π, where π is approximately equal to 3.14.

Now we know that

$$\sin (x + 2\pi) = \sin x,$$

and hence the curve from 2π to 4π is a repetition of the curve from 0 to 2π; the same is true from 4π to 6π, from -2π to 0, and so on. For this reason, sin x is said to be *periodic of period* 2π.

Example 13

Sketch the graph of the equation $y = \cos x$.

Solution: Since cos x is also periodic of period 2π, it suffices to sketch the graph between 0 and 2π as was done in the preceding example. The graph is sketched in Figure 105. This graph is so much like that of the

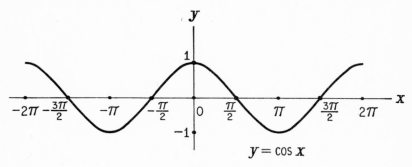

Figure 105

preceding example that we omit any further discussion. Actually, the graph of the equation $y = \cos x$ can be obtained from that of the equation $y = \sin x$ by moving the y-axis $\pi/2$ units to the right. This is readily seen to be a consequence of the fact that cos $(x - \pi/2) = \sin x$ for all x.

Example 14

Discuss and sketch the graph of the equation $y = \tan x$.

Solution: Since tan $0 = 0$, the y-intercept is the origin. Setting $y = 0$, the equation tan $x = 0$ is satisfied for $x = n\pi$ where n is any integer; and hence the x-intercepts are $(n\pi, 0)$ for every integer n.

It is important to note that $|\tan x|$ becomes as large as we may desire if x is taken sufficiently near to $\pi/2$, and tan $(\pi/2)$ does not exist. Hence, in contrast to the graphs of the two preceding examples, no two lines parallel to the x-axis can be found such that the graph of $y = \tan x$ lies between them.

Clearly tan $(x + 2\pi) = \tan x$, as is the case for all the trigonometric functions. However, for tan x it is also true that tan $(x + \pi) = \tan x$. Hence tan x is *periodic of period* π. In drawing the graph we can therefore restrict attention to any segment of the x-axis of length π. The following table, obtained by use of Table I of the appendix, makes it possible to draw the graph from $x = 0$ to $x = \pi/2$. Since the curve is symmetric

x	0	$\pi/12$	$\pi/6$	$\pi/4$	$\pi/3$	$5\pi/12$
$y = \tan x$	0	.27	.58	1	1.73	3.73

with respect to the origin (why?), it is then easy to draw the curve from $x = -\pi/2$ to $x = 0$.

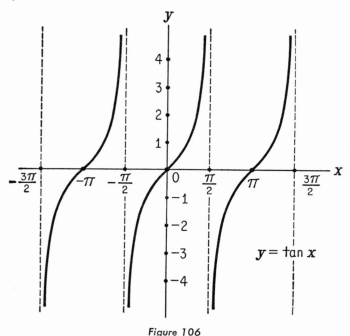

Figure 106

The graph is shown in Figure 106.   The dotted lines in the figure are the lines $x = \pm\pi/2, \pm 3\pi/2, \cdots$.   Since tan x is not defined for these values of x, the dotted lines do not intersect the graph but are, in fact, asymptotes of the graph.

By making use of the graphs of the three examples just given, it is possible to determine easily the general shape of the graphs of somewhat more complicated trigonometric equations.   For example, suppose that one wishes to draw the graph of the equation

$$y = a \sin bx,$$

where a and b are given real numbers.   Now the values of sin bx will repeat after the angle bx has varied from 0 to 2π, that is, after x has varied from 0 to $2\pi/b$.   Hence the graph will be periodic of period $2\pi/b$.   Of course, the presence of the coefficient a merely means that the values of $\sin bx$ must be multiplied by the constant a in order to obtain the corresponding values of y.

Example 15

Sketch the graph of the equation $y = 3 \sin 2x$.

Solution: In view of the remarks just made, it is clear that the curve has period π; so we can draw the rest of the graph as soon as we have deter-

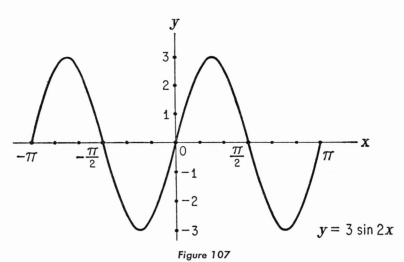

$$y = 3 \sin 2x$$

Figure 107

mined it for $0 \leq x \leq \pi$. Moreover, as x varies from 0 to π, $\sin 2x$ will take on all the values that $\sin x$ takes as x varies from 0 to 2π. Thus the graph will resemble that of Figure 104 except that the period will be π instead of 2π. However, in the present case the values of $\sin 2x$ must be multiplied by 3 to get the corresponding values of y; therefore y will take values between -3 and $+3$. The graph is sketched in Figure 107.

EXERCISES

Sketch the graph of each of the following equations.

1. $y = 2 \sin x$.
2. $y = -\cos x$.
3. $y = \sin 2x$.
4. $y = 3 \cos x$.
5. $y = \sin (x/2)$.
6. $y = \cos (x/2)$.
7. $y = 2 \sin 3x$.
8. $y = 3 \cos 3x$.
9. $y = \tan 2x$.
10. $y = 1 + \sin x$.

11. $y = 1 - \cos x$.   12. $y = x + \sin x$.

13. $y = 2 \tan (x/2)$.   14. $y = 1 + \tan x$.

15. $2y = \sin \pi x$.   16. $y = 3 \cos \pi x$.

17. $y = \sin^2 x$.   18. $y = \tan^2 x$.

19. $\sin y = x$.   20. $\cos y = x$.

21. $\tan y = x$.   22. $y^2 = \tan x$.

23. $y^2 = \sin x$.   24. $y^2 = \cos x$.

53.   EXPONENTIAL AND LOGARITHMIC CURVES

We conclude this chapter with a brief discussion of curves associated with equations of the type

$$y = a^x \qquad \text{or} \qquad y = \log_a x,$$

where in either case a is a positive real number different from 1.

Example 16

Sketch the graph of the equation $y = 2^x$.

Solution: For every value of x, $2^x > 0$, so the curve lies completely above the x-axis.   For increasingly large positive x, 2^x increases indefinitely; but for increasing large negative x, 2^x becomes arbitrarily small and therefore the x-axis is an asymptote of this curve.   The reader may easily verify the following table, from which the graph can be sketched as in Figure 108.

x	-4	-3	-2	-1	0	1	2	3	4
y	1/16	1/8	1/4	1/2	1	2	4	8	16

Actually, for any $a > 1$, the graph of the equation $y = a^x$ is similar in general shape to the curve of Figure 108.   However, if $a < 1$, the situation is different, as indicated in the next example.

Example 17

Sketch the graph of the equation $y = (1/2)^x$.

Solution: The graph is sketched in Figure 109, making use of the following table.

x	-4	-3	-2	-1	0	1	2	3	4
y	16	8	4	2	1	1/2	1/4	1/8	1/16

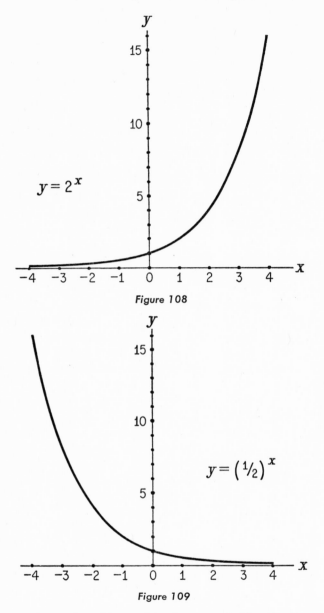

Figure 108

Figure 109

It is apparent from the table, and is also revealed by the figure, that the graph of the equation $y = (1/2)^x$ is the image with respect to the y-axis of the graph of the equation $y = 2^x$.

The tables in the two preceding examples were easily constructed, since we used only integral values of x. To find values of y corresponding to other values of x, it would be necessary to use tables of logarithms. For many choices of the number a, this would also be convenient even for integral values of x. For example, in advanced mathematics one often needs to consider e^x, where e is an irrational constant approximately equal to 2.718. We shall illustrate the procedure in the following example. Of course, tables exist which give at once the values of e^x corresponding to different values of x. For our purposes, however, the logarithm tables are adequate, as will be explained in the following example.

Example 18

Sketch the graph of the equation $y = e^x$.

Solution: Since $e > 1$, we know that the graph will resemble the curve of Figure 108, but we shall compute an actual table of values.

By taking logarithms of both sides of the equation $y = e^x$, we obtain

$$\log_{10} y = x \log_{10} e.$$

From Table II of the appendix (giving logarithms to the base 10) we find that $\log_{10} 2.718 = .4343$; so we have

$$\log_{10} y = (.4343)x.$$

Thus to find, for example, the value of y corresponding to $x = -2$, we find first that

$$\log_{10} y = (.4343)(-2) = -.8686,$$

or

$$\log_{10} y = .1314 - 1.$$

Thus from Table II we find that $y = .1353$, approximately. Of course, for the purpose of drawing the graph, it is not necessary to carry out the calculations to four decimal places. In the table below we record $y = .14$ for $x = -2$. The other values can be obtained in a similar manner. The graph is shown in Figure 110.

x	-3	-2	-1	0	1	2	3
y	.05	.14	.37	1	2.72	7.39	20.1

Since, by definition, $y = \log_a x$ is equivalent to $a^y = x$, it is clear that the graph of a logarithmic curve will be closely related to the graph of an exponential curve. Actually, the graph of the equation $y = \log_a x$ can be obtained from the graph of $y = a^x$ by interchanging the roles of x and y. Thus we can find immediately from Figure 110 that the graph of the equation

$$y = \log_e x$$

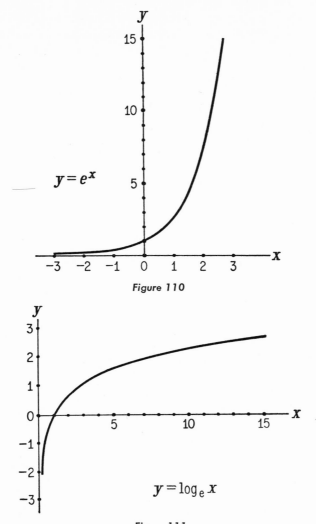

Figure 110

Figure 111

is as shown in Figure 111.   In this case, there are no points on the curve
for negative values of x, the y-axis is an asymptote, and the values of y
increase indefinitely as x increases.

As already indicated, the values of $\log_{10} x$ can be found by use of
Table II.   Moreover, it is known that

$$\log_a x = \frac{\log_{10} x}{\log_{10} a},$$

and this relation can be used to compute a table of values for the equation

$$y = \log_a x.$$

Note that the values of $\log_a x$ are obtained by multiplying the corresponding values of $\log_{10} x$ by the constant factor $1/(\log_{10} a)$.

EXERCISES

Sketch the graph of each of the following equations.

1. $y = 3^x$.

2. $y = (1/3)^x$.

3. $y = -2^x$.

4. $y = 3e^x$.

5. $y = 2^{x/2}$.

6. $y = 2^{-x^2}$.

7. $y = 2^{x^2}$.

8. $y = 3^{1-x}$.

9. $y = 3^{-2x}$.

10. $y = e^{2x+1}$.

11. $y = \log_2 x$.

12. $y = \log_{1/2} x$.

13. $y = \log_3 (4x)$.

14. $y = \log_2 x^2$.

15. $y = \log_{10} x$.

16. $y = \log_{10} (1/x)$.

17. $y = x + \log_{10} x$.

18. $y = x + 2^x$.

19. $y^2 = \log_{10} x$.

20. $y^2 = e^x$.

chapter 9

Polar Coordinates

In the rectangular coordinate system, which we have used heretofore, a point is determined by its directed distances from two mutually perpendicular lines. However, another coordinate system, called the *polar coordinate* system, is also used frequently in analytic geometry. In this system a point is determined by its distance from a fixed point and its direction angle from a fixed half-line. In the present chapter we shall define the polar coordinate system and describe some of its uses.

54. DEFINITIONS

Let l be a coordinate half-line in the plane; that is, l is that part of a coordinate line containing those points with zero or positive coordinates (Figure 112). In the discussion to follow, the half-line l is called the

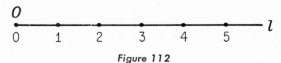

Figure 112

polar axis and its endpoint O is called the **pole**. Throughout this chapter, when we speak of the terminal side of an angle it is to be understood that its vertex is the pole and its initial side is the polar axis, and we shall follow the usual convention of considering an angle to be positive or negative according as it is generated by a counterclockwise or clockwise rotation. The angles may be measured either in degrees or in radians.

As a simple illustration of the idea of polar coordinates, let us consider Figure 113 in which the point A is two units from the pole and on the terminal side of an angle of $5\pi/4$ radians (225°). We therefore say that $(2, 5\pi/4)$ are polar coordinates of A, and write $A(2, 5\pi/4)$ to indicate this fact. However, the position of A can also be described by saying that it is two units from the pole and on the half-line which is obtained by extending through the pole the terminal side of an angle of $\pi/4$ radians (45°). We shall therefore say that $(-2, \pi/4)$ is also a pair of polar coor-

171

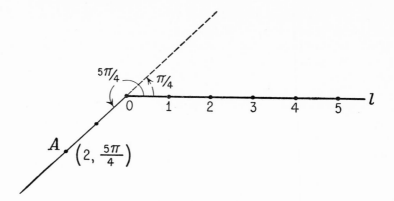

Figure 113

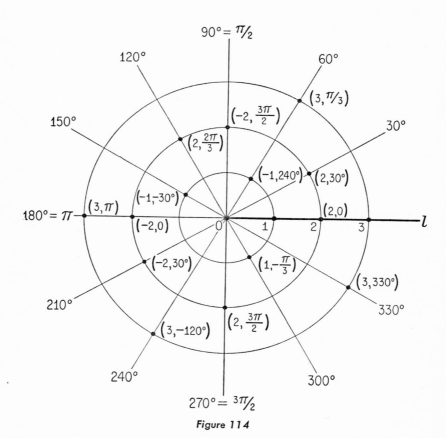

Figure 114

dinates of A; and we may also write $A(-2, \pi/4)$.   With this example in mind, we shall now describe polar coordinates in general.

If $r > 0$, the point P with **polar coordinates** (r, θ) is the point r units from the pole and on the terminal side of angle θ.   If $r < 0$, the point P with **polar coordinates** (r, θ) is the point $|r|$ units from the pole and on the half-line which is obtained by extending through the pole the terminal side of angle θ.   The point $(0, \theta)$ is the pole, no matter what the angle θ.   Some examples are given in Figure 114.

It is clear that to each pair (r, θ) of numbers there corresponds a unique point of the plane.   However, it is not true that each point of the plane has unique polar coordinates.   We have already observed that the point A in Figure 113 has coordinates $(2, 5\pi/4)$, and also has coordinates $(-2, \pi/4)$.   Acutally, since there are many different angles with the same terminal side, each point has many different pairs of polar coordinates.

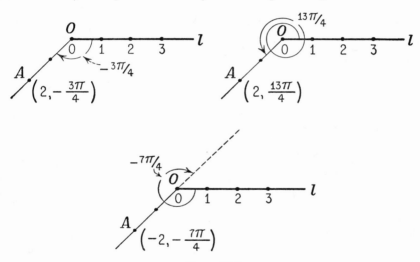

Figure 115

For example, Figure 115 indicates that the point $A(2, 5\pi/4)$ also has coordinates $(2, -3\pi/4)$, $(2, 13\pi/4)$, and $(-2, -7\pi/4)$.

In general, since the angles

$$\theta, \; \theta + 2\pi, \; \theta + 4\pi, \; \cdots \; ; \qquad \theta - 2\pi, \; \theta - 4\pi, \; \cdots \; ,$$

have the same terminal side, it follows that

9·1 $\quad (r, \theta), \; (r, \theta + 2\pi), \; (r, \theta + 4\pi), \; \cdots \; ; \qquad (r, \theta - 2\pi),$
$$(r, \theta - 4\pi), \; \cdots \; ,$$

are polar coordinates of the same point P.   Also

9·2 $\quad (-r, \theta + \pi), \; (-r, \theta + 3\pi), \; (-r, \theta + 5\pi), \; \cdots \; ; \qquad (-r, \theta - \pi),$
$$(-r, \theta - 3\pi), \; \cdots \; ,$$

are polar coordinates of the same point $P(r, \theta)$, since these angles have as terminal side the extension through the pole of the terminal side of angle θ.

Every point P in the plane other than the pole has unique polar coordinates (r, θ) if we restrict r and θ so that $r > 0$ and $0 \leq \theta < 2\pi$. However, we shall not generally make any such restriction.

The plotting of points in a polar coordinate system is made much easier by the use of polar coordinate paper. The use of this paper is illustrated in Figure 114, as well as in many of the other figures of this chapter.

EXERCISES

In each of Exercises 1–6, plot the given points in a polar coordinate system.

1. $(2, 30°)$, $(-2, 30°)$, $(2, -30°)$, $(-2, -30°)$.

2. $(3, \pi/3)$, $(4, 7\pi/3)$, $(-1, -3\pi/2)$, $(-5, -\pi)$.

3. $(4, 0)$, $(0, \pi/4)$, $(-2, 9\pi/4)$, $(2, 3\pi/4)$.

4. $(-1, -90°)$, $(1, 210°)$, $(3, 570°)$, $(-4, -150°)$.

5. $(0, 60°)$, $(-3, 750°)$, $(6, -390°)$, $(2, 240°)$.

6. $(1/2, \pi/8)$, $(3/2, 4\pi/9)$, $(-1/3, -\pi/3)$, $(-4/3, 5\pi/9)$.

7. Find the polar coordinates of the vertices of a square with center at the pole and two sides parallel to the polar axis if the length of a side of the square is a units.

8. The center of a regular pentagon is at the pole and one vertex is on the polar axis. If the distance from the center to a vertex is a, find the polar coordinates of the vertices of the pentagon.

9. Do the same as in Exercise 8 for a regular hexagon.

10. Show that $((-1)^n r, \theta + n\pi)$, n any integer, are all the polar coordinates of the point $P(r, \theta)$.

55.   GRAPHS OF EQUATIONS

In analogy with our definition (3·1) of the graph of an equation when rectangular coordinates are used, we make the following definition. The *graph* of an equation in r and θ consists of those and only those points P having a pair (r, θ) of polar coordinates that satisfies the equation. Note that not all the different pairs of polar coordinates of P need satisfy the equation, but that at least one pair must do so.

We now give some examples of the sketching of the graph of an equation in r and θ.

Example 1

Sketch the graph of each of the following equations:

$$(a) \quad r = 3, \qquad (b) \quad \theta = \pi/4.$$

Solution: (a) Since the point (3, θ) is on the graph of the equation $r = 3$ for each value of θ, clearly the graph is a circle of radius 3 having its center at the pole (Figure 116).   As an illustration of the fact that *not all* pairs of coordinates of a point need satisfy an equation in order for the point to be on the graph, it may be observed that the pair $(-3, 5\pi/4)$ does not

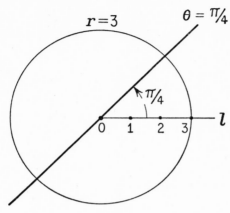

Figure 116

satisfy the equation $r = 3$.   However, the point with these coordinates is on the graph of this equation, since the same point also has coordinates $(3, \pi/4)$ and this pair does satisfy the equation.

(b) The point $(r, \pi/4)$ is on the graph of the equation $\theta = \pi/4$ for each choice of r, whether it be positive, negative, or zero.   Therefore the graph of this equation is the complete line passing through the pole and making an angle of $\pi/4$ with the polar axis (Figure 116).

In general, the graph of the equation $r = a$ is a circle of radius $|a|$ having its center at the pole, whereas the graph of the equation $\theta = a$ is a line passing through the pole and making an angle of a radians with the polar axis.

Example 2

Sketch the graph of the equation $r = \theta/\pi$.

Solution: The accompanying table of values has been computed by assigning values to θ and solving for the corresponding values of r.   The graph, shown in Figure 117, is seen to be a spiral.   The dotted spiral

θ	0	$\pi/2$	π	$3\pi/2$	2π	3π	4π
r	0	1/2	1	3/2	2	3	4

shown in the figure is that part of the graph obtained by using negative values of θ, in which case the values of r also are negative.

So far we have used radian measure, but we could have used degree measure just as well. In the next examples we shall measure the angle θ

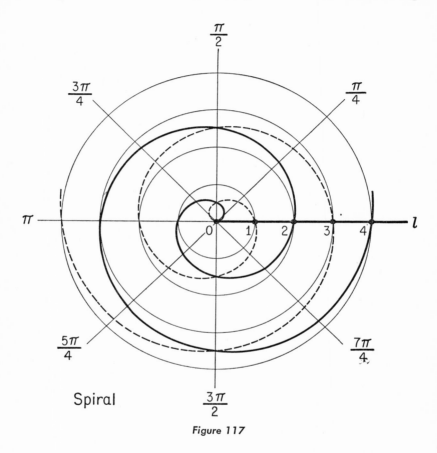

Spiral

Figure 117

in degrees although, again, radian measure could have been used to yield the same results.

Example 3

Sketch the graph of the equation $r = 2 \cos \theta$.

Solution: Since the cosine function has period $360°$, it is clear that the complete graph will be obtained if we let θ range from $0°$ to $360°$. The following table gives a number of corresponding values of θ and r. Using the table, we may sketch the graph as shown in Figure 118.

θ	0°	30°	60°	90°	120°	150°	180°
r	2	$\sqrt{3}$	1	0	−1	$-\sqrt{3}$	−2

θ	210°	240°	270°	300°	330°	360°
r	$-\sqrt{3}$	−1	0	1	$\sqrt{3}$	2

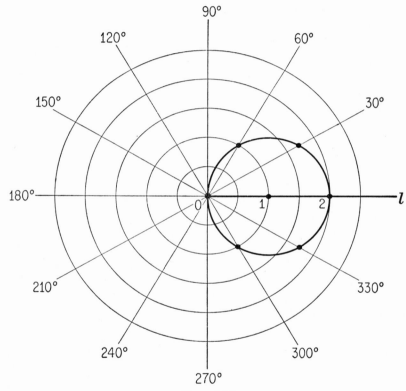

Figure 118

If these points are plotted, it will be observed that, in fact, the complete figure is obtained when θ varies from 0° to 180°, and it is retraced completely as θ varies from 180° to 360°. The upper half of the graph is obtained as θ varies from 0° to 90°, in which case r is positive; whereas the lower half is obtained as θ varies from 90° to 180°, the values of r now being negative. However, the lower half could just as well be obtained by letting θ vary from 0° to −90°, in which case r is positive for this range of values of θ.

The graph appears to be a circle.   That it is a circle of radius 1 and with center at $(1, 0°)$ will be proved in the next section.   We may note in passing that the graph of this equation is symmetric with respect to the polar axis, since $\cos(-\theta) = \cos\theta$ for every θ.   Thus the point $(r, -\theta)$ is on the graph whenever the point (r, θ) is.

Example 4

Sketch the graph of the equation $r = 2\cos\theta - 1$.

Solution: We can obtain a table of values for this equation simply by

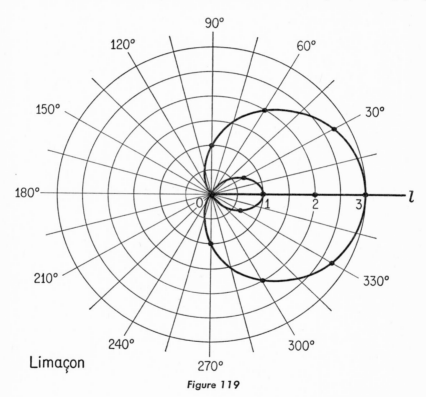

Limaçon

Figure 119

subtracting 1 from each value of r in the preceding table.   In this way we obtain the following table in which we have used 1.7 as an approximation of $\sqrt{3}$.

θ	0°	30°	60°	90°	120°	150°	180°
r	1	.7	0	-1	-2	-2.7	-3

θ	210°	240°	270°	300°	330°	360°
r	-2.7	-2	-1	0	$.7$	1

The graph is sketched in Figure 119. The inner loop is obtained as θ varies from 0° to 60° and from 300° to 360°, the corresponding values of r being positive. On the outer loop the values of r are always negative. In the case of this equation it was necessary to let θ vary from 0° to 360° to obtain the complete graph. Clearly, the graph is symmetric with respect to the polar axis. This curve is called a limaçon.

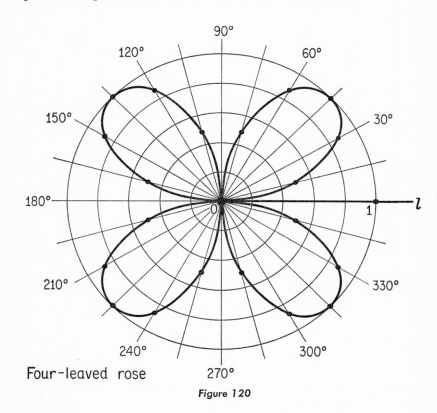

Four-leaved rose

Figure 120

Example 5

Sketch the graph of the equation $r = \sin 2\theta$.

Solution: The graph is sketched in Figure 120, using the following table of values.

θ	0°	15°	30°	45°	60°	75°	90°	105°	120°	135°	150°	165°	180°
r	0	.5	.87	1	.87	.5	0	$-.5$	$-.87$	-1	$-.87$	$-.5$	0

θ	195°	210°	225°	240°	255°	270°	285°	300°	315°	330°	345°	360°
r	.5	.87	1	.87	.5	0	$-.5$	$-.87$	-1	$-.87$	$-.5$	0

It may be well to emphasize that in each case it is the point (r, θ) that is plotted, although 2θ appears in the given equation. Thus, for example, if we let $\theta = 45°$, then $2\theta = 90°$ and $r = \sin 90° = 1$. Hence the point $(1, 45°)$ is a point on the graph.

The graph of either of the equations

$$r = a \sin n\theta, \qquad r = a \cos n\theta, \qquad (n \text{ a positive integer})$$

is called an *n-leaved rose* if n is an odd integer, and a *2n-leaved rose* if n is an even integer. The reason for the name is suggested by the graph of Figure 120 for the special case in which $n = 2$.

EXERCISES

In each of the following, sketch the graph of the given equation.

1. $r = 4$.
2. $\theta = 2\pi/3$.
3. $\theta = -\pi/2$.
4. $r = 3/2$.
5. $r = 4 \sin \theta$.
6. $r = 3 \cos \theta$.
7. $r = -2 \cos \theta$.
8. $r = -6 \sin \theta$.
9. $r = 1 + \cos \theta$ (Cardioid).
10. $r = 2(1 - \sin \theta)$ (Cardioid).
11. $r = 2 + \sin \theta$ (Limaçon).
12. $r = 2 - 3 \cos \theta$ (Limaçon).
13. $r = \sin^2 \theta$.
14. $r = 4 \cos^2 \theta$.
15. $r = 3 \tan \theta$.
16. $r \cos \theta = 2$.
17. $r = \cos 2\theta$ (Four-leaved rose).
18. $r = 2 \sin 3\theta$ (Three-leaved rose).
19. $r = a \sin 5\theta$.
20. $r = \cos 4\theta$.
21. $r^2 = a^2 \cos 2\theta$ (Lemniscate).
22. $r^2 = a^2 \sin 2\theta$ (Lemniscate).
23. $r = a(1 + \sin^2 \theta)$.
24. $r = a \csc \theta$.
25. $r\theta = 2\pi$ (Hyperbolic spiral).
26. $r = 2 \sec \theta + 1$ (Conchoid).
27. $r = \csc \theta + 2$.
28. $r^2\theta = \pi$.

56. ASSOCIATED RECTANGULAR COORDINATE SYSTEM

Let both a rectangular and a polar coordinate system in the plane be given, with the origin and the positive half of the x-axis of the rectangular

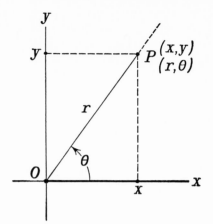

Figure 121

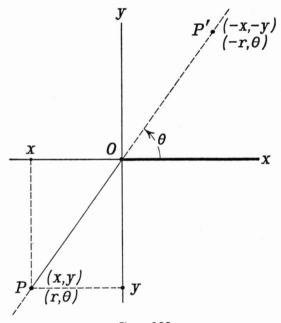

Figure 122

coordinate system being the pole and polar axis, respectively, of the polar coordinate system.   Then associated with each point P in the plane are rectangular coordinates (x, y) and polar coordinates (r, θ).   Except for the special case in which P is the pole (origin), either r is a positive number and P is a point on the terminal side of angle θ (Figure 121), or r is a negative number and P is a point on the extension of the terminal side of angle θ through the pole (Figure 122).   In this latter case, the image of P

in the origin O is the point P' with rectangular coordinates $(-x, -y)$ and polar coordinates $(-r, \theta)$.

If $r > 0$ and P is a point on the *terminal side* of angle θ, by the very definitions of the trigonometric functions of an angle θ, we have

$$\sin \theta = \frac{y}{r}, \qquad \cos \theta = \frac{x}{r}.$$

If $r < 0$, as in Figure 122, where P' (instead of P) is on the *terminal side* of angle θ, P' is at a distance $-r$ from the origin. Therefore, even in this case, we have

$$\sin \theta = \frac{-y}{-r} = \frac{y}{r}, \qquad \cos \theta = \frac{-x}{-r} = \frac{x}{r}.$$

We conclude that rectangular and polar coordinates of a point P in the plane are always related by the equations

9·3
$$\begin{aligned} x &= r \cos \theta, \\ y &= r \sin \theta. \end{aligned}$$

If we know polar coordinates of a point P, these equations make it possible to find the rectangular coordinates of P. For example, if P has polar coordinates $(2, 4\pi/3)$, we find at once from 9·3 that

$$x = 2 \cos \frac{4\pi}{3} = -1,$$

$$y = 2 \sin \frac{4\pi}{3} = -\sqrt{3},$$

and hence P has rectangular coordinates $(-1, -\sqrt{3})$.

We now consider the problem of changing from rectangular to polar coordinates. Using the identity, $\sin^2 \theta + \cos^2 \theta = 1$, it is clear from 9·3 that

$$r^2 = x^2 + y^2.$$

Thus, if we choose r to be positive, the point P with rectangular coordinates (x, y) has polar coordinates (r, θ) given by

9·4
$$r = \sqrt{x^2 + y^2},$$
$$\sin \theta = \frac{y}{r}, \qquad \cos \theta = \frac{x}{r}.$$

There is a *unique* angle θ between 0 and 2π satisfying the latter pair of equations. Of course, after we have found one pair of polar coordinates of P, other pairs are given by 9·1 and 9·2.

As an example of the use of 9·4, suppose that P has rectangular coordinates $(-2, 2)$. Then, from 9·4, we have $r = 2\sqrt{2}$ and

$$\sin \theta = \frac{\sqrt{2}}{2}, \qquad \cos \theta = -\frac{\sqrt{2}}{2}.$$

It follows that $\theta = 3\pi/4$ (135°), and therefore $(2\sqrt{2}, 3\pi/4)$ is one pair of polar coordinates of P.

It is clear from 9·4 that $\tan \theta = y/x$, and therefore that

$$\theta = \arctan \frac{y}{x}.$$

However, this equation does not completely determine θ, since there are two angles between 0 and 2π having y/x as their tangent.

From a given equation in x and y we may derive an equation in r and θ by use of 9·3. The graph in the polar coordinate system of the resulting polar equation coincides with the graph of the given equation in the rectangular coordinate system. Conversely, given an equation in r and θ, we may obtain a corresponding equation in x and y by use of 9·4. We now give some examples.

Example 6

Change the equation $x^2 = 4y$ into polar form.

Solution: Using 9·3, we at once obtain

$$r^2 \cos^2 \theta = 4r \sin \theta.$$

Now since r is a factor of both sides of this equation, its graph consists of the graph of the equation $r = 0$ (which is just the pole), together with the graph of the equation

$$r \cos^2 \theta = 4 \sin \theta.$$

However, it is easily verified that the pole is on the graph of this latter equation; therefore the factor r can be discarded without affecting the graph. Thus the desired equation is

$$r \cos^2 \theta = 4 \sin \theta,$$

which may be put in the form

$$r = 4 \tan \theta \sec \theta.$$

Example 7

Change the equation $r = 2 \cos \theta$ into rectangular form.

Solution: We find it convenient to multiply the equation by r, and thus to write it in the form

$$r^2 = 2r \cos \theta.$$

For the reasons explained in the preceding example, the graph of this equation is the same as that of the original equation.   Now, using 9·4, we obtain the equation

$$x^2 + y^2 = 2x,$$

in rectangular coordinates.   This equation may be put in the form

$$(x - 1)^2 + y^2 = 1,$$

which we recognize as the equation of a circle of radius 1 and with center $(1, 0)$.   This proves that the graph in Example 3 is a circle.

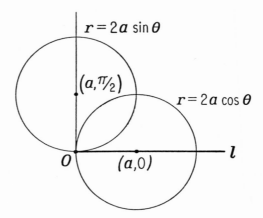

Figure 123

In a similar manner it is easy to show that the equation

$$r = 2a \cos \theta$$

has as its graph a circle of radius $|a|$ with center at $(a, 0)$, whereas the graph of the equation

$$r = 2a \sin \theta$$

is a circle of radius $|a|$ with center at $(a, \pi/2)$, as indicated in Figure 123.

Example 8

Change the equation $r^2 = 4 \sin 2\theta$ into rectangular form.

Solution: Since $\sin 2\theta = 2 \sin \theta \cos \theta$, the given equation may be put in the form

$$r^2 = 8 \sin \theta \cos \theta.$$

To simplify the use of 9·4, we now multiply by r^2 and write the equation in the form

$$r^4 = 8r^2 \sin \theta \cos \theta.$$

Now, using 9·4, we may write this equation in the form

$$(x^2 + y^2)^2 = 8xy,$$

in rectangular coordinates.

Example 9

Find the equation of a line in a polar coordinate system.

Solution: We have already seen in Section 55 that any line through the pole has an equation of the form $\theta = k$, where k is a real number. Accordingly, we can now exclude this case and consider only lines that do not pass through the pole. In the rectangular coordinate system we know that any such line has an equation of the form

$$ax + by = c,$$

with $c \neq 0$. If we use 9·3, this equation becomes

$$ar \cos \theta + br \sin \theta = c,$$

or

9·5
$$r = \frac{c}{a \cos \theta + b \sin \theta}, \qquad (c \neq 0).$$

This, then, is the general equation of a line (not through the pole) in polar coordinates. By giving first a, and then b, the value 0 in 9·5, we see that

$$r = k \csc \theta, \qquad r = k \sec \theta,$$

are equations of lines respectively parallel and perpendicular to the polar axis. (Why?)

EXERCISES

In each of Exercises 1–8, change the given equation into polar form.

1. $x^2 + y^2 = 16$.
2. $x = -3$.
3. $x^2 - y^2 = 1$.
4. $y^2 = 8x$.
5. $xy = 9$.
6. $2x^2 + y^2 = 4$.
7. $x^2 + y^2 - 2x + 4y = 0$.
8. $x = \sqrt{3}\,y$.

In each of Exercises 9–16, change the given equation into rectangular form.

9. $r = 4 \sin \theta$.
10. $r = 3$.
11. $\theta = \pi/2$.
12. $r^2 = a^2 \cos \theta$.
13. $r = a(1 + \cos \theta)$.
14. $r = a \tan \theta$.
15. $r = a \sec^2 \theta$.
16. $r = a \sin 3\theta$.

57.   THE DISTANCE FORMULA

In this section we give a formula for the distance between two points in terms of polar coordinates of the points.

Let $P_1(r_1, \theta_1)$ and $P_2(r_2, \theta_2)$ be two given points. By 9·3, it follows at once that these points have respective coordinates $(r_1 \cos \theta_1, r_1 \sin \theta_1)$ and $(r_2 \cos \theta_2, r_2 \sin \theta_2)$ in the associated rectangular coordinate system. Now using the distance formula (1·5) in a rectangular coordinate system, the distance $|P_1P_2|$ between P_1 and P_2 satisfies the equation

$$
\begin{aligned}
|P_1P_2|^2 &= (r_1 \cos \theta_1 - r_2 \cos \theta_2)^2 + (r_1 \sin \theta_1 - r_2 \sin \theta_2)^2 \\
&= r_1{}^2(\cos^2 \theta_1 + \sin^2 \theta_1) + r_2{}^2(\cos^2 \theta_2 + \sin^2 \theta_2) \\
&\qquad\qquad - 2r_1r_2(\cos \theta_1 \cos \theta_2 + \sin \theta_1 \sin \theta_2).
\end{aligned}
$$

By use of familiar trigonometric identities, this equation yields the following result.

9·6   Distance Formula

The distance between the points $P_1(r_1, \theta_1)$ and $P_2(r_2, \theta_2)$ is given by

$$
|P_1P_2| = \sqrt{r_1{}^2 + r_2{}^2 - 2r_1r_2 \cos (\theta_2 - \theta_1)}.
$$

Example 10

Find the distance between the points $P_1(3, \pi/7)$ and $P_2(2, 10\pi/21)$.

Solution: By 9·6, we find at once that

$$
\begin{aligned}
|P_1P_2| &= \sqrt{3^2 + 2^2 - 2 \cdot 3 \cdot 2 \cos (10\pi/21 - \pi/7)} \\
&= \sqrt{13 - 12 \cos (\pi/3)} = \sqrt{7}.
\end{aligned}
$$

Of course, this example is rather special, since the angle $\theta_2 - \theta_1$ is an angle whose cosine can be determined without use of tables. In general, tables would have to be used to obtain a numerical answer.

EXERCISE

Use the distance formula to find the polar equation of the circle with center (r_1, θ_1) and radius a.

58.   THE CONIC SECTIONS

In discussing polar equations of the conic sections, we shall find it convenient to use the focus-directrix definition given in 5·23. According to this definition, a conic section is the locus of all points P such that the ratio of the distance between P and a fixed point F (a focus) to the distance between P and a fixed line k (a directrix) is a constant e (the eccentricity). We recall that the conic section is an ellipse, a parabola, or a hyperbola according as $e < 1$, $e = 1$, or $e > 1$.

In order to find the polar equation of a given conic section having focus F, directrix k, and eccentricity e, let us place the pole at F and the polar axis perpendicular to k, with k to the left of the pole, as in Figure 124.

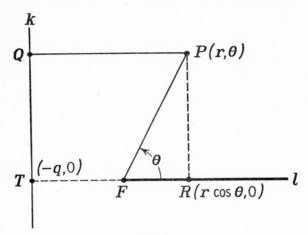

Figure 124

If q denotes the distance between F and k, then k crosses the extension of the polar axis at the point $T(-q, 0)$. Now let $P(r, \theta)$ be any point on the given conic section, and let Q and R be the respective projections of P on k and the polar axis (or its extension). The point R has coordinates $(r \cos \theta, 0)$. (Why?) It follows from the definition of a conic section that

9·7
$$\frac{|FP|}{|PQ|} = e.$$

We shall show that each point P on the given conic section has a pair of coordinates (r, θ) satisfying the equation

9·8
$$r = \frac{eq}{1 - e \cos \theta}.$$

This is done in two separate cases as follows.

First, if P is on the same side of k as F, as in Figure 124, let P have coordinates (r, θ) with $r > 0$. Then

$$|FP| = r, \qquad |PQ| = |TR| = r \cos \theta + q,$$

and by 9·7 we have

$$\frac{r}{r \cos \theta + q} = e.$$

Solving this equation for r, we obtain 9·8.

In the second case, if P is on the opposite side of k from F (which can happen only if $e > 1$), as in Figure 125, let P have coordinates (r, θ) with $r < 0$.   Then

$$|FP| = -r, \qquad |PQ| = |RT| = -q - r \cos \theta,$$

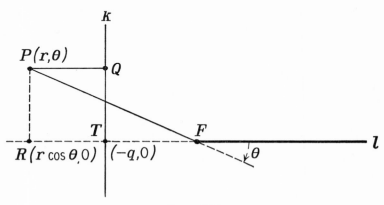

Figure 125

and by 9·7 we have

$$\frac{-r}{-q - r \cos \theta} = e.$$

When solved for r, this equation again reduces to 9·8.

Thus we conclude that every point P on the conic section has at least one pair (r, θ) of coordinates satisfying 9·8.   Conversely, it can be shown that each point $P(r, \theta)$ satisfying 9·8 is on the conic section, and therefore 9·8 is the equation of the conic section.

Other equations of the conic sections are the following:

9·9
$$r = \frac{eq}{1 + e \cos \theta},$$

9·10
$$r = \frac{eq}{1 - e \sin \theta},$$

9·11
$$r = \frac{eq}{1 + e \sin \theta}.$$

In each of Equations 9·8–9·11, the conic section has a focus at the pole, has eccentricity e, and has the positive number q as the distance between the focus and the directrix. For Equation 9·9, the directrix is perpendicular to the polar axis and to the *right* of the pole. For Equations 9·10 and 9·11, the directrix is parallel to the polar axis. It is *below* the pole for Equation 9·10 and *above* the pole for Equation 9·11.

In the case of each of the conics, the *vertices* are the points of intersection of the conic with the line on the focus which is perpendicular to the directrix. If we know the vertices and a focus of a conic section, we may describe it completely by using our previous knowledge of the conic sections.

Example 11

Describe and sketch the graph of the equation

$$r = \frac{9}{5 - 4 \cos \theta}.$$

Solution: This equation may be put in the form 9·8 by dividing numerator and denominator by 5, yielding

$$r = \frac{9/5}{1 - (4/5) \cos \theta}.$$

Thus $e = 4/5 < 1$, and hence this equation is the equation of an ellipse. The major axis is along the polar axis, and therefore the vertices may be

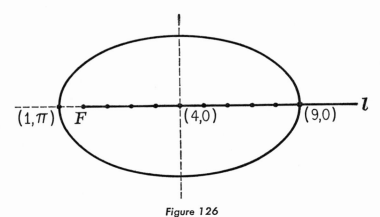

Figure 126

found by letting $\theta = 0$ and $\theta = \pi$. It follows that the vertices are $(9, 0)$ and $(1, \pi)$. The distance between the vertices is 10, so that $a = 5$. (See Section 34.) Since $e = c/a$, clearly $c = 4$; and $b^2 = a^2 - c^2$, so that $b = 3$. The center of the ellipse is the point $(4, 0)$ which is halfway between the vertices. This ellipse is sketched in **Figure 126**.

Example 12

Describe and sketch the graph of the equation

$$r = \frac{4}{1 + \sin \theta}.$$

Solution: This equation, of the form 9·11, has a parabola as its **graph,** since $e = 1$.   The vertex, on the line $\theta = \pi/2$, is easily found to be

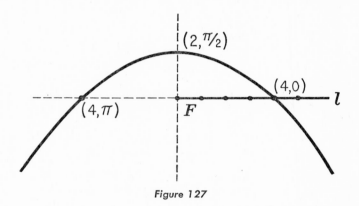

Figure 127

$(2, \pi/2)$.   The points $(4, 0)$ and $(4, \pi)$ are the ends of the latus rectum (why?), so that the curve is as sketched in Figure 127.

Example 13

Describe and sketch the graph of the equation

$$r = \frac{16}{3 - 5 \sin \theta}.$$

Solution: This equation may be put in the form 9·10 by dividing numerator and denominator by 3, to obtain the equation

$$r = \frac{16/3}{1 - (5/3) \sin \theta}.$$

Since $e = 5/3 > 1$, the graph is a hyperbola.   The vertices are on the line perpendicular to the polar axis at the pole, and it follows that the vertices are $(-8, \pi/2)$ and $(2, -\pi/2)$.   Therefore $2a = 6$ and $a = 3$. Since $c/a = e = 5/3$, we have $c = 5$.   For the hyperbola, $b^2 = c^2 - a^2$, and hence $b = 4$.   The graph is sketched in Figure 128.

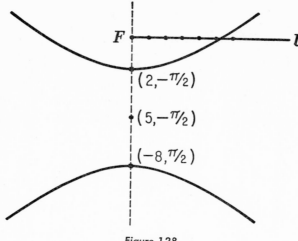

F

$(2, -\pi/2)$

$(5, -\pi/2)$

$(-8, \pi/2)$

Figure 128

Example 14

Find the polar equation of the hyperbola having eccentricity 2, a focus at the pole, and $V(3, 0)$ as the vertex nearer the pole.

Solution: Since the vertices are on the polar axis, the equation is of the form 9·8 or 9·9 with $e = 2$. Now, by 9·1 and 9·2, the vertex $V(3, 0)$ has other pairs of coordinates

$$(3, 2\pi), (3, 4\pi), \cdots ; \qquad (-3, \pi), (-3, 3\pi), \cdots .$$

Since $2q > 0$, it is easy to verify that none of these will satisfy Equation 9·8. However, the Equation 9·9,

$$r = \frac{2q}{1 + 2 \cos \theta},$$

will be satisfied by $(3, 0)$ if $q = 9/2$, and by $(-3, \pi)$ if $q = 3/2$. It is easily verified that the vertices of the hyperbola

$$r = \frac{9}{1 + 2 \cos \theta}$$

are the points $V(3, 0)$ and $(-9, \pi)$, whereas the vertices of the hyperbola

$$r = \frac{3}{1 + 2 \cos \theta}$$

are $V(-3, \pi)$ and $(1, 0)$. Since it is required that V be the vertex nearer the pole, the desired equation is

$$r = \frac{9}{1 + 2 \cos \theta}.$$

EXERCISES

In each of Exercises 1–10, describe and sketch the graph of the given equation.

1. $r = \dfrac{2}{1 + \cos\theta}.$

2. $r = \dfrac{3}{1 - \sin\theta}.$

3. $r = \dfrac{6}{2 + \sin\theta}.$

4. $r = \dfrac{16}{5 - 3\cos\theta}.$

5. $r = \dfrac{1}{1 - \sqrt{2}\sin\theta}.$

6. $r = \dfrac{6}{1 + \cos\theta}.$

7. $r = \dfrac{24}{1 - 4\cos\theta}.$

8. $r = \dfrac{12}{1 + 3\sin\theta}.$

9. $r = \dfrac{12}{3 + \cos\theta}.$

10. $r = \dfrac{1}{\sqrt{2} - \sin\theta}.$

In each of Exercises 11–20, find the polar equation of the conic section which has a focus at the pole and satisfies the given conditions.

11. Eccentricity 1, equation of directrix $r\cos\theta = -2$.

12. Eccentricity 3/2, equation of directrix $r\sin\theta = 1$.

13. Eccentricity 2/3, equation of directrix $r\sin\theta = -5$.

14. Eccentricity 2, equation of directrix $r\cos\theta = 3$.

15. Eccentricity 1, vertex $(2, \pi)$.

16. Eccentricity 3/5, with $(4, \pi/2)$ the vertex nearer the pole.

17. Vertices $(2, 0)$ and $(6, 0)$.

18. Vertices $(1, \pi/2)$ and $(4, -\pi/2)$.

19. Parabola, vertex $(4, -\pi)$.

20. Focus $(-6, 0)$, vertex $(9, \pi)$.

21. Prove that the length of the latus rectum of each of the conic sections 9·8–9·11 is $2eq$.

22. On the assumption that $e \neq 1$, find the center of each of the conic sections 9·8–9·11.

23. On the assumption that $e \neq 1$, find the distance between the vertices of each of the conic sections 9·8–9·11.

59. EQUIVALENT EQUATIONS AND INTERSECTIONS OF CURVES (OPTIONAL)

One interesting consequence of the fact that a point has different pairs of polar coordinates is that equations which are algebraically different may nevertheless have identical graphs. As a simple example, the two equations $r = 2$ and $r = -2$ have the same graph, namely, the circle with center at the pole and radius 2. We shall find it convenient to say that two equations are *equivalent* if they have the same graph, even though neither can be obtained from the other by algebraic operations. Thus the equations $r = 2$ and $r = -2$ are equivalent.

As a somewhat more interesting example, let us consider the equation

9·12
$$r = 2 \cos \theta - 1,$$

the graph of which is the limaçon discussed in Example 4. Motivated by the fact that (r, θ) and $(-r, \theta + 180°)$ are different coordinates of the same point, let us formally replace (r, θ) in 9·12 by $(-r, \theta + 180°)$; that is, let us replace r by $-r$ and θ by $\theta + 180°$. This replacement yields the equation

$$-r = 2 \cos (\theta + 180°) - 1,$$

which reduces to

9·13
$$r = 2 \cos \theta + 1.$$

If the point P has coordinates (r, θ) satisfying 9·12, then the point P has coordinates $(-r, \theta + 180°)$ satisfying 9·13. Thus each point P on the graph of 9·12 is on the graph of 9·13. Since, conversely, for each point P having coordinates (r, θ) that satisfy 9·13, P also has coordinates $(-r, \theta - 180°)$ that satisfy 9·12, evidently the graphs of 9·12 and 9·13 coincide.

In general, as illustrated by this example, if in an equation in r and θ we replace (r, θ) by any other pair of coordinates of the same point (as given in 9·1 and 9·2), the resulting equation will be equivalent to the given equation. In the case of the particular Equation 9·12, it may be verified that any equivalent equation obtained by this process will reduce algebraically to 9·12 or 9·13.

We now turn to the problem of finding the intersections of two curves, the equations of which are given in polar coordinates. The first step in any such problem is to draw a reasonably accurate figure showing the two curves. This will make it possible to know when all the points of intersection have been found. It is important to notice whether both curves pass through the pole. If they do, this point is a point of intersection even though the values of θ that make $r = 0$ may be different for the two curves. The next step is to solve the two equations simultaneously. However, it may happen that the figure will show points of intersection not obtained by this process. In this case, it may be necessary to solve simultaneously other pairs of equivalent equations of the given curves. Why this is so, and how one can proceed, will be illustrated in the following example.

Example 15

Find the points of intersection of the parabola and the limaçon with respective equations

$$r = \frac{1}{2 + 2 \cos \theta} \quad \text{and} \quad r = 2 \cos \theta - 1.$$

Solution: These curves are shown in Figure 129; an examination of the figure indicates that there are four points of intersection.   Clearly, the parabola does not pass through the pole; so the pole is not a point of inter-

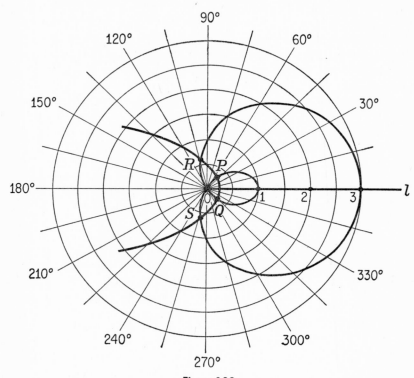

Figure 129

section.   We proceed to solve the two equations simultaneously.   If we equate the expressions for r in the two equations, we obtain

$$\frac{1}{2 + 2 \cos \theta} = 2 \cos \theta - 1,$$

which simplifies to the equation

$$4 \cos^2 \theta + 2 \cos \theta - 3 = 0.$$

Using the quadratic formula to solve for $\cos \theta$, we obtain

$$\cos \theta = \frac{-1 \pm \sqrt{13}}{4},$$

from which it follows that (approximately)

$$\cos \theta = -1.1514 \qquad \text{or} \qquad \cos \theta = .6514.$$

The first value is impossible, since always $|\cos \theta| \leq 1$. Using the second value, we find by use of Table I in the appendix that the only possible angles θ between $0°$ and $360°$ are

$$\theta = 49° \; 21' \qquad \text{and} \qquad \theta = 310° \; 39'.$$

Since $\cos \theta = .6514$, it follows from either of the given equations that $r = .3028$. Hence the two simultaneous solutions give the points $(.3028, 49° \; 21')$ and $(.3028, 310° \; 39')$. It is clear that these are the points P and Q in Figure 129.

Let us now consider why we failed to obtain the points R and S of the figure. As was pointed out when the curve was discussed in Example 4, the outer loop of the limaçon arises from negative values of r; hence as points on the graph of the equation $r = 2 \cos \theta - 1$, R and S occur with negative values of r. However, for the parabola r is always positive, so that as points of the parabola R and S occur with positive values of r. Thus neither R nor S can have a single pair of coordinates that satisfies both equations.

We now remember that we obtained above another equation for the limaçon, namely, Equation 9·13. The method of obtaining this equation from Equation 9·12 shows that a point (r, θ) which satisfies 9·12 will occur as a point $(-r, \theta + 180°)$ on the graph of Equation 9·13. Thus it is not surprising that the points R and S can be obtained by solving simultaneously the given equation of the parabola and the alternate equation 9·13 of the limaçon. Solving these simultaneously, we find

$$\cos \theta = \frac{-3 \pm \sqrt{5}}{4};$$

that is,

$$\cos \theta = -1.3090 \qquad \text{or} \qquad \cos \theta = -.1910.$$

Again, the first value is impossible and the second yields

$$\theta = 101° \; 1' \qquad \text{or} \qquad \theta = 258° \; 59'.$$

The corresponding value of r turns out to be $r = .6180$. Hence the two common points obtained in this way are the points $(.6180, 101° \; 1')$ and $(.6180, 258° \; 59')$. Clearly, these are, respectively, the points R and S of the figure, and we have now obtained all points of intersection.

This example reveals the care that must be taken with certain types of problems involving polar coordinates, owing to the fact that a point is not represented uniquely by a pair of coordinates in the polar system. For example, the point R is on the graph of each of the given equations of

Example 15 since the coordinates (.6180, 101° 1′) of R satisfy the equation of the parabola, and the coordinates (−.6180, 281° 1′) of R satisfy the equation of the limaçon.   However, no pair of coordinates of R satisfies both equations simultaneously.

EXERCISES

Find the points of intersection of each of the following pairs of curves.

1. $r = \dfrac{2}{1 + \cos\theta}$, $\theta = 60°$.

2. $r = \dfrac{6}{1 + \sin\theta}$, $\theta = 150°$.

3. $r = \dfrac{12}{1 + 3\sin\theta}$, $\theta = 210°$.

4. $r = \dfrac{16}{5 - 3\cos\theta}$, $\theta = -60°$.

5. $r = 3\cos\theta$, $r = 3\sin\theta$.

6. $r = 2$, $r = \cos\theta - 2$.

7. $r = \cos\theta$, $r = 1 - \cos\theta$.

8. $r = \dfrac{1}{1 - \sin\theta}$, $r = 1 - 3\sin\theta$.

9. $r = \dfrac{3}{\cos\theta}$, $r = 1 + 4\cos\theta$.

10. $r = 2\cos\theta - 3$, $r = 2$.

11. $r = \csc\theta + 2$, $r = \dfrac{1}{1 - \sin\theta}$.

12. $r = 3 - 4\sin\theta$, $r = 2 + 3\sin\theta$.

chapter 10

Parametric Equations

60. PARAMETRIC EQUATIONS

As an illustration of the concept to be presented in this chapter, let us consider the following pair of equations:

10·1
$$x = 4t - 2, \qquad y = 4t^2.$$

With each value of t we shall associate a point (x, y) in the coordinate plane, where x and y are determined from Equations 10·1. For example, if $t = 1$ in 10·1, we find $x = 2$, $y = 4$; hence corresponding to $t = 1$ we have the point $(2, 4)$. Similarly, $t = 2$ yields the point $(6, 16)$. The totality of all points obtained by letting t be a real number in 10·1 is called the *graph* of these equations. In the accompanying table, we indicate the values of x and y that correspond to certain values of t, and the points (x, y) are plotted in Figure 130.

t	-2	$-3/2$	-1	$-1/2$	0	$1/2$	1	$3/2$	2
x	-10	-8	-6	-4	-2	0	2	4	6
y	16	9	4	1	0	1	4	9	16

A smooth curve drawn through these points then approximates the desired graph.

From the figure it appears that the graph is a parabola, and we proceed to verify that this is indeed the case. By solving the first of Equations 10·1 for t, we obtain

$$t = \frac{x + 2}{4}.$$

Now, if this value of t is substituted in the second of Equations 10·1, we obtain

$$y = \frac{(x + 2)^2}{4},$$

or

10·2 $(x + 2)^2 = 4y.$

This equation must therefore be satisfied by every pair of numbers (x, y) obtained from 10·1 by assigning a real value to t.   Since the graph of Equation 10·2 is known to be a parabola, it follows that every point on the

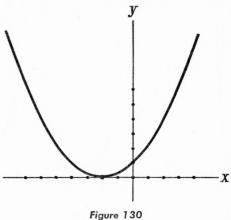

Figure 1 30

graph of Equations 10·1 must be a point on this parabola.   Actually, it is easy to verify in this particular example that every point on the graph of Equation 10·2 can be obtained as a point on the graph of Equations 10·1 by suitable choice of t; hence the two graphs are identical.

Equations such as 10·1 in which x and y are expressed in terms of some other letter t to which can be assigned arbitrary real values, are called **parametric equations**; and t is called the **parameter**.   The process by which we obtained Equation 10·2 from Equations 10·1 is called "eliminating the parameter."   In many cases, this process may be difficult or even impossible to carry out.   It is sometimes convenient to call Equation 10·2 the *rectangular* equation of the parabola to distinguish it from the parametric equations.

In the example under discussion, it is possible to give a geometric meaning to the parameter t.   Let us compute the slope of the line on the vertex $(-2, 0)$ and on any other point $P(x, y)$ of the parabola.   By 2·4 and 10·1, this slope is just

$$\frac{y}{x + 2} = \frac{4t^2}{4t} = t,$$

and thus the value of the parameter t which gives the point P is just the slope of the line on P and the vertex of the parabola.

Frequently, as in this example, the parameter can be given some geometric or physical meaning, but this need not always be the case. We may also remark that although a given pair of parametric equations has a uniquely determined graph, the same curve may be the graph of many different pairs of parametric equations.   For example, the reader may verify that the parametric equations

$$x = 4t + 2, \qquad y = 4(t + 1)^2$$

have the same graph as Equations 10·1.

It may very well be true that the graph of a rectangular equation obtained by eliminating the parameter has points on it that are not on the graph of the given parametric equations, although this did not happen in the case of Equations 10·1.   As an example, consider the parametric equations

10·3 $$x = 4s^2 - 2, \qquad y = 4s^4,$$

with s the parameter.   If we eliminate the parameter from these equations, we again get Equation 10·2, and thus all points on the graph of Equations 10·3 must lie on the parabola with Equation 10·2.   However, from the first of Equations 10·3 we see that $x + 2 = 4s^2$, and thus $x + 2 \geqq 0$ for every choice of the real number s.   Actually, the graph of Equations 10·3 consists of that part of the parabola of Figure 130 which is to the right of the vertex $(-2, 0)$.   Thus—and this is most important—we see that the graph of a pair of parametric equations may give only a part of the graph of the rectangular equation obtained by eliminating the parameter.

61.   THE PATH OF A PROJECTILE

In this section we give an example in which it is convenient to use the *time* as the parameter.

Suppose that a projectile is fired from the origin with an initial velocity of v_0 feet per second and at an angle α from the horizontal, as indicated in Figure 131.   The projectile may be thought of as an artillery

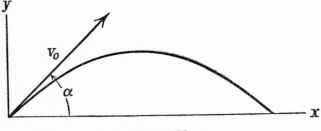

Figure 131

shell, a baseball, or any other material object. We assume, however, that the friction of the air can be neglected, so that while the projectile is in flight the only force acting on it is the force of gravity. Under this assumption, it is shown in elementary physics that at a time t seconds after the projectile is fired its coordinates are

10·4 $$x = (v_0 \cos \alpha)t, \qquad y = (v_0 \sin \alpha)t - 16t^2,$$

with the understanding that x and y are given in feet. Accordingly, these are parametric equations of the path of the projectile.

By eliminating t from Equations 10·4, we find that the path of the projectile is along the curve with rectangular equation

10·5 $$y = x \tan \alpha - \frac{16 \sec^2 \alpha}{v_0^2} x^2.$$

This is readily recognized as the equation of a parabola; so the path of the projectile is along an arc of a parabola. We observe, however, that Equations 10·4 give us important information not obtainable from Equation 10·5 in that the actual position of the projectile at any given time is immediately obtainable from Equations 10·4.

Example 1

A ball is thrown from the ground at an initial velocity of 80 feet per second, and at an angle of 30° from the horizontal. Determine when and where the ball will strike the ground.

Solution: In the notation used above, we have $v_0 = 80$ and $\alpha = 30°$. Hence the equations (10·4) of the path become

$$x = 40 \sqrt{3}\, t, \qquad y = 40t - 16t^2.$$

It is clear that the ball is at the ground if and only if $y = 0$, hence if and only if

$$40t - 16t^2 = 0.$$

The solutions of this equation are $t = 0$ and $t = 40/16 = 2.5$. Naturally, $t = 0$ is the time that the ball is thrown, and therefore it returns to the ground 2.5 seconds later. At this instant, we have

$$x = 40 \sqrt{3}\ (2.5) = 173 \text{ feet (approximately)}.$$

We find therefore that the ball strikes the ground 2.5 seconds after it is thrown, and at a point 173 feet from the throwing point.

EXERCISES

In each of Exercises 1–14, sketch the graph of the given parametric equations by assigning values to the parameter. Then find the rectangular equation of the graph by eliminating the parameter.

1. $x = 2t, y = 1 - 3t.$

2. $x = t^2 + 1, y = 4 + 5t^2.$

3. $x = \dfrac{t}{1-t}, y = \dfrac{1}{1-t}.$

4. $x = \dfrac{1}{t}, y = 4t.$

5. $x = t^2 + 1, y = 1 - t.$

6. $x = \sqrt{t}, y = 4t - 3.$

7. $x = 1 + \dfrac{1}{t}, y = t - \dfrac{1}{t}.$

8. $x = 3 - t, y = 4t^2.$

9. $x = 2t, y = 2t^3.$

10. $x = 4t^2, y = 8t^3.$

11. $x = \dfrac{1}{t}, y = \dfrac{1-t^2}{t^2}.$

12. $x = 1 - t^4, y = t - t^3.$

13. $x = \dfrac{2(1-t^2)}{1+t^2}, y = \dfrac{4t}{1+t^2}.$

14. $x = \dfrac{3t}{1+t^3}, y = \dfrac{3t^2}{1+t^3}.$

15. An arrow is shot with an initial velocity of 200 feet per second and at an angle of 45° from the horizontal. Find when and where the arrow will strike the ground.

16. A golfer hits a ball with an initial velocity of 120 feet per second and at an angle of 30° from the horizontal. Find when and where the ball will hit the ground.

17. Will the ball of the previous example clear a fence 10 feet high and at a distance of 350 feet from the golfer?

18. With what initial velocity must a ball be thrown from the ground at an angle of 30° from the horizontal if it is to travel a horizontal distance of 300 feet?

19. A batter hits a ball with an initial velocity of 96 feet per second and at an angle of 60° from the horizontal. Find the maximum height attained by the ball.

62. PARAMETRIC EQUATIONS OF THE CIRCLE AND THE ELLIPSE

Frequently it is convenient to use an angle as a parameter, in which case the parametric equations may very well involve the trigonometric functions of the angle. Therefore it is important to always keep in mind the definitions of the trigonometric functions. In particular, if $P(x, y)$ is a point on the terminal side of an angle ϕ in standard position, and the distance between P and the origin is a, we have by definition

$$\cos \phi = \frac{x}{a}, \qquad \sin \phi = \frac{y}{a};$$

or

10·6 $$x = a \cos \phi, \qquad y = a \sin \phi.$$

Now, if a is a fixed positive number, and ϕ varies from 0 to 2π, it is clear that $P(x, y)$ with coordinates given by 10·6 moves around the circle with center at the origin and with radius a (Figure 132). Hence 10·6 are

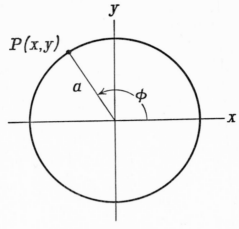

Figure 132

parametric equations of this circle.   It is easy to find the familiar rectangular equation of the circle by squaring each of Equations 10·6 and adding.   We obtain in this way

$$x^2 + y^2 = a^2 (\sin^2 \phi + \cos^2 \phi),$$

which reduces to

$$x^2 + y^2 = a^2.$$

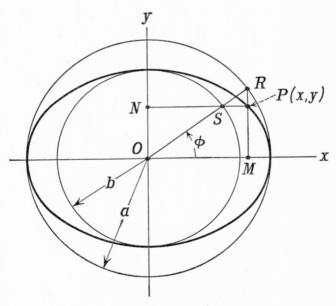

Figure 133

We shall now give a geometric construction of points on an ellipse and find parametric equations of an ellipse.

Let a and b be positive numbers with $a > b$, and consider the two circles with center the origin and with radii a and b respectively (Figure 133). Let ϕ be an arbitrary angle in standard position, and let the terminal side of ϕ cut the two circles at R and S, respectively. Through S draw a line parallel to the x-axis, and through R a line parallel to the y-axis; let these lines intersect at point $P(x, y)$. We proceed to express the coordinates of P in terms of the angle ϕ.

If M and N are the respective projections of R and S on the x- and y-axes, then

$$\cos \phi = \frac{\overline{OM}}{a} = \frac{x}{a}, \qquad \sin \phi = \frac{\overline{ON}}{b} = \frac{y}{b}.$$

Thus the coordinates of P are as follows:

10·7 $$x = a \cos \phi, \qquad y = b \sin \phi.$$

We now consider these to be parametric equations of some curve, and can easily identify the curve by finding its rectangular equation. Using the identity, $\sin^2 \phi + \cos^2 \phi = 1$, it follows that when ϕ is eliminated from Equations 10·7, the following equation results:

$$\frac{x^2}{a^2} + \frac{y^2}{b^2} = 1.$$

We know this equation to be that of an ellipse with major axis along the x-axis and center at the origin. Thus Equations 10·7 are parametric equations of this ellipse, and the points P determined by the geometric construction described above always lie on this ellipse. Note that if $a = b$, Equations 10·7 of an ellipse reduce to Equations 10·6 of a circle.

63. THE CYCLOID

In this and the next section we give examples in which a curve is specified by some geometric or physical condition, and the parametric equations are then obtained directly from the given condition.

The path of a fixed point on a circle which rolls on a straight line is called a **cycloid.** We shall proceed to find parametric equations of a cycloid.

Let us assume that the rolling circle has radius a, that we seek the path of point P, and that the circle rolls to the right on the x-axis from a starting position with P at the origin.

In Figure 134, the fixed radius CP has turned through the angle ϕ, which we assume to be measured in radians. Moreover, we consider ϕ to be a positive angle even though the rotation of CP is in a clockwise direction. We shall obtain parametric equations of the cycloid by expressing the coordinates (x, y) of P in terms of the angle ϕ.

Let M and M' be the respective projections of C on the x- and y-axes, and N and N' the respective projections of P on the x- and y-axes, as

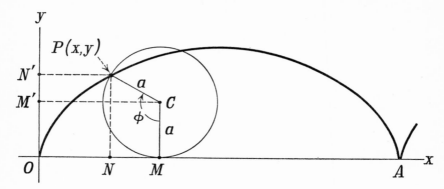

Figure 134

indicated in Figure 134. By the definition of the cycloid, arc $\widehat{MP}$ has length $|OM| = \overline{OM}$. Since ϕ is measured in radians, arc $\widehat{MP}$ has length $a\phi$, and hence

$$\overline{OM} = a\phi.$$

Evidently

$$\overline{OM'} = a.$$

Thus

$$x = \overline{ON} = \overline{OM} - \overline{NM} = a\phi - \overline{NM},$$
$$y = \overline{ON'} = \overline{OM'} - \overline{N'M'} = a - \overline{N'M'}.$$

Now, somewhat detailed, but elementary, trigonometric calculations will show that

$$\overline{NM} = a \sin \phi, \qquad \overline{N'M'} = a \cos \phi,$$

regardless of the magnitude of angle ϕ. (The reader should verify this for the case in which ϕ is as indicated in Figure 134.) Hence in terms of the parameter ϕ, the cycloid has parametric equations

10·8
$$x = a(\phi - \sin \phi),$$
$$y = a(1 - \cos \phi).$$

The cycloid consists of a succession of equal arches, the maximum height being the diameter $2a$ of the rolling circle. Furthermore, the point P will first return to the x-axis at a point A such that $|OA| = 2\pi a$, the circumference of the rolling circle. Of course, point A is the point obtained by setting $\phi = 2\pi$ in Equations 10·8.

One of the most interesting properties of the cycloid can be described as follows.   Let us consider a thin wire in the shape of a single inverted arch of a cycloid (Figure 135), and a bead which can slide on the wire without friction.   If Q is the lowest point on the arch, then the time that it takes for the bead to slide down the curve to point Q is independent of the starting point.   It is assumed, of course, that the bead starts from

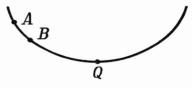

Figure 135

rest and is acted on only by the force of gravity.   For example, in Figure 135, the time the bead takes to slide to Q is the same whether it starts at A or at B.

Another property of considerable interest in advanced mathematics is the following.   If A and B are two points on a cycloid, as in Figure 135, a bead will slide from A to B in less time along the cycloid than along any other curve passing through A and B.

64.   EPICYCLOID AND HYPOCYCLOID

In this section we shall consider the path of a point on a circle which rolls on another circle.   The path is called an **epicycloid** if the rolling circle is *outside* the fixed circle, and a **hypocycloid** if the rolling circle is *inside* the fixed circle.

We now proceed to find parametric equations of the epicycloid.   Let a be the radius of the fixed circle, and b that of the rolling circle.   Let P be the point on the rolling circle, the path of which we seek, and denote by C the center of the rolling circle.   We assume that the center of the fixed circle is at the origin, that the rolling circle moves around the fixed circle in a counterclockwise direction, and that in the initial position P coincides with the point A on the fixed circle and the x-axis.

A typical poisition of the rolling circle is shown in Figure 136, in which the fixed radius CP of the rolling circle has turned through the angle α, and the line OC has turned through the angle ϕ.   We shall consider these angles to be measured in radians, and shall express the coordinates (x, y) of P in terms of the parameter ϕ.

We now consider new x'- and y'-axes with origin at C and parallel to the original x- and y-axes, respectively.   The angle $\pi + \phi + \alpha$ is in standard position relative to the x'- and y'-axes and has CP as its terminal side.   Since $|CP| = b$, it follows from the definitions of the trigonometric functions that the x'- and y'-coordinates of P are

$$x' = b \cos (\pi + \phi + \alpha) = -b \cos (\phi + \alpha),$$
$$y' = b \sin (\pi + \phi + \alpha) = -b \sin (\phi + \alpha).$$

Similarly, since $|OC| = a + b$ and angle ϕ is in standard position relative to the x- and y-axes, the point C has coordinates $((a + b) \cos \phi, (a + b) \sin \phi)$ relative to the original axes. By the formulas (6·1) for translation

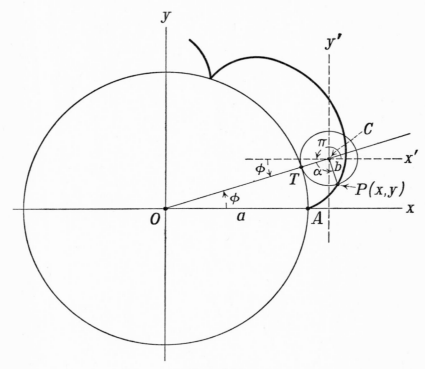

Figure 136

of axes, the cooordinates (x, y) of P relative to the original axes are as follows:

10·9
$$x = (a + b) \cos \phi - b \cos (\phi + \alpha),$$
$$y = (a + b) \sin \phi - b \sin (\phi + \alpha).$$

Since P was originally at A, it is clear that the arcs $\overparen{AT}$ and $\overparen{PT}$ have equal lengths, and hence that

$$a\phi = b\alpha.$$

If we use this equation to express α in terms of ϕ, Equations 10·9 can be written in the following form:

$$x = (a + b) \cos \phi - b \cos \frac{a + b}{b} \phi,$$

10·10

$$y = (a + b) \sin \phi - b \sin \frac{a + b}{b} \phi.$$

These are the desired parametric equations of the epicycloid.

If the moving circle rolls *inside* the fixed circle, the path of the point P is a hypocycloid. It can be shown, although we omit the proof, that equations of the hypocycloid can be obtained from 10·10 by replacing b with $-b$. Thus parametric equations of the hypocycloid are

$$x = (a - b) \cos \phi + b \cos \frac{a - b}{b} \phi,$$

10·11

$$y = (a - b) \sin \phi - b \sin \frac{a - b}{b} \phi.$$

For either the epicycloid or hypocycloid, the special case in which a/b is an integer n is of particular interest. In this case it is clear that after the moving circle has completed n rotations, the point P will be back to A and the complete curve will have been obtained. As an illustration, let us consider the hypocycloid with $n = 4$. If we set $b = a/4$ in Equations 10·11, we obtain

$$x = (3a/4) \cos \phi + (a/4) \cos 3\phi,$$
$$y = (3a/4) \sin \phi - (a/4) \sin 3\phi.$$

Using the trigonometric identities,

$$\cos 3\phi = 4 \cos^3 \phi - 3 \cos \phi,$$
$$\sin 3\phi = 3 \sin \phi - 4 \sin^3 \phi,$$

these reduce to

10·12

$$x = a \cos^3 \phi,$$
$$y = a \sin^3 \phi.$$

The graph of these equations is indicated in Figure 137, and is called a *hypocycloid of four cusps*.

Although it may be impossible to eliminate the parameter in Equations 10·11, it is quite easy to do so in the special case of Equations 10·12. From these equations we see that

$$\cos^2 \phi = \left(\frac{x}{a}\right)^{2/3} \quad \text{and} \quad \sin^2 \phi = \left(\frac{y}{a}\right)^{2/3},$$

and hence

$$\left(\frac{x}{a}\right)^{2/3} + \left(\frac{y}{a}\right)^{2/3} = 1.$$

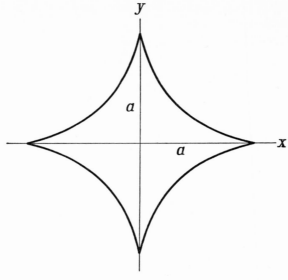

This rectangular equation of the hypocycloid of four cusps is usually written in the form

$$x^{2/3} + y^{2/3} = a^{2/3}.$$

Some other special cases of hypocycloids and epicycloids will appear in the following list of exercises.

EXERCISES

In each of Exercises 1–10, sketch the graph of the given parametric equations; then find the rectangular equation of the graph by eliminating the parameter.

1. $x = 3 \cos \phi$, $y = 3 \sin \phi$.   2. $x = 2 \sin \phi$, $y = 2 \cos \phi$.

3. $x = 4 \sin \phi$, $y = 2 \cos \phi$.   4. $x = \cos \phi$, $y = 5 \sin \phi$.

5. $x = 1 + \sin \phi$, $y = 2 - \cos \phi$.

6. $x = 2 - 3 \cos \phi$, $y = -1 + 2 \cos \phi$.

7. $x = \cos^4 \phi$, $y = \sin^4 \phi$.   8. $x = \sec \phi$, $y = \tan \phi$.

9. $x = 3 \tan \phi$, $y = 4 \sec \phi$.   10. $x = 1 + \sin \phi$, $y = -2 + \cos^2 \phi$.

11. Plot some points and sketch the graph of the cycloid (10·8) with $a = 4$.

12. Plot some points and sketch the graph of the hypocycloid of four cusps (10·12) with $a = 4$.

13. Show that the hypocycloid of two cusps ($a/b = 2$ in 10·11) is just a diameter of the fixed circle.

14. Find equations of the hypocycloid of three cusps ($a/b = 3$ in 10·11) and sketch its graph.

15. Find equations of the epicycloid for which $a = 4b$, and sketch the curve.

16. Do the same as in Exercise 15 with $a = 3b$.

17. Do the same as in Exercise 15 with $a = 2b$.

18. Do the same as in Exercise 15 with $a = b$.

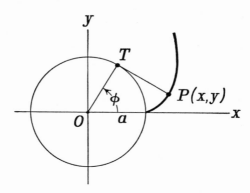

Figure 1 38

19. Show that parametric equations of the path of a point b units from the center of a circle of radius a which rolls along the x-axis are

$$x = a\phi - b \sin \phi, \qquad y = a - b \cos \phi.$$

20. Sketch the graph of the equations of Exercise 19 if $a = 2$ and $b = 1$.

21. If a thread which has been wound around a fixed circle is unwound in such a way that the thread is kept taut, the end of the thread traces out a curve called the *involute* of the circle. If the circle is of radius a and has its center at the origin (Figure 138), show that parametric equations of the involute are

$$x = a(\cos \phi + \phi \sin \phi), \qquad y = a(\sin \phi - \phi \cos \phi).$$

[*Hint:* In the figure, $|TP| = a\phi$, and angle OTP is a right angle.]

22. Sketch the graph of the involute of a circle if $a = 1$.

chapter 11

Tangents to the Conic Sections

In Euclidean geometry a tangent to a circle is usually defined as a line which cuts the circle in exactly one point, and the line is said to be tangent to the circle at this point. It is then proved that the tangent to a circle at a given point is perpendicular to the radius drawn to this point. In Chapter 4 we assumed that the reader was acquainted with the basic ideas concerning tangents to circles, and hence included illustrative examples in which these ideas were used.

The definition of a tangent to a general curve involves the concept of **limit,** a concept of fundamental importance in that branch of mathematics known as the **calculus.** Although a rigorous treatment of limits is essential for a full discussion of tangents, an intuitive treatment is sufficient for our purposes in finding tangents to the conics. After giving the definition of the tangent to a conic at a given point on the curve, we shall discuss some general properties of tangents to conics and shall indicate some of the physical applications of these properties.

65. THE CONCEPT OF TANGENT LINE

Let us begin with a discussion of tangents to the parabola having the simple equation

$$y = x^2.$$

This will allow us to introduce the general method of finding tangents, at the same time keeping the computations to a minimum.

We start by choosing a fixed point on this parabola, say the point $P(2, 4)$, and by discussing what is meant by the tangent to the parabola at this point. If Q is any point on the parabola other than P, the line s on P and Q is called a **secant line** of the parabola (Figure 139). For convenience, we denote the coordinates of Q by $(2 + h, 4 + k)$. Thus, for example, if Q were the particular point $(3, 9)$, we would have $h = 1$ and $k = 5$. With this notation, the slope m of the secant line s is given by

$$m = \frac{(4 + k) - 4}{(2 + h) - 2} = \frac{k}{h}.$$

Since the point $Q(2 + h, 4 + k)$ is on the parabola, the coordinates of Q satisfy the equation of the parabola; that is,

$$4 + k = (2 + h)^2.$$

On simplification, this yields

$$k = h(4 + h),$$

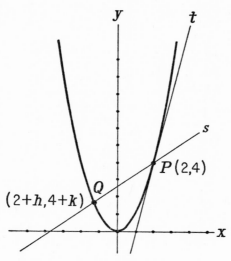

Figure 139

and hence the slope m of s is given by

11·1
$$m = 4 + h.$$

The clue to the definition of the tangent line at $P(2, 4)$ is that if Q is taken close to P, the secant line s will be close to what we choose to regard as the tangent line t at P. Therefore, the *slope* of the secant line s will be close to the *slope* of the tangent line t at P. However, if Q is close to P, then h (which is the difference between the x-coordinates of Q and P) will be close to zero, and the slope m of s will be close to 4. In terms of limits, we say that "the limit of m as h approaches zero is 4." *This limit is defined to be the slope of the tangent line t at P.* Thus the slope of the tangent line at the point $P(2, 4)$ is 4.

Since the slope of the tangent line t is now known to be 4, and since the point $P(2, 4)$ is on t, the equation of t is

$$y - 4 = 4(x - 2),$$

or

11·2
$$4x - y - 4 = 0.$$

In order to illustrate further the more general calculations of the next section, we shall now obtain a formula for the equation of the tangent to this parabola at a fixed but unspecified point $P(x_1, y_1)$ on the parabola. As in the discussion above, we let $Q(x_1 + h, y_1 + k)$ be any other point on the parabola, and we let the secant line s on P and Q (Figure 140) have

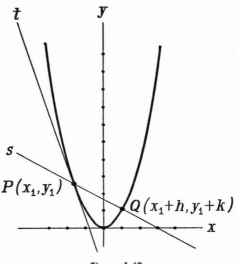

Figure 140

slope m.   Clearly, $m = k/h$ as before.   Since P and Q are on the parabola, we must have

$$y_1 = x_1{}^2$$

and

$$y_1 + k = (x_1 + h)^2.$$

On subtracting the first equation from the second, we obtain

$$k = h(2x_1 + h).$$

Thus the slope m of the secant line s is given by

11·3
$$m = \frac{k}{h} = 2x_1 + h.$$

Note that if we put $x_1 = 2$, we obtain Equation 11·1 as a special case.

It is clear from 11·3 that if Q is close to P, that is, if h is close to zero, then m is close to $2x_1$.   Hence the tangent line t at $P(x_1, y_1)$ is *defined* to be the line on P with slope $2x_1$.   As examples, the slope of the tangent line at $P(2, 4)$ is $2 \cdot 2 = 4$; at $P(3, 9)$ the slope is $2 \cdot 3 = 6$; at $P(-2, 4)$ the slope is $2(-2) = -4$.

Since the slope of the tangent line at the point $P(x_1, y_1)$ is $2x_1$, the equation of this tangent line is

$$y - y_1 = 2x_1(x - x_1),$$

or

$$y = 2x_1x + y_1 - 2x_1{}^2.$$

By making use of the fact that $y_1 = x_1{}^2$, we may express this latter equation in the form

11·4 $$y = 2x_1x - y_1.$$

Naturally, if we set $x_1 = 2$ and $y_1 = 4$, this equation reduces to Equation 11·2 obtained above.

66.   THE TANGENT AT ANY POINT OF A CONIC SECTION

The following theorem generalizes the results of the preceding section.

11·5   Theorem

Let t be the line which is tangent to the conic section having the equation

11·6 $$Ax^2 + Cy^2 + Dx + Ey + F = 0$$

at the point $P(x_1, y_1)$ on the conic.   Then

(a)   *the slope of the line t is*

11·7 $$-\frac{2Ax_1 + D}{2Cy_1 + E},$$

(b)   *the equation of the line t is*

11·8 $$Ax_1x + Cy_1y + D\left(\frac{x_1 + x_2}{2}\right) + E\left(\frac{y_1 + y_2}{2}\right) + F = 0.$$

Proof: Let $Q(x_1 + h, y_1 + k)$ be any point, other than $P(x_1, y_1)$, on the conic section, and let m be the slope of the secant line on P and Q.   As before, it follows that $m = k/h$.   Since the coordinates of P, and also those of Q, must satisfy Equation 11·6, we have

11·9 $$Ax_1{}^2 + Cy_1{}^2 + Dx_1 + Ey_1 + F = 0,$$

and

11·10 $$A(x_1 + h)^2 + C(y_1 + k)^2 + D(x_1 + h) + E(y_1 + k) + F = 0.$$

If we expand the terms in 11·10 and subtract 11·9, the following equation results:

$$2Ax_1h + Ah^2 + 2Cy_1k + Ck^2 + Dh + Ek = 0.$$

We now divide each term by h and replace k/h by m, thus obtaining the equation

$$2Ax_1 + Ah + 2Cy_1m + Ckm + D + Em = 0.$$

When solved for m, this equation yields

$$m = -\frac{2Ax_1 + Ah + D}{2Cy_1 + Ck + E}.$$

Now that we have a formula for the slope m of the secant line on P and Q, we seek the "limit of m as h approaches zero." This expression is given a precise meaning in the calculus, but here we shall use our intuitive ideas in finding this limit. Since h is the difference of the x-coordinates of the points Q and P on the conic section, and k is the difference of their y-coordinates, it follows that k is small if h is small. That is, as h approaches zero, so does k, and m approaches the limiting value

$$-\frac{2Ax_1 + D}{2Cy_1 + E}.$$

The tangent line to the conic section at the point $P(x_1, y_1)$ therefore has slope given by 11·7.* This completes the proof of part (a) of the theorem.

The tangent line t is the line on $P(x_1, y_1)$ with slope given by 11·7, and hence its equation is

11·11 $$y - y_1 = -\frac{2Ax_1 + D}{2Cy_1 + E}(x - x_1).$$

The proof of the theorem will be completed by showing that this equation can be written in the form 11·8.

If we multiply both sides of Equation 11·11 by $2Cy_1 + E$, the resulting equation can be put in the form

11·12 $2Ax_1x + 2Cy_1y + Dx + Ey = 2(Ax_1{}^2 + Cy_1{}^2) + Dx_1 + Ey_1.$

However, from 11·9 we see that

$$Ax_1{}^2 + Cy_1{}^2 = -Dx_1 - Ey_1 - F.$$

Making this substitution on the right of 11·12 and simplifying, we obtain

$$2Ax_1x + 2Cy_1y + Dx + Ey = -Dx_1 - Ey_1 - 2F.$$

Clearly, this can be written in the desired form 11·8, and the proof is completed.

An easy way to remember Equation 11·8 is to observe that one can formally obtain it from Equation 11·6 by replacing

x^2 by x_1x, y^2 by y_1y, x by $(x + x_1)/2$,   and y by $(y + y_1)/2$.

---

* If it should happen in a special case that the denominator of 11·7 is zero, with the numerator different from zero, the tangent at P will have no slope; that is, it will be parallel to the y-axis.

In the preceding theorem we have considered a conic section, the equation of which has no term involving xy. This case is sufficiently general for our purposes, since we know that by a proper choice of coordinate axes the equation of any conic can be written in this form. Although the calculations will be slightly more complicated, the same general method can be used to find the equation of the tangent even when there is a term involving xy. (See Exercise 18 below.)

It may be of interest to verify that for the special case of a circle our new definition of tangent line coincides with the familiar definition of elementary geometry. We shall therefore show that a tangent line is perpendicular to the radius drawn to the point of tangency.

Let $P(x_1, y_1)$ be a fixed point on the circle with center (c, d) and radius r. The equation of this circle is known to be

$$(x - c)^2 + (y - d)^2 = r^2,$$

or

$$x^2 + y^2 - 2cx - 2dy + c^2 + d^2 - r^2 = 0.$$

This equation can be identified with Equation 11·6 by setting $A = C = 1$, $D = -2c$, $E = -2d$, $F = c^2 + d^2 - r^2$. It follows at once from 11·7 that the slope of the tangent to this circle at the point $P(x_1, y_1)$ is

$$- \frac{x_1 - c}{y_1 - d}.$$

Since the line on the center (c, d) and the point P has slope

$$\frac{y_1 - d}{x_1 - c},$$

the two lines are perpendicular by 2·5.

Example 1

Find the equation of the tangent to the hyperbola with equation

$$\frac{x^2}{16} - \frac{y^2}{9} = 1$$

at the point $(5, 9/4)$ on the hyperbola.

Solution: If we let $x_1 = 5$ and $y_1 = 9/4$ in 11·8, we obtain the desired equation

$$\frac{5x}{16} - \frac{(9/4)y}{9} = 1,$$

which simplifies to

$$45x - 36y - 144 = 0.$$

Example 2

Find the point on the parabola with equation $y = 6x - 2x^2$ at which the tangent line is parallel to the line with equation $2x - y = 1$.

Solution: We write the equation of the parabola in the form

$$2x^2 - 6x + y = 0$$

and identify this equation with Equation 11·6 by setting $A = 2$, $C = 0$, $D = -6$, $E = 1$, and $F = 0$.   By 11·7, the slope of the tangent at any point $P(x_1, y_1)$ on the parabola is $-(4x_1 - 6)$, or $6 - 4x_1$.   However, we seek the tangent line that is parallel to the line with equation $2x - y = 1$, a line with slope 2.   Hence we must have

$$6 - 4x_1 = 2,$$

from which it follows that $x_1 = 1$.   Substituting $x_1 = 1$ in the equation of the parabola, we find that $y_1 = 4$.   Hence the tangent at the point (1, 4) on the parabola is parallel to the given line.

Example 3

The tangent at any point P of the parabola $y^2 = 4px$ cuts the y-axis at a point A.   Show that this tangent line is perpendicular to the line on A and the focus of the parabola (Figure 141).

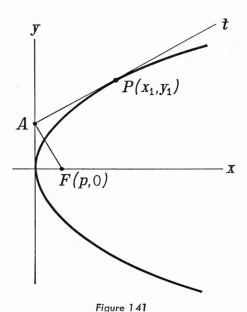

Figure 141

Solution: If P has coordinates (x_1, y_1), then by 11·8 the equation of the tangent line t at P is

$$y_1 y - 2p(x + x_1) = 0.$$

Giving x the value 0 in this equation, we obtain $(0, 2px_1/y_1)$ as the coordinates of A. Since the focus F has coordinates $(p, 0)$, the slope m_1 of the line on A and F is given by

$$m_1 = \frac{(2px_1)/y_1}{-p} = -\frac{2x_1}{y_1}.$$

The slope m_2 of the tangent line at P is given by

$$m_2 = \frac{2p}{y_1}.$$

Hence

$$m_1 m_2 = -\frac{4px_1}{y_1{}^2}.$$

Since $P(x_1, y_1)$ is on the parabola, $y_1{}^2 = 4px_1$, and it follows that $m_1 m_2 = -1$. By 2·5, the two lines are perpendicular, as we wished to show.

EXERCISES

In each of Exercises 1–10, find the equation of the tangent line to the given conic at the given point.

1. $y = 3x^2$, $(2, 12)$.
2. $y = -4x^2$, $(-1, -4)$.
3. $y^2 = 2x$, $(2, -2)$.
4. $4x^2 + 9y^2 = 36$, $(5/2, 1)$.
5. $4x^2 + y^2 = 4$, $(1/2, -\sqrt{3})$.
6. $x^2 - y^2 = 3$, $(-2, -1)$.
7. $x^2 - 6x + y^2 + 8y = 0$, $(6, 0)$.
8. $x^2 + y^2 + 10x - 24y = 0$, $(7, 7)$.
9. $y^2 - 4y = x^2 + 6x + 14$, $(1, 7)$.
10. $3x^2 + 4y^2 - 6x + 8y = 9$, $(3, -2)$.

11. Find the equation of the tangent line to the parabola $y = x^2 + x - 2$ that is parallel to the line $3x + y - 5 = 0$.

12. Find the equation of the tangent line to the parabola $y^2 = x + 3$ that is perpendicular to the line $y = 4x$.

13. Show that the tangent lines to the parabola $y^2 = 4px$ at the ends of the latus rectum are perpendicular to each other, and intersect on the directrix.

14. Let F be the focus of the parabola $y^2 = 4px$, P any point on this parabola, and Q the point of intersection of the tangent line to the parabola at P and the x-axis. Prove that FPQ is an isosceles triangle.

15. Let F and F' be the foci of an ellipse, P any point on the ellipse, and l the tangent line to the ellipse at P. Show that the product of the distances of F to l and F' to l is a constant (that is, that the product is the same for every choice of P).

16. Do the same as in Exercise 15 for a hyperbola instead of an ellipse.

17. A tangent line to a conic has only one point in common with the conic. Prove this for the ellipse.

18. Show that the tangent line to the conic

$$Ax^2 + Bxy + Cy^2 + Dx + Ey + F = 0$$

at the point $P(x_1, y_1)$ on the curve has equation

$$Ax_1x + B\left(\frac{x_1y + y_1x}{2}\right) + Cy_1y + D\left(\frac{x + x_1}{2}\right) + E\left(\frac{y + y_1}{2}\right) + F = 0.$$

In each of the following, use the result of Exercise 18 to find the equation of the tangent line to the given conic at the given point.

19. $xy = 4$, $(1, 4)$.   20. $xy + x + y = 3$, $(1, 1)$.

21. $x^2 + xy + y^2 = 7$, $(-2, 3)$.   22. $y^2 - 2xy + x + 3 = 0$, $(4, 1)$.

67. REFLECTION PROPERTIES OF THE CONICS

We first consider a parabola with coordinate axes so chosen that its equation has the simple form

$$y^2 = 4px.$$

Let l be the tangent line at an arbitrary point $P(x_1, y_1)$ on the parabola, and let k be the line on P parallel to the x-axis (Figure 142). We shall prove that the angle u from k to l is equal to the angle v from l to the line

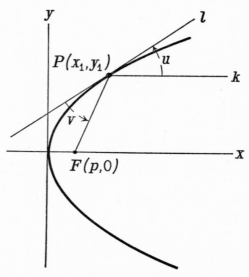

Figure 142

on P and F.   Since u is the inclination of l, $\tan u$ is the slope of l.   However, by Example 3 above, the slope of l also is $2p/y_1$; therefore

$$\tan u = \frac{2p}{y_1}.$$

The slope of the line on P and F is $y_1/(x_1 - p)$, and thus by 2·6 we have

$$\tan v = \frac{\dfrac{y_1}{x_1 - p} - \dfrac{2p}{y_1}}{1 + \dfrac{y_1 \cdot 2p}{(x_1 - p)y_1}} = \frac{y_1{}^2 - 2px_1 + 2p^2}{x_1y_1 + py_1}.$$

Since $y_1{}^2 = 4px_1$, this equation reduces to

$$\tan v = \frac{2p(x_1 + p)}{y_1(x_1 + p)} = \frac{2p}{y_1}.$$

Thus $\tan u = \tan v$, and since both angles are less than $180°$, it follows that $u = v$, as we wished to show.

Now suppose that one has a reflecting surface in the shape of a paraboloid obtained by revolving a section of a parabola about its axis. The property just proved assures us that if a source of light is placed at the focus, all rays of light that strike the reflecting surface will be reflected parallel to the axis of the paraboloid (since the angle of incidence equals the angle of reflection); hence one will obtain a narrow beam of light. It is for this reason that searchlights are often made in the shape of parabolic surfaces. Reversing the process, light coming from a distance source, such as the sun or a star, so that the rays are essentially parallel, will be reflected to the focus, provided the reflecting surface is turned so that the rays are parallel to the axis (Figure 143). As a matter of fact, heat rays as well as light rays will be reflected to the focus F so that if the reflector is turned toward the sun, inflammable material placed at the focus may well be ignited. In this connection is is interesting to observe that the word *focus* comes from the Latin and means *hearth* or *fireplace*.

We may also remark that the reflecting mirrors in reflecting telescopes are made in the shape of parabolic surfaces, and it is this reflection property of the parabola that is used in these modern telescopes.

An ellipse has a reflection property which may be stated as follows. Let P be any point of an ellipse with foci F and F' (Figure 144). If l is the tangent line at P, then the angle from l to the line on P and F' is equal to the angle from the line on P and F to l. Thus one finds that if a reflecting surface is in the form of an ellipsoid, obtained by revolving an ellipse about its major axis, any ray of light emanating from a source at one focus will be reflected so as to pass through the other focus. The laws of reflection of sound are similar to those for reflection of light, so the same type of

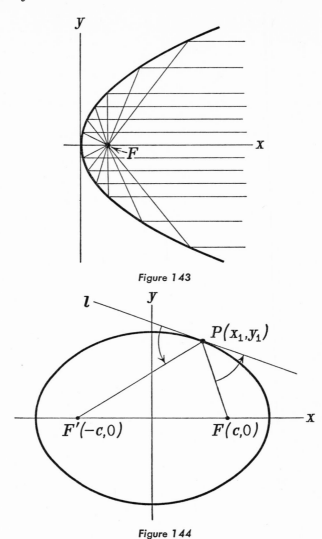

Figure 143

Figure 144

surface would serve as a "whispering gallery." That is, a weak sound at *F* might be heard rather distinctly at *F'* owing to reflection of the sound from the surface—even though it might be inaudible to someone much closer to *F*.

EXERCISES

1. Prove the reflection property of the ellipse stated above.
2. Prove that if *P* is any point on a hyperbola with foci *F* and *F'*, the tangent at *P* bisects the angle *F'PF*.

68. SOME OTHER PROPERTIES OF TANGENTS TO CONICS (OPTIONAL)

In the list of exercises given below a number of properties of tangents to conics are stated. Most of these are rather difficult to prove by the methods of analytic geometry, not because of any lack of knowledge as to procedure, but merely because of the rather detailed algebraic manipulations required. We shall illustrate a method of attack on such problems by an example.

Example 4

Let A and B be any two points on a parabola with vertex V; let l be the line on the vertex which is perpendicular to the axis of the parabola. Points R, S, and T are defined as follows: R is the point where the line on V and B intersects the line on A which is parallel to the axis of the parabola, S is the point where the line on A and B intersects the axis of the parabola, and T is the point where the tangent to the parabola at A intersects the line l. Show that R, S, and T are collinear and that T is the midpoint of the segment RS.

Solution: We find it convenient to choose coordinate axes in such a way that the equation of the parabola takes the simple form

$$y^2 = 4px.$$

It follows that the line l is the y-axis, and the axis of the parabola is the x-axis. Let A and B have coordinates (x_1, y_1) and (x_2, y_2), respectively (Figure 145). The problem now resolves itself into finding the coordinates of the points R, S, and T. Since each of these is the point of intersection of two lines, we proceed to display the equations of these lines. The reader may verify these equations by familiar calculations.

Equation of the line on A and R: $y = y_1$.
Equation of the line on B and V: $y = (y_2/x_2)x$.

Equation of the line on A and B: $y - y_1 = \dfrac{y_2 - y_1}{x_2 - x_1}(x - x_1)$.

Equation of the tangent line at A: $y_1 y = 2p(x + x_1)$.

By solving simultaneously the appropriate equations, we may easily verify that R, S, and T have coordinates as follows:

$$R(x_2 y_1/y_2, \, y_1), \qquad S\left(\frac{y_2 x_1 - y_1 x_2}{y_2 - y_1}, \, 0\right), \qquad T(0, \, 2px_1/y_1).$$

We now compute the coordinates of the midpoint of the segment RS. By 1·7, the x-coordinate of this midpoint is

$$\frac{1}{2}\left[\frac{x_2 y_1}{y_2} + \frac{y_2 x_1 - y_1 x_2}{y_2 - y_1}\right],$$

which simplifies to

$$\frac{y_2{}^2 x_1 - y_1{}^2 x_2}{2y_2(y_2 - y_1)}.$$

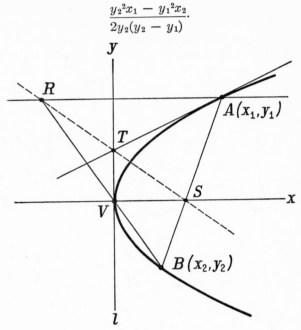

Figure 145

On substitution of $y_2{}^2 = 4px_2$ and $y_1{}^2 = 4px_1$, this reduces to 0.   Similarly, the y-coordinate of the midpoint of the segment RS is

$$\frac{y_1}{2} = \frac{y_1{}^2}{2y_1} = \frac{2px_1}{y_1}.$$

Thus T is the midpoint of the segment RS, and the proof is completed.

EXERCISES

1. Let F be the focus of a parabola, P an arbitrary point on the parabola, and Q the point of intersection of the directrix and the tangent line to the parabola at P.   Show that the line on F and Q is perpendicular to the line on F and P.

2. Let A, B, V, and l be as described in Example 4, and let X, Y, and Z be defined as follows: X is the point where the line on A and B intersects l, Y is the point where the line on B and V intersects the tangent to the parabola at A, and Z is the point where the line on A and V intersects the tangent to the parabola at B.   Show that X, Y, and Z are collinear.

3. In an ellipse let B and B' be the ends of the minor axis, and let P be any other point on the ellipse except a vertex. Each side of the triangle BPB' is extended until it intersects the tangent to the ellipse at the opposite vertex of the triangle. Show that the three points thus obtained are collinear.

4. Let V be one of the vertices of an ellipse, B one of the ends of the minor axis, and P any point on the ellipse other than an end of one of the axes. The points R, S, and T are as follows: R is the point where the line on P and V intersects the line on B which is parallel to the major axis, S is the point where the line on P and B intersects the line on V which is parallel to the minor axis, and T is the point where the line on B and V intersects the tangent to the ellipse at P. Prove that R, S, and T are collinear.

5. Let the tangent at any point P on a hyperbola intersect the asymptotes at Q and R. Show that P is the midpoint of the segment QR.

6. Let l_1 and l_2 be the asymptotes of a hyperbola, and let P be any point on the hyperbola. If the line on P which is parallel to l_1 cuts l_2 at R, and the line on P which is parallel to l_2 cuts l_1 at S, show that the line on R and S is parallel to the tangent at P.

chapter 12

Solid Analytic Geometry

So far in this book we have studied *plane* analytic geometry; that is, we have restricted attention to a fixed coordinate plane. However, many of the results of plane analytic geometry can be extended to three-dimensional space. In the present chapter we shall give a brief introduction to this so-called *solid* analytic geometry.

69. DEFINITIONS

In order to introduce a coordinate system in space, we select any three mutually perpendicular planes. It may be helpful to visualize these planes as the floor and two adjacent walls of a room. Each pair of these planes intersects in a line, and the three lines so obtained are mutually perpendicular and intersect in a point O. We now make each of these lines into a coordinate line in the usual way, taking O as the origin and using the same unit on each line. These three coordinate lines are called the *x-axis*, the *y-axis*, and the *z-axis;* together they are called the **coordinate axes.**

It is clearly impossible to construct a three-dimensional figure on a plane piece of paper, but it is possible to draw *in perspective* such a figure on a plane. A photograph of a building, for example, shows the building in perspective on a plane. In perspective, the three mutually perpendicular axes of our coordinate system might appear as in Figure 146. The x- and z-axes are in the plane of the paper, whereas the y-axis is to be visualized as perpendicular to the plane of the paper. The plane containing the x- and y-axes is called the *xy-plane;* the yz- and xz-planes are defined similarly. These three planes may be called the **coordinate planes.**

We now proceed to define the coordinates of a point in space. If P is an arbitrary point in space, let us denote by R, S, and T the respective projections of P on the yz-plane, the xz-plane, and the xy-plane (Figure 147). Obviously, the point P is determined by the directed distances $\overline{RP}$, $\overline{SP}$, and $\overline{TP}$ of P from the three coordinate planes. It is assumed,

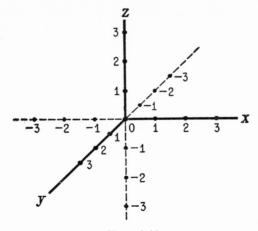

Figure 146

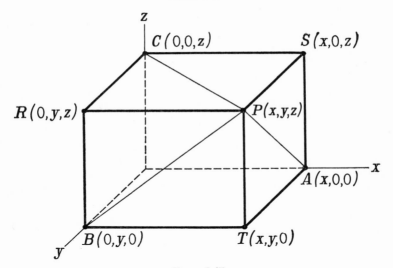

Figure 147

of course, that a line parallel to a coordinate axis has the same direction as that axis. Thus, for example, $\overline{TP}$ is positive or negative according as P is above or below the xy-plane. We now set $x = \overline{RP}$, $y = \overline{SP}$, and $z = \overline{TP}$. These three numbers are called the **coordinates** of P, and we write $P(x, y, z)$ to indicate that the point P has x, y, and z as its coordinates. In this way, with each point P in space a unique triple (x, y, z) of numbers is associated. Conversely, with each triple (x, y, z) of numbers is associated a unique point P in space having coordinates (x, y, z). We have thus introduced a **rectangular coordinate system** in space.

It is obvious that the points in the xy-plane have zero for z-coordinate; similarly, those in the xz-plane have zero for y-coordinate, and those in the yz-plane have zero for x-coordinate.

In Figure 147 the respective projections of P on the x- , y- , and z-axes are the points A, B, and C. As a point on the coordinate line which we have chosen as x-axis, A has coordinate x; and similarly, the points B and C have respective coordinates y and z. Thus we may also think of the three coordinates of P as the coordinates of the respective projections of P on the three coordinate axes.

Figure 147 also indicates that if P is a point not on one of the coordinate planes, the projections of P on the coordinate axes and coordinate planes, together with the origin and the point P itself, are the vertices of a rectangular parallelopiped.

The three coordinate planes divide space into eight regions, each of which is called an **octant**. The *first* octant contains every point P all of whose coordinates are positive numbers. The other octants are not numbered, since we have no need to refer to them explicitly.

70. DISTANCE AND MIDPOINT FORMULAS

The following formula gives the distance between two points in space in terms of the coordinates of the points.

12·1 Distance Formula

The distance $|P_1P_2|$ between the points $P_1(x_1, y_1, z_1)$ and $P_2(x_2, y_2, z_2)$ is given by

$$|P_1P_2| = \sqrt{(x_2 - x_1)^2 + (y_2 - y_1)^2 + (z_2 - z_1)^2}.$$

Proof: Through each of the given points construct three planes parallel to the three coordinate planes. As indicated in Figure 148, these six planes bound a rectangular parallelopiped, the edges of which are parallel to the coordinate axes. If the points A and B are selected as in the figure, the lines AB, BP_1, and AP_2 are parallel to the three coordinate axes, and we evidently have

$$|AB| = |x_2 - x_1|, \qquad |BP_1| = |y_2 - y_1|, \qquad |AP_2| = |z_2 - z_1|.$$

Thus, by the Pythagorean Theorem,

$$\begin{aligned}
|P_1P_2|^2 &= |AP_1|^2 + |AP_2|^2 \\
&= |AB|^2 + |BP_1|^2 + |AP_2|^2 \\
&= (x_2 - x_1)^2 + (y_2 - y_1)^2 + (z_2 - z_1)^2,
\end{aligned}$$

and the desired result follows.

A slight modification of this proof is required if the line P_1P_2 is parallel to a coordinate plane. If, for example, P_1P_2 is parallel to the xy-plane, the points A and P_2 of Figure 148 coincide. Hence

$$|P_1P_2|^2 = (x_2 - x_1)^2 + (y_2 - y_1)^2.$$

However, this agrees with 12·1 since in this case we must have $z_2 = z_1$. (Why?)

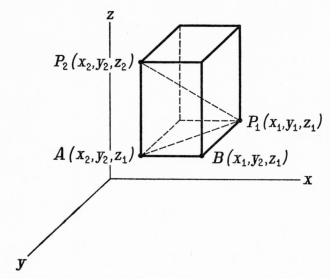

Figure 148

From 12·1 it follows at once that the distance $|OP|$ of the point $P(x, y, z)$ from the origin O is given by

$$|OP| = \sqrt{x^2 + y^2 + z^2}.$$

Example 1

Prove that the points $A(3, 2, 4)$, $B(6, 10, -1)$, and $C(9, 4, 1)$ are the vertices of an isosceles right triangle.

Solution: Using 12·1, we find the lengths of the sides of triangle ABC to be as follows:

$$|AB| = \sqrt{(3 - 6)^2 + (2 - 10)^2 + (4 + 1)^2} = \sqrt{98} = 7\sqrt{2},$$

$$|AC| = \sqrt{(3 - 9)^2 + (2 - 4)^2 + (4 - 1)^2} = \sqrt{49} = 7,$$

$$|BC| = \sqrt{(6 - 9)^2 + (10 - 4)^2 + (-1 - 1)^2} = \sqrt{49} = 7.$$

Since $|AC| = |BC|$, the triangle is isosceles; and since

$$|AC|^2 + |BC|^2 = |AB|^2,$$

the triangle is a right triangle with right angle at C.

We now state without proof the following midpoint formula, since the proof for the plane case (1·7) carries over with little modification.

12·2   Midpoint Formula

If $P_1(x_1, y_1, z_1)$ and $P_2(x_2, y_2, z_2)$ are any two points of space, the midpoint of the segment P_1P_2 has coordinates

$$\left(\frac{x_1 + x_2}{2}, \frac{y_1 + y_2}{2}, \frac{z_1 + z_2}{2}\right).$$

Example 2

Find the coordinates of the midpoints of the sides of triangle ABC of Example 1.

Solution: The midpoint D of side AB has coordinates

$$\left(\frac{3 + 6}{2}, \frac{2 + 10}{2}, \frac{4 - 1}{2}\right),$$

or $D(9/2, 6, 3/2)$.   Similarly, the midpoints E and F of AC and BC have the respective coordinates $E(6, 3, 5/2)$ and $F(15/2, 7, 0)$.

EXERCISES

In sketching a rectangular coordinate system of space in perspective on a plane, it is convenient to take the x- and z-axes as being perpendicular, and to take the y-axis as making an angle of $135°$ both with the x-axis and the z-axis (as in Figures 146–148).   The unit distance on the y-axis is then shortened to $\sqrt{2}/2$ (approximately .7) times that on the x- and z-axes.

In each of Exercises 1–4, plot the given points, sketching the rectangular parallelopiped associated with each point (as in Figure 147).

1. $(1, 2, 3)$, $(4, 1, 5)$, $(2, 4, 3)$.

2. $(-1, 2, 4)$, $(3, 0, 2)$, $(4, -3, 4)$.

3. $(2, 3, 0)$, $(-3, -3, 1)$, $(5, 0, 0)$.

4. $(-4, -2, -3)$, $(0, 1, -1)$, $(0, 2, 0)$.

In each of Exercises 5–8, plot the two given points and sketch the rectangular parallelopiped having these points as opposite vertices (as in Figure 148).   Find the volume of each parallelopiped.

5. $(1, 4, 1)$ and $(5, 1, 5)$.

6. $(6, 0, 0)$ and $(2, 8, 6)$.

7. $(-2, 2, 4)$ and $(2, -2, 1)$.

8. $(-3, -4, 1)$ and $(1, 6, -2)$.

In each of Exercises 9–16, show that the three given points are either the vertices of a right triangle, or the vertices of an isosceles triangle, or both. Sketch the triangle.

9. $(1, 5, 0)$, $(6, 6, 4)$, $(0, 9, 5)$.   10. $(4, 9, 4)$, $(0, 11, 2)$, $(1, 0, 1)$.

11. $(1, 0, 2)$, $(4, 3, 2)$, $(0, 7, 6)$.   12. $(2, 3, 4)$, $(8, -1, 2)$, $(-4, 1, 0)$.

13. $(7, 4, 4)$, $(2, -1, 3)$, $(1, 0, -4)$.

14. $(1, 10, 5)$, $(-4, 0, -10)$, $(1, -10, -5)$.

15. $(4, 0, 1)$, $(2, 0, 0)$, $(3, 2, -2)$.   16. $(2, 2, 2)$, $(3, 4, 0)$, $(5, 4, 1)$.

17. Show that the points $(1, 6, 1)$, $(1, 3, 4)$, $(4, 3, 1)$, and $(0, 2, 0)$ are the vertices of a regular tetrahedron. Sketch.

18. Show that the points $(3, -1, 3)$, $(1, -1, 2)$, $(2, 1, 0)$, and $(4, 1, 1)$ are the vertices of a rectangle.

19. Under what conditions on x, y, and z is the point $P(x, y, z)$ equidistant from the points $(3, -1, 4)$ and $(-1, 5, 0)$?

20. Let A, B, C, and D be any four points in space such that no three are collinear. Prove that the figure formed by joining in order the midpoints of AB, BC, CD, DA, and AB is a parallelogram.

71. TRANSLATION OF AXES

Given a coordinate system in space and a point $O'(h, k, m)$, let us construct on O' lines parallel to the x- , y- , and z-axes. We consider these lines as new coordinate axes and label them the x'- , y'- , and z'-axes (Figure 149).

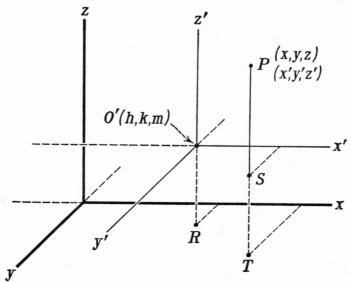

Figure 149

Just as in the plane case (Section 42), this process of selecting new axes parallel to a given set of axes is called **translation of axes** or **translation of the origin.**

Any point P in space has two sets of coordinates; coordinates (x, y, z) in the original coordinate system, and coordinates (x', y', z') in the new coordinate system. Let R be the projection of O' on the xy-plane, and S and T the respective projections of P on the $x'y'$- and xy-planes. It follows easily that

$$z = \overline{TP} = \overline{TS} + \overline{SP}$$
$$= \overline{RO'} + \overline{SP}$$
$$= m + z'.$$

Similarly, by taking projections on the yz- and xz-planes, we obtain

$$x = h + x', \qquad y = k + y'.$$

We have therefore shown that if we translate the axes to the new origin $O'(h, k, m)$, a point $P(x, y, z)$ in the original coordinate system has coordinates (x', y', z') in the new coordinate system, where

12·3 $\qquad x' = x - h, \qquad y' = y - k, \qquad z' = z - m.$

This result will be used later.

72.   DIRECTION ANGLES AND DIRECTION COSINES OF A LINE

Given a line l in space, construct a half-line parallel to l with endpoint at the origin. Clearly there are two choices k and k' of this half-line, as indicated in Figures 150 and 151. Associated with each of these half-lines are three angles, namely, the angles of least measure between the half-line and each of the positive coordinate axes. In Figure 150 the angles between k and the positive x- , y- , and z-axes are denoted respectively by α, β, and γ; whereas in Figure 151 the angles between k' and the positive x- , y- , and z-axes are denoted respectively by α', β', and γ'. Clearly $0 \leqq \alpha \leqq 180°$, and the same inequality holds for each of the other five angles. Moreover, α, and α' are supplementary angles, as are β and β', γ and γ'. The angles α, β, and γ (or the angles α', β', and γ') are called **direction angles** of the line l. Thus a line has two sets of direction angles, the angles of one set being the respective supplements of the angles of the other set. It follows immediately from the definition that parallel lines have the same direction angles.

If α, β, and γ are direction angles of the line l, then the numbers $\cos \alpha$, $\cos \beta$, and $\cos \gamma$ are called **direction cosines** of the line l. Since there are two sets of direction angles of a line l, there are two sets of direction cosines of l. However, if α and α' are supplementary angles, then necessarily $\cos \alpha' = -\cos \alpha$. Thus the two sets of direction cosines of l are $\cos \alpha$, $\cos \beta$, $\cos \gamma$ and $-\cos \alpha$, $-\cos \beta$, $-\cos \gamma$.

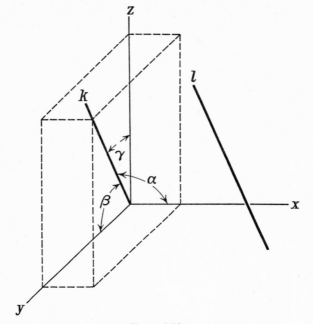

Figure 150

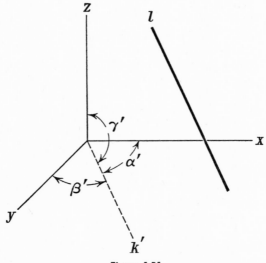

Figure 151

The following observation, which will be used presently, is merely a restatement of the definition of the cosine of an angle. If θ is an angle having its vertex at the origin and its initial side on the positive half of a coordinate line l, and P is a point on the terminal side of θ at a distance of p units from the origin (Figure 152), then the projection A of P on l has coordinate $p \cos \theta$.

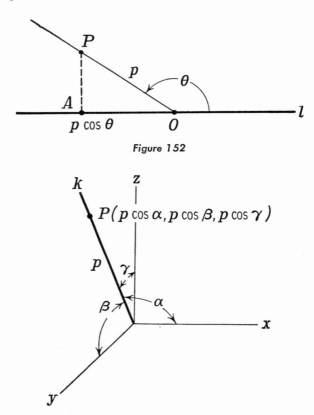

Figure 152

Figure 153

Now suppose that k is a half-line in space having its endpoint at the origin, and let α, β, and γ be the direction angles of k (Figure 153). If P is the point on k at a distance of p units from the origin, then by the remark just made it follows that the projections of P on the x- , y- , and z-axes have respective coordinates $p \cos \alpha$, $p \cos \beta$, and $p \cos \gamma$. But these are just the coordinates of the point P in space, and hence P is the point $(p \cos \alpha, p \cos \beta, p \cos \gamma)$, as indicated in the figure. As an important special case, if $p = 1$, then P has coordinates $(\cos \alpha, \cos \beta, \cos \gamma)$, and by the distance formula (12·1) we have

$$|OP| = \sqrt{\cos^2 \alpha + \cos^2 \beta + \cos^2 \gamma} = 1.$$

It follows that

12·4 $$\cos^2 \alpha + \cos^2 \beta + \cos^2 \gamma = 1,$$

and we have proved that *the sum of the squares of the direction cosines of any line is equal to* 1.

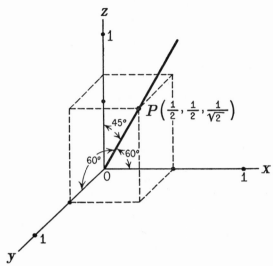

Figure 154

Conversely, it is easy to see that any three numbers r, s, and t such that

$$r^2 + s^2 + t^2 = 1$$

are direction cosines of some line l. One has only to select the line l as the line on the origin and the point $P(r, s, t)$. In view of our previous discussion (Figure 153), if α, β, γ are the direction angles of the half-line on P with endpoint at the origin, then

$$r = \cos \alpha, \qquad s = \cos \beta, \qquad t = \cos \gamma.$$

For example, 1/2, 1/2, and $1/\sqrt{2}$ are direction cosines of a line since the sum of their squares is equal to 1. Therefore the angles 60°, 60°, and 45° are direction angles of the line on the origin and the point $P(1/2, 1/2, 1/\sqrt{2})$ (Figure 154).

73. DIRECTION NUMBERS OF A LINE

We have seen that the direction of a line in space is determined by its direction angles or by its direction cosines. The direction cosines are usually more convenient to use than the direction angles, and we shall see presently that it is not necessary to specify the direction cosines themselves but merely any three numbers that are proportional to the direction cosines.

It is convenient to call any three numbers a, b, and c that are proportional to the direction cosines of a line l **direction numbers** of l. Thus, if α, β, and γ are direction angles of l, then a, b, and c are direction numbers of l if and only if

$$a = p \cos \alpha, \quad b = p \cos \beta, \quad c = p \cos \gamma,$$

for some nonzero number p.

Any three numbers a, b, and c, not all equal to zero, are direction numbers of some line, namely, the line on the origin and the point $P(a, b, c)$. For if $|OP| = p > 0$, then it is clear (Figure 153) that

$$a = p \cos \alpha, \quad b = p \cos \beta, \quad c = p \cos \gamma.$$

Given a set a, b, and c of direction numbers of a line l, it is easy to find a set of direction cosines of l. Such a set is

$$\frac{a}{\sqrt{a^2 + b^2 + c^2}}, \quad \frac{b}{\sqrt{a^2 + b^2 + c^2}}, \quad \frac{c}{\sqrt{a^2 + b^2 + c^2}},$$

since these numbers are proportional to a, b, c, and the sum of their squares is 1.

Two sets a, b, c and a', b', c' of numbers are direction numbers of the same line if and only if they are proportional. Thus, for example, 2, -1, 3 and -8, 4, -12 are direction numbers of the same line since

$$-8 = (-4) \cdot 2, \quad 4 = (-4) \cdot (-1), \quad -12 = (-4) \cdot 3.$$

Direction *cosines* of this line are $2/\sqrt{14}$, $-1/\sqrt{14}$, $3/\sqrt{14}$.

If we know two points on a line, direction numbers of the line can easily be found by use of the following theorem.

12·5   Theorem

If $P_1(x_1, y_1, z_1)$ and $P_2(x_2, y_2, z_2)$ are two points on a line l, then

$$x_2 - x_1, \quad y_2 - y_1, \quad z_2 - z_1$$

are direction numbers of l.

Proof: Consider a translation of axes with new origin P_1, as indicated in Figure 155. By 12·3, the coordinates of P_2 relative to the new axes are $(x_2 - x_1, y_2 - y_1, z_2 - z_1)$. In view of the discussion above, it is clear that $x_2 - x_1$, $y_2 - y_1$, $z_2 - z_1$ are direction numbers of l with reference to the new coordinate axes. Since the direction angles of a line are unchanged by a translation of axes, it follows that these are also direction numbers of l relative to the original axes.

Example 3

Find direction cosines and direction angles of the line l on the points $P(-3, 4, 2)$ and $Q(4, -5, 7)$.

Solution: Since $4 - (-3) = 7$, $-5 - 4 = -9$, and $7 - 2 = 5$, the preceding theorem shows that 7, -9, and 5 are direction numbers of l. Hence

$$\frac{7}{\sqrt{155}}, \quad \frac{-9}{\sqrt{155}}, \quad \frac{5}{\sqrt{155}}$$

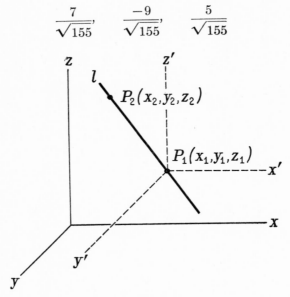

Figure 155

are direction cosines of l. These numbers are approximately equal to

$$.5623, \quad -.7229, \quad .4016.$$

Thus, by Table I, the direction angles of l are approximately

$$55° \ 47', \quad 136° \ 18', \quad 66° \ 19'.$$

EXERCISES

In each of Exercises 1–6, find direction cosines and direction angles of the line on the origin and the given point.

1. $(2, 2, 2\sqrt{2})$.
2. $(2, 2, -1)$.
3. $(-1, 1, \sqrt{2})$.
4. $(12, -6, 4)$.
5. $(1, 1, 1)$.
6. $(8, 1, -4)$.

In each of Exercises 7–12, find direction numbers, direction cosines, and direction angles of the line on the two given points.

7. $(1, -2, 0)$, $(5, -10, 1)$.   8. $(0, 5, 7)$, $(1, 9, -1)$.

9. $(6, 5, -3)$, $(4, 1, 1)$.   10. $(2, -2, 4)$, $(-3, 3, 4)$.

11. $(1, -5, 1)$, $(4, -5, 4)$.   12. $(-3, 4, -1)$, $(-3, 4, 4)$.

13. Find the direction cosines and direction angles of the x-axis; of the y-axis; of the z-axis.

14. If two of the direction angles of a line are 45° and 60°, find the third direction angle.

15. If two of the direction angles of a line are $2\pi/3$ and $3\pi/4$, find the third direction angle.

16. If the direction angles of a line are all equal, what must they be?

17. Prove that at least two of the direction angles of a line must be greater than or equal to 45°.

18. If a line is parallel to a coordinate plane, what can be said about its direction cosines?

19. If a line is parallel to a coordinate axis, what can be said about its direction cosines?

20. The line l has direction angles α, β, and γ. If $\alpha = \beta$ and $\gamma = 2\alpha$, prove that l is parallel or perpendicular to the xy-plane.

74. EQUATIONS OF A LINE

We are now in a position to find parametric equations of a line in space.

12·6 Theorem

The line l on the point $P(x_1, y_1, z_1)$ and with direction numbers a, b, and c has parametric equations

$$x = x_1 + at, \qquad y = y_1 + bt, \qquad z = z_1 + ct.$$

Proof: Let $Q(x, y, z)$ be any point on l distinct from P (Figure 156). By 12·5, we know that $x - x_1$, $y - y_1$, and $z - z_1$ are direction numbers of l, and these numbers must therefore be proportional to the given direction numbers a, b, and c; that is, a nonzero number t must exist such that

$$x - x_1 = at, \qquad y - y_1 = bt, \qquad z - z_1 = ct.$$

Clearly, then, the coordinates (x, y, z) of Q satisfy the desired equation. The coordinates of P itself satisfy the given equation for $t = 0$.

Conversely, if $Q(x, y, z)$ is a point different from P, the coordinates of which satisfy the given equations, then the numbers $x - x_1$, $y - y_1$, $z - z_1$ are proportional to a, b, c; and hence also are direction numbers of l. Thus the line on P and Q, having the point P in common with l, must coincide with l. Hence every point with coordinates which satisfy the given equations is on l, and therefore these equations have l as their graph.

Parametric equations of a line are not unique, for, obviously, different equations will be obtained by starting with a different point on l and using different direction numbers.

We may remark that a line is parallel to a coordinate plane if and only if one of its direction numbers is zero (why?), and that it is parallel

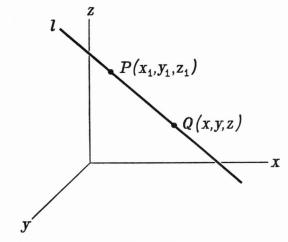

Figure 156

to two coordinate planes if and only if two of its direction numbers are zero (why?). Thus, for example, the line with the parametric equations

$$x = 2 - t, \qquad y = -3 + t, \qquad z = 4$$

is parallel to the xy-plane.

Example 4

(a) Find parametric equations of the line l on the points $P(2, 3, 2)$ and $Q(6, 5, -2)$.

(b) Find the points where the line l intersects the coordinate planes.

Solution: By 12·5, we see that 4, 2, −4 are direction numbers of l. Then, by the preceding theorem, it follows that

$$x = 2 + 4t, \qquad y = 3 + 2t, \qquad z = 2 - 4t$$

are parametric equations of l. In order to find where the line cuts the yz-plane, we set $x = 0$ and find that $t = -1/2$. For this value of t, $y = 2$ and $z = 4$. Thus $(0, 2, 4)$ is the desired point. Similarly, $(-4, 0, 8)$ and $(4, 4, 0)$ are the points of l on the xz-plane and the xy-plane, respectively. The line is sketched in Figure 157.

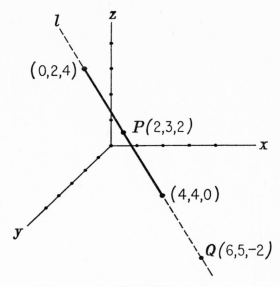

Figure 157

It is evident that two nonparallel lines in space need not intersect. If two lines do intersect, their point of intersection may be found by solving their parametric equations simultaneously, as indicated in the next example.

Example 5

Find the point of intersection, if such exists, of the lines with respective parametric equations

$$x = -2 + t, \qquad y = 2 + 2t, \qquad z = 3 - t$$

and

$$x = 6 - 5s, \qquad y = -4 + s, \qquad z = 1 + 2s.$$

Solution: It is necessary that different letters be used for the parameters in each case, as we see below.   If the point $P(x, y, z)$ is on both lines, then for proper choices of t and s we must have

$$-2 + t = 6 - 5s, \qquad 2 + 2t = -4 + s, \qquad 3 - t = 1 + 2s.$$

Solving the first equation for t,

$$t = 8 - 5s,$$

and substituting in the second equation, we obtain

$$18 - 10s = -4 + s,$$

from which it follows that $s = 2$. Then $t = -2$ from the first equation. It is now easy to verify that these values of s and t also satisfy the third equation. Hence the point $P(-4, -2, 5)$ obtained from the given equations by letting $t = -2$ (or $s = 2$) is the point of intersection of the given lines.

If the direction numbers a, b, and c of the line l are all different from zero, each of the parametric equations of l, given by 12·6, can be solved for t as follows:

$$t = \frac{x - x_1}{a}, \qquad t = \frac{y - y_1}{b}, \qquad t = \frac{z - z_1}{c}.$$

Thus we have

12·7
$$\frac{x - x_1}{a} = \frac{y - y_1}{b} = \frac{z - z_1}{c}.$$

These equations are called the **symmetric form** of the equations of the line l. Again, these equations are not unique since one may use any fixed point on l in place of (x_1, y_1, z_1), and any set of direction numbers of l in place of a, b, and c.

EXERCISES

In each of Exercises 1–10, find parametric equations of the line on the two given points. Also find the points of intersection of the line with the coordinate planes.

1. $(1, 1, 1)$, $(-1, 3, 3)$.   2. $(4, -1, 7)$, $(-2, 2, -5)$.

3. $(2, -3, -11)$, $(-1, 6, 13)$.   4. $(-1, 1, 4)$, $(2, 1, 5)$.

5. $(1, 1, 0)$, $(1, 0, 1)$.   6. $(-4, -3, 5)$, $(3, 1, -1)$.

7. $(-2, 2, 4)$, $(2, 6, 0)$.   8. $(0, 0, 0)$, $(2, 1, -3)$.

9. $(6, 5, -6)$, $(-2, -15, 6)$.   10. $(-5, 5, -5)$, $(4, 7, 3)$.

In each of Exercises 11–14, the lines l_1, l_2, and l_3 with given parametric equations are the sides of a triangle. Find the vertices of the triangle.

11. $l_1: x = -1 + 3r,\ y = 3 - 3r,\ z = 2 - r.$
    $l_2: x = 6 + 2s,\ y = 2 + s,\ z = -3 - 2s.$
    $l_3: x = -6 + 5t,\ y = 5 - 2t,\ z = 5 - 3t.$

12. $l_1: x = -2 + r,\ y = 3 - r,\ z = 5 - r.$
    $l_2: x = 4 + s,\ y = 1,\ z = 15 + 3s.$
    $l_3: x = 13 + 2t,\ y = -6 - t,\ z = 14 + 2t.$

13. $l_1: x = 7 + 2r,\ y = 10 + 3r,\ z = -12 - 5r.$
    $l_2: x = -1 + 2s,\ y = 14 - 5s,\ z = -8 + 3s.$
    $l_3: x = -5 + 6t,\ y = 8 - 7t,\ z = 2 + t.$

14. $l_1: x = -3 + r, y = -3 + r, z = -3 + r.$
   $l_2: x = 6 + s, y = -4 - s, z = -4 - s.$
   $l_3: x = -6 + 5t, y = 2 + t, z = 2 + t.$

In each of Exercises 15–20, write in symmetric form the equations of the line with the given parametric equations.

15. $x = 3 - t, y = 4 + 2t, z = -1 - 5t.$

16. $x = 2 + t, y = 3 + 4t, z = -1 + 3t.$

17. $x = 2t, y = 3t, z = 4 - 2t.$

18. $x = -5 - 3t, y = 4 + t, z = 7t.$

19. $x = 7 + 5t, y = 4 - t, z = 3 + 5t.$

20. $x = 1 + t, y = 1 + t, z = 1 + t.$

21. Find parametric equations of the x-axis; of the y-axis; of the z-axis.

22. Find parametric equations of the line on the point (a, b, c) and parallel to the x-axis; to the y-axis; to the z-axis.

75.   ANGLE BETWEEN TWO LINES

If l_1 and l_2 are two lines in space, let us select half-lines k_1 and k_2 with endpoints at the origin and respectively parallel to l_1 and l_2 (Figure 158). If l_1 and l_2 intersect, as in the figure, clearly the angle θ between k_1 and k_2 is equal to the angle of intersection of l_1 and l_2.   Even if l_1 and l_2 do not intersect, it is customary to call θ the angle between the two lines.   Since there are two choices of each of the half-lines k_1 and k_2, it is clear that there are two different angles between the lines l_1 and l_2.   However, these

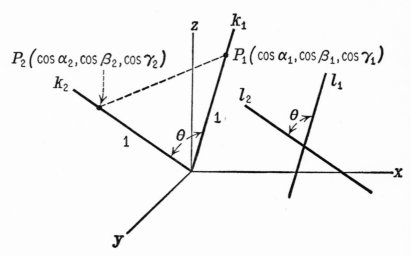

Figure 158

angles are supplementary, and we shall find it convenient to consider either of them as the angle between the two lines.

If α_1, β_1, γ_1 and α_2, β_2, γ_2 are the direction angles of k_1 and k_2, respectively, then the points P_1 and P_2 on k_1 and k_2, respectively, at a distance of 1 unit from the origin have coordinates $P_1(\cos \alpha_1, \cos \beta_1, \cos \gamma_1)$ and $P_2(\cos \alpha_2, \cos \beta_2, \cos \gamma_2)$. By the law of cosines, it follows that

$$|P_1P_2|^2 = 1^2 + 1^2 - 2 \cdot 1 \cdot 1 \cdot \cos \theta.$$

Replacing $|P_1P_2|$ by its value given by the distance formula 12·1, we have

$$(\cos \alpha_2 - \cos \alpha_1)^2 + (\cos \beta_2 - \cos \beta_1)^2 + (\cos \gamma_2 - \cos \gamma_1)^2$$
$$= 2 - 2 \cos \theta.$$

This reduces to

$$(\cos^2 \alpha_1 + \cos^2 \beta_1 + \cos^2 \gamma_1) + (\cos^2 \alpha_2 + \cos^2 \beta_2 + \cos^2 \gamma_2)$$
$$- 2(\cos \alpha_1 \cos \alpha_2 + \cos \beta_1 \cos \beta_2 + \cos \gamma_1 \cos \gamma_2)$$
$$= 2 - 2 \cos \theta.$$

Using 12·4 and simplifying, we obtain

$$\cos \theta = \cos \alpha_1 \cos \alpha_2 + \cos \beta_1 \cos \beta_2 + \cos \gamma_1 \cos \gamma_2.$$

We have therefore established the following result.

12·8   Theorem

If the lines l_1 and l_2 have respective direction cosines $\cos \alpha_1$, $\cos \beta_1$, $\cos \gamma_1$ and $\cos \alpha_2$, $\cos \beta_2$, $\cos \gamma_2$, then the angle between l_1 and l_2 is the angle θ of measure between $0°$ and $180°$ that satisfies the equation

$$\cos \theta = \cos \alpha_1 \cos \alpha_2 + \cos \beta_1 \cos \beta_2 + \cos \gamma_1 \cos \gamma_2.$$

Example 6

Find the angle between the two intersecting lines of Example 5.

Solution: The coefficients of the parameter in each set of equations are direction numbers of the corresponding line. Thus $1, 2, -1$ and $-5, 1, 2$ are direction numbers of the given lines, and

$$\frac{1}{\sqrt{6}}, \frac{2}{\sqrt{6}}, -\frac{1}{\sqrt{6}} \quad \text{and} \quad -\frac{5}{\sqrt{30}}, \frac{1}{\sqrt{30}}, \frac{2}{\sqrt{30}}$$

are direction cosines of these lines. Hence if θ is the angle between these lines, we have, by 12·8, that

$$\cos \theta = \left(\frac{1}{\sqrt{6}}\right)\left(-\frac{5}{\sqrt{30}}\right) + \left(\frac{2}{\sqrt{6}}\right)\left(\frac{1}{\sqrt{30}}\right) + \left(-\frac{1}{\sqrt{6}}\right)\left(\frac{2}{\sqrt{30}}\right) = -\frac{\sqrt{5}}{6},$$

and we obtain $\cos \theta = -.3727$, approximately. Using Table I, we find that $\theta = 111° 53'$.   The acute angle between these lines is the supplement of θ, namely, $68° 7'$.

Two lines are parallel if and only if they have the same direction cosines, or, if and only if they have proportional direction numbers.

Since $\cos 90° = 0$, we find from 12·8 that two lines are perpendicular if and only if

$$\cos \alpha_1 \cos \alpha_2 + \cos \beta_1 \cos \beta_2 + \cos \gamma_1 \cos \gamma_2 = 0,$$

where α_1, β_1, γ_1 and α_2, β_2, γ_2 are direction angles of the two lines.   The following theorem shows that this condition for perpendicularity of two lines can easily be expressed in terms of direction *numbers* of the lines.

12·9   Theorem

The lines l_1 and l_2 with direction numbers a_1, b_1, c_1 and a_2, b_2, c_2, respectively, are perpendicular if and only if

$$a_1 a_2 + b_1 b_2 + c_1 c_2 = 0.$$

Proof: If α_1, β_1, γ_1 and α_2, β_2, γ_2 are direction angles of l_1 and l_2, respectively, then

$$a_1 = p_1 \cos \alpha_1, \qquad b_1 = p_1 \cos \beta_1, \qquad c_1 = p_1 \cos \gamma_1,$$

and

$$a_2 = p_2 \cos \alpha_2, \qquad b_2 = p_2 \cos \beta_2, \qquad c_2 = p_2 \cos \gamma_2,$$

for some nonzero numbers p_1 and p_2.   Thus

$$a_1 a_2 + b_1 b_2 + c_1 c_2 = p_1 p_2 (\cos \alpha_1 \cos \alpha_2 + \cos \beta_1 \cos \beta_2 + \cos \gamma_1 \cos \gamma_2),$$

which by our previous remarks equals zero if and only if l_1 and l_2 are perpendicular.

Example 7

Find equations of the line l_1 on the point $P(5, 7/2, 5)$ and intersecting at right angles the line l_2 with equations

$$x = 4 + 3t, \qquad y = 1 + t, \qquad z = -3t.$$

Solution: The numbers 3, 1, -3 are direction numbers of l_2.   If $Q(x, y, z)$ is the point of intersection of l_1 and l_2 (Figure 159), then, by 12·5, direction numbers of l_1 are $x - 5$, $y - 7/2$, $z - 5$.   Hence, by 12·9, we must have

$$3(x - 5) + (y - 7/2) - 3(z - 5) = 0.$$

Replacing x, y, and z by their values in terms of t from the given equations of l_2, we obtain

$$3(3t - 1) + (t - 5/2) - 3(-3t - 5) = 0,$$

from which it follows that $t = -1/2$. Since this is the value of t that yields the point Q on l_2, Q has coordinates $(5/2, 1/2, 3/2)$. We now

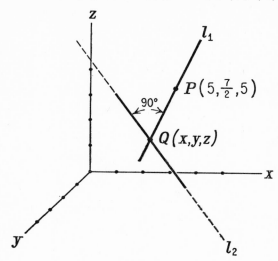

Figure 159

know the coordinates of two points on l_1, and it is easy to find that l_1 has direction numbers 5, 6, 7. Hence

$$x = 5 + 5t, \qquad y = 7/2 + 6t. \qquad z = 5 + 7t$$

are equations of l_1.

EXERCISES

In each of Exercises 1–6, find the angle between two lines with the given direction numbers.

1. 2, 2, −1; 1, 2, −6.

2. 6, 1, 2; −2, 2, 1.

3. 8, −4, 1; 1, 1, −1.

4. 2, −1, 3; 4, 5, 2.

5. 3, 0, 4; 0, 4, −3.

6. −3, 1, 7; −4, 4, −7.

In each of Exercises 7–12, find parametric equations of the line on the given point P and intersecting at right angles the line with the given parametric equations.

7. $P(11, 4, -6); x = 4 - t, y = 7 + 2t, z = -1 + t.$

8. $P(-7, 3, -6); x = 2 - 3t, y = 4 + t, z = -5 - 2t.$

9. $P(13, 9, -1); x = t, y = 2t, z = 4 - t.$

10. $P(-5, 49, 4); x = -5 + 4t, y = 2 - 3t, z = 6 + 2t.$

11. $P(5, -4, 4); x = -t, y = 1 + 3t, z = -2t.$

12. $P(6, 0, 26); x = 2 - t, y = 3, z = 4 + 7t.$

13. Find parametric equations of the line on the point $P(2, 2, -3)$ and perpendicular to each of two lines with direction numbers $-3, 2, -4$ and $2, 1, 5$.

14. Find parametric equations of the line on the origin and perpendicular to each of two lines with direction numbers $2, -1, -1$ and $-3, 4, 3$.

15. Find parametric equations of the line intersecting at right angles each of the following lines:

$$x = 3 + 2t, \quad y = 4 + t, \quad z = -1 + t,$$
$$x = -1 + s, \quad y = 6 - 4s, \quad z = 5 + 2s.$$

16. Find parametric equations of the line intersecting at right angles each of the following lines:

$$x = 4 + 2t, \quad y = 2t, \quad z = 1 - t,$$
$$x = -4 + 3s, \quad y = 6 + 4s, \quad z = -3.$$

17. In a room 12 feet long, 12 feet wide, and 8 feet high, lines are run from adjacent corners of the floor to the same one of the opposite corners of the ceiling. Find the angle of intersection of these lines.

18. Work the previous exercise if the lines run from adjacent corners of the floor to the midpoint of the opposite wall.

76. EQUATION OF A PLANE

We next turn to the problem of finding the equation of a plane in space.   It will now be convenient to let p denote a plane, just as we have used l to denote a line.

A line l is said to be a **normal line** of a plane p if l is perpendicular to p.   Of course, this means that l is perpendicular to every line on the plane p which passes through the point of intersection of l and p.

12·10   Theorem

If the line l with direction numbers A, B, and C is normal to the plane p, then the equation of p is of the form

$$Ax + By + Cz + D = 0$$

for some constant D.   Conversely, the graph of any equation of this form is a plane whose normal lines have direction numbers A, B, and C.

Proof: Let $P_1(x_1, y_1, z_1)$ be the point of intersection of l and p, and let $P(x, y, z)$ be any other point on p (Figure 160).   The line l_1 on P and P_1 lies on the plane p, and hence is perpendicular to l.   Since $x - x_1, y - y_1,$ and $z - z_1$ are direction numbers of l_1, we have, by 12·9, that

$$A(x - x_1) + B(y - y_1) + C(z - z_1) = 0.$$

Every point $P(x, y, z)$ on the plane p (including the given point P_1) has coordinates satisfying this equation, and every point $P(x, y, z)$ with coordinates satisfying this equation is necessarily on the plane p, since every

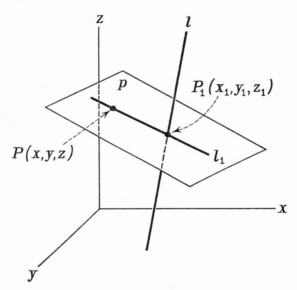

Figure 160

line perpendicular to l at P_1 lies on p. Thus the equation of the plane p is

$$Ax + By + Cz - (Ax_1 + By_1 + Cz_1) = 0,$$

and this proves the first statement of the theorem with

$$D = -(Ax_1 + By_1 + Cz_1).$$

The proof of the converse is essentially the reverse of the above proof, and so is omitted.

We saw in Chapter 2 that in a coordinate plane the graph of an equation of the first degree in x and y is a line. We have now proved that the graph in space of an equation of the first degree in x, y, and z is a plane.

Example 8

Find the equation of the plane p passing through the point $P(4, -2, 3)$ if a normal line of p has direction numbers 2, -1, and 3.

Solution. By the preceding theorem, the equation of p has the form

$$2x - y + 3z + D = 0$$

for some constant D. Since $P(4, -2, 3)$ is on p, its coordinates must satisfy this equation, and therefore we must have

$$2 \cdot 4 - (-2) + 3 \cdot 3 + D = 0,$$

or $D = -19$. Hence the desired equation is

$$2x - y + 3z - 19 = 0.$$

Any three noncollinear points in space determine a plane. The following example illustrates how to find the equation of a plane through three given points.

Example 9

Find the equation of the plane through the points $P(-1, 0, 1)$, $Q(3, 2, -1)$, and $R(-2, 4, 3)$.

Solution: We know that the desired equation has the form

$$Ax + By + Cz + D = 0$$

for proper choice of A, B, C, and D. Since the coordinates of the given points must satisfy this equation, we have

$$\begin{aligned} -A + C + D &= 0, \\ 3A + 2B - C + D &= 0, \\ -2A + 4B + 3C + D &= 0. \end{aligned}$$

Our problem is to solve these equations simultaneously for A, B, C, and D. Actually, we shall solve for A, B, and C in terms of D. If we eliminate C between the first and second equations, and also between the first and third equations, we obtain

$$\begin{aligned} A + B + D &= 0, \\ A + 4B - 2D &= 0. \end{aligned}$$

Now, if we solve these two equations for A and B in terms of D, we obtain

$$A = -2D, \qquad B = D.$$

Substituting these values in any one of the three original equations, we find that $C = -3D$. To summarize, we have found that

$$A = -2D, \qquad B = D, \qquad C = -3D.$$

Now, D can have any arbitrary nonzero value. If we set $D = -1$, we get

$$2x - y + 3z - 1 = 0$$

as the desired equation. Another choice of D would have the effect merely of multiplying this equation by a nonzero constant.

The yz- , xz- , and xy-planes have respective equations

$$x = 0, \qquad y = 0, \qquad z = 0;$$

whereas a plane parallel to one of these planes has an equation of the form $x = d$, $y = d$, or $z = d$, where d is a constant.

An equation of the form

$$Ax + By + D = 0$$

is the equation of a plane parallel to the z-axis, for if the point $P_1(x_1, y_1, z_1)$ is on this plane, so is the point $P(x_1, y_1, z)$ for *any* choice of z (why?), and thus the line passing through the point P_1 and parallel to the z-axis lies in this plane. The same conclusion can be reached by observing that the third direction number of the normal to this plane is zero, and hence that the normal is perpendicular to the z-axis. The plane itself must then be parallel to the z-axis.

Similar remarks hold for planes with equations of either of the forms

$$Ax + Cz + D = 0, \qquad By + Cz + D = 0.$$

Two planes are perpendicular if and only if their normal lines are perpendicular. Hence, in view of 12·9 and 12·10, the planes with equations

$$A_1x + B_1y + C_1z + D_1 = 0$$

and

$$A_2x + B_2y + C_2z + D_2 = 0$$

are perpendicular if and only if

$$A_1A_2 + B_1B_2 + C_1C_2 = 0.$$

Since the xy-plane has equation $z = 0$, the preceding remark gives still another proof that a plane with an equation of the form

$$Ax + By + D = 0$$

is perpendicular to the xy-plane, and hence is parallel to the z-axis.

The points of a given plane that lie on the coordinate axes are called the **intercepts** of the plane. The intercepts may be used to aid in sketching the graph of a plane, as indicated in the following examples.

Example 10

Find the intercepts of the equation

$$2x + y + 2z - 4 = 0,$$

and sketch its graph.

Solution: If we put $y = 0$ and $z = 0$ in this equation, we find that $x = 2$. Thus $(2, 0, 0)$ is the x-intercept of this plane. Similarly, $(0, 4, 0)$ and $(0, 0, 2)$ are the y- and z-intercepts. The plane is sketched in Figure 161.

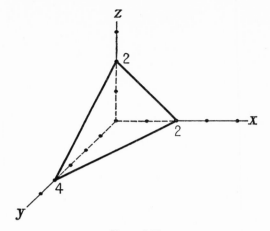

Figure 161

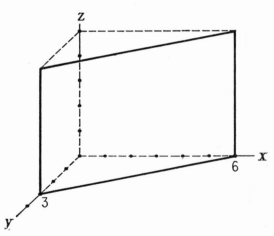

Figure 162

Example 11

Find the intercepts of the equation

$$x + 2y - 6 = 0,$$

and sketch its graph.

Solution: It is easy to verify that the x-intercept is $(6, 0, 0)$ and the y-intercept is $(0, 3, 0)$. Since the plane is parallel to the z-axis, there is no z-intercept. The graph of this equation is the plane sketched in Figure 162.

EXERCISES

In each of Exercises 1–6, find the equation of the plane that passes through the given point P and is perpendicular to a line with the given direction numbers.

1. $P(-1, 3, 2)$; 4, 1, 3.
2. $P(2, 0, -5)$; 4, -4, 2.
3. $P(2, -4, 1)$; -1, -1, 2.
4. $P(1, -3, 7)$; 0, 1, 3.
5. $P(1, 0, -1)$; 1, 0, -4.
6. $P(7, 5, -4)$; 3, -5, 2.

In each of Exercises 7–12, find the equation of the plane through the three given points.

7. $(2, 1, 1)$, $(6, 3, 1)$, $(-2, 1, 2)$.
8. $(1, -2, 1)$, $(0, 3, 2)$, $(2, -2, -1)$.
9. $(1, -1, 2)$, $(-3, -2, 6)$, $(5, 0, 1)$.
10. $(2, 3, 1)$, $(-1, -2, 5)$, $(2, -1, 3)$.
11. $(-1, 1, 1)$, $(5, -8, -2)$, $(4, 1, 0)$.
12. $(1, -3, 2)$, $(2, 1, 5)$, $(-1, 2, -4)$.

In each of Exercises 13–18, find the intercepts of the given equation and sketch its graph.

13. $x + y + 3z - 3 = 0$.
14. $2x + 3y + z - 6 = 0$.
15. $3x - 2y + 6z - 6 = 0$.
16. $x - 2y + 2 = 0$.
17. $2y - z + 5 = 0$.
18. $3x - 2z + 12 = 0$.

19. Find the equation of the plane through the points $(1, 0, 1)$ and $(2, 2, 1)$, and perpendicular to the plane $x - y - z + 4 = 0$.

20. Find the equation of the plane through the points $(3, 1, 1)$ and $(7, 4, -1)$, and perpendicular to the xy-plane.

21. Find parametric equations of the line of intersection of the planes $x + y - z + 1 = 0$ and $x - y + 2z - 3 = 0$.

22. Find parametric equations of the line of intersection of the planes $x + y = 1$ and $y - z = 2$.

23. Find the equation of the plane through the point $(3, -1, 1)$ and perpendicular to each of the planes $4x + 2y + z + 1 = 0$ and $2x + y + 3z - 5 = 0$.

24. Find the equation of the plane through the point $(2, 1, 2)$ and perpendicular to each of the planes $3x + 2y - 5z - 1 = 0$ and $x + y = 0$.

25. Let p be the plane with equation $Ax + By + Cz + D = 0$, with $C > 0$, and let $P(a, b, c)$ be a point above the plane p. Prove that $Aa + Bb + Cc + D > 0$. State and prove the analogous result when P is below the plane p. [*Hint:* See Section 18].

26. Let p be the plane with equation $Ax + By + Cz + D = 0$, with $C > 0$, and let a, b, and c be numbers such that $Aa + Bb + Cc + D > 0$. Prove that the point $P(a, b, c)$ is above the plane p. State and prove the analogous result when $Aa + Bb + Cc + D < 0$. [*Hint:* See Section 18.]

27. Prove the converse part of Theorem 12·10.

77.   DISTANCE BETWEEN A POINT AND A PLANE

The distance between a point P and a plane p is defined to be the distance between P and the projection Q of P on the plane p.   The following theorem shows that the distance between a point and a plane can be found in much the same way as the distance between a point and a line in a coordinate plane (Theorem 2·18).

12·11   Theorem

The distance d between the point $P(x_1, y_1, z_1)$ and the plane p with equation

$$Ax + By + Cz + D = 0$$

is given by

$$d = \frac{|Ax_1 + By_1 + Cz_1 + D|}{\sqrt{A^2 + B^2 + C^2}}.$$

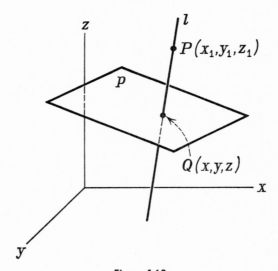

Figure 163

Proof: The line l normal to p and passing through the point P (Figure 163) has direction numbers A, B, and C, and parametric equations

$$x = x_1 + At, \qquad y = y_1 + Bt, \qquad z = z_1 + Ct.$$

If $Q(x, y, z)$ is the point of intersection of p and l, the coordinates of Q satisfy both the equations of l and the equation of p.   Hence

$$A(x_1 + At) + B(y_1 + Bt) + C(z_1 + Ct) + D = 0,$$

and, solving for t, we obtain

$$t = -\frac{Ax_1 + By_1 + Cz_1 + D}{A^2 + B^2 + C^2}.$$

This, then, is the value of t that gives the point Q on l.   It follows that

$$\begin{aligned} d = |PQ| &= \sqrt{(x - x_1)^2 + (y - y_1)^2 + (z - z_1)^2} \\ &= \sqrt{A^2t^2 + B^2t^2 + C^2t^2} \\ &= |t| \cdot \sqrt{A^2 + B^2 + C^2} \\ &= \frac{|Ax_1 + By_1 + Cz_1 + D|}{\sqrt{A^2 + B^2 + C^2}}, \end{aligned}$$

and the proof is completed.

Example 12

Find the distance between the point $P(3, -4, -2)$ and the plane with the equation

$$2x - 2y + 3z - 7 = 0.$$

Solution: From the preceding theorem we find at once that the desired distance d is given by

$$d = \frac{|2 \cdot 3 - 2(-4) + 3(-2) - 7|}{\sqrt{2^2 + (-2)^2 + 3^2}} = \frac{1}{\sqrt{17}}.$$

EXERCISES

In each of Exercises 1–10, find the distance between the given point and the given plane.

1. $(1, 3, 4)$, $2x + y + 2z - 1 = 0$.
2. $(-1, 0, 3)$, $3x - 2y + 6z + 3 = 0$.
3. $(3, 4, -7)$, $6x - 2y + 3z - 3 = 0$.
4. $(2, -3, 1)$, $5x + 14y - 2z + 1 = 0$.
5. $(4, -2, -1)$, $x - y + z - 6 = 0$.
6. $(0, 5, -11)$, $3x - y + z + 7 = 0$.
7. $(-5, -1, 0)$, $8x + y - 4z + 2 = 0$.
8. $(-3, 1, 7)$, $2x + 2y - z + 14 = 0$.
9. $(3, 3, 3)$, $3x - 5y + 8z + 3 = 0$.
10. $(4, -3, 8)$, $7x + 3y - 5z - 2 = 0$.

In each of Exercises 11–14, find the distance between the given parallel planes.

11. $8x - y + 4z - 5 = 0$, $8x - y + 4z + 4 = 0$.

12. $x - 2y - 2z + 6 = 0$, $-x + 2y + 2z + 9 = 0$.

13. $4x - 2y + 4z - 1 = 0$, $2x - y + 2z - 7 = 0$.

14. $3x + y + z - 7 = 0$, $6x + 2y + 2z + 13 = 0$.

15. Sketch the tetrahedron with vertices $(4, 0, 0)$, $(0, 4, 0)$, $(0, 0, 4)$, and $(5, 3, 8)$. Find its volume.

16. Sketch the tetrahedron with vertices $(2, 0, 0)$, $(0, 8, 0)$, $(0, 0, 1)$, and $(1, 4, 9)$. Find its volume.

17. Show that the distance between the parallel planes

$$Ax + By + Cz + D_1 = 0 \qquad \text{and} \qquad Ax + By + Cz + D_2 = 0$$

is

$$\frac{|D_1 - D_2|}{\sqrt{A^2 + B^2 + C^2}}.$$

18. A plane p intersects the x-, y-, and z-axes in the points with coordinates a, b, and c, respectively. If d is the distance between the origin and the plane p, show that

$$\frac{1}{d^2} = \frac{1}{a^2} + \frac{1}{b^2} + \frac{1}{c^2}.$$

19. Prove that the distance d between the point $P(x_1, y_1, z_1)$ and the line with parametric equations

$$x = x_0 + at, \qquad y = y_0 + bt, \qquad z = z_0 + ct$$

is given by

$$d = \sqrt{\frac{(bx_2 - ay_2)^2 + (cx_2 - az_2)^2 + (cy_2 - bz_2)^2}{a^2 + b^2 + c^2}},$$

where $x_2 = x_1 - x_0$, $y_2 = y_1 - y_0$, $z_2 = z_1 - z_0$. [*Hint:* Translate the axes to the new origin (x_0, y_0, z_0), and find the distance between the point $P'(x_2, y_2, z_2)$ and the line with parametric equations $x = at$, $y = bt$, $z = ct$.]

78. SURFACES

By the graph in space of an equation in x, y, and z we mean, of course, the collection of all points with coordinates which satisfy the equation. The graph of an equation in x, y, and z is called a **surface.** Thus, in particular, a plane is a surface, since it is the graph of an equation of the form

$$Ax + By + Cz + D = 0.$$

Henceforth we shall be concerned primarily with surfaces that are graphs of equations of the second degree, that is, of equations of the form

$$12\cdot12 \quad Ax^2 + By^2 + Cz^2 + Dxy + Exz + Fyz + Gx + Hy + Jz + K = 0,$$

in which A, B, C, D, E, and F are not all zero.

In considering the graph of an equation of the second degree there are some special cases illustrated by the graphs of the following equations:

$$(a) \quad (x + y - z + 2)^2 = 0,$$
$$(b) \quad (2x - y + z + 4)(x + y + z) = 0,$$
$$(c) \quad x^2 + y^2 = 0,$$
$$(d) \quad x^2 + y^2 + z^2 = 0.$$

If the equation is factorable, as in (a) or (b), the graph consists of one or two planes. The graph of equation (c) is the z-axis, since $x^2 + y^2 = 0$ implies that $x = 0$ *and* $y = 0$, whereas the graph of equation (d) is just the origin.

The graph of an equation of the second degree is called a **quadric surface** if it contains more than one point and is not simply a line, a plane, or two planes. In the following sections we shall illustrate all the different types of quadric surfaces.

In discussion of a surface, the following observations about symmetry are sometimes useful. If $P(x, y, z)$ is a given point in space, it is easy to verify that the point $(-x, y, z)$ is the image of P in the yz-plane, the point $(-x, -y, z)$ is the image of P in the z-axis, and the point $(-x, -y, -z)$ is the image of P in the origin. Thus (Section 26) it follows that a surface is symmetric with respect to the yz-plane if its equation is unchanged when x is replaced by $-x$; it is symmetric with respect to the z-axis if its equation is unchanged when x is replaced by $-x$ and y is replaced by $-y$; and it is symmetric with respect to the origin if its equation is unchanged when x, y, and z are respectively replaced by $-x$, $-y$, and $-z$.

79.   CYLINDERS

When we speak of an equation in x, y, and z, we do not mean to imply that the equation must contain all these letters. Before we proceed, let us consider the following example.

Example 13

Discuss the graph in space of the equation

$$x^2 + y^2 = 25.$$

Solution: The points *in the xy-plane* with coordinates which satisfy this equation are the points on the circle of radius 5 and with center at the origin. Moreover, if $P(x, y, 0)$ is a point on this circle, then for *every* choice of z the coordinates of the point $Q(x, y, z)$ satisfy the given equation. Thus the entire line parallel to the z-axis and passing through the point P is on the graph. For example, the point $(3, 4, z)$ is on the graph for every choice of z, and hence the line parallel to the z-axis and passing through the point (3, 4, 0) is on the graph.   The graph in question, sketched in Figure 164, is commonly called a **right circular cylinder.**

In general, a surface is called a **cylinder** if for each point P on the surface all points on the line through P and parallel to some fixed line l are also on the surface.

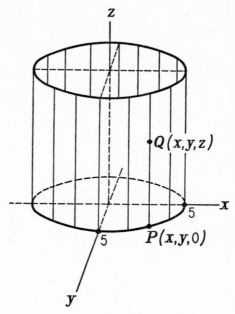

Figure 164

We may think of a cylinder as being generated by a line perpendicular to a given plane as it moves along a curve in this plane.   Thus the cylinder in the preceding example is generated by a line perpendicular to the xy-plane as it moves along the circle $x^2 + y^2 = 25$ in this plane. The curve along which the line moves is called the **directrix** * of the cylinder, and each of the lines passing through the directrix and perpendicular to the plane of the directrix is called a **ruling** of the cylinder.

It is clear from Example 13 that the graph in space of an equation in x and y is a cylinder with rulings parallel to the z-axis and with a directrix which is the graph in the xy-plane of the given equation.   Similarly, if x or y is missing from an equation, the graph will be a cylinder with rulings parallel to the axis of the missing letter.

If the equation of a clyinder is an equation of the second degree, the directrix of the cylinder will be one of the conic sections.   We now give additional examples of cylinders.

---

* Not to be confused with the directrix of a parabola or of a conic in general.

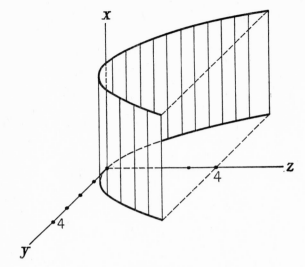

Figure 165

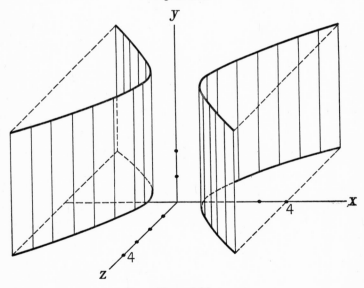

Figure 166

Example 14

Discuss the graph in space of the equation

$$y^2 = 4z.$$

Solution: The letter x is missing in this equation, and therefore the graph is a cylinder with rulings parallel to the x-axis. The directrix of this cylinder is the parabola in the yz-plane with equation $y^2 = 4z$. The graph is called a **parabolic cylinder** and is sketched in Figure 165. Note that in this figure the x- and z-axes have been interchanged.

Example 15

Discuss the graph in space of the equation

$$x^2 - z^2 = 1.$$

Solution: The rulings of this cylinder are parallel to the y-axis, and the directrix is the hyperbola in the xz-plane with the given equation. This cylinder, which consists of two separate parts, is called a **hyperbolic cylinder.** It is sketched in Figure 166.

EXERCISES

Discuss and sketch the graph in space of each of the following equations:

1. $x^2 + y^2 = 4.$ 2. $x^2 = 4y.$
3. $x^2 + 4y^2 = 4.$ 4. $y^2 + z^2 = 9.$
5. $4z^2 - 9y^2 = 36.$ 6. $y^2 - 9z^2 = 9.$
7. $z = x^2.$ 8. $xy = 1.$
9. $16y^2 + 9z^2 = 144.$ 10. $x^2 - y^2 = 0.$
11. $xz = 4.$ 12. $4x^2 + z^2 = 16.$
13. $z^2 = 4.$ 14. $y = 4 - x^2.$
15. $9 - y^2 = z.$ 16. $x^2 + y^2 = 2x.$

80.   THE SPHERE

A **sphere** is defined to be the locus of all points in space at a given distance (the radius) from a fixed point (the center). It is clear from the distance formula that

$$x^2 + y^2 + z^2 = r^2$$

is the equation of a sphere of radius r with its center at the origin.   More generally,

12·13 $$(x - h)^2 + (y - k)^2 + (z - m)^2 = r^2$$

is the equation of a sphere of radius r with its center at the point (h, k, m). On multiplying out Equation 12·13, we see that it is an equation of the form

12·14 $$x^2 + y^2 + z^2 + Gx + Hy + Jz + K = 0.$$

Thus every sphere has an equation of the form 12·14. Conversely, if an equation of the form 12·14 has a graph consisting of more than one point, its graph is a sphere. Just as in the case of the circle, the center and radius can be found by completing squares. This is illustrated in the following example.

Example 16

Discuss the graph of the equation

$$x^2 + y^2 + z^2 - 4x + 2y - 6z - 11 = 0.$$

Solution: This equation is of the form 12·14, but we proceed to write it in the form 12·13 by completing squares as follows:

$$(x^2 - 4x + 4) + (y^2 + 2y + 1) + (z^2 - 6z + 9) = 11 + 4 + 1 + 9,$$

or

$$(x - 2)^2 + (y + 1)^2 + (z - 3)^2 = 25.$$

Thus the graph is a sphere of radius 5 and with center at the point $(2, -1, 3)$.

81. THE ELLIPSOID

The graph of an equation of the form

12·15
$$\frac{x^2}{a^2} + \frac{y^2}{b^2} + \frac{z^2}{c^2} = 1$$

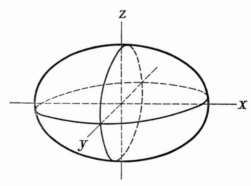

Figure 167

is called an **ellipsoid** (Figure 167). It is symmetric with respect to each of the coordinate planes, to each of the coordinate axes, and to the origin.

The reason for the name will be clear if we consider the various plane sections of an ellipsoid. By a *plane section* of a surface we mean the curve of intersection of a plane with the surface. The plane section of the ellipsoid 12·15 in the plane $x = 0$ (the yz-plane), found by setting $x = 0$ in 12·15, has the equation

$$\frac{y^2}{b^2} + \frac{z^2}{c^2} = 1.$$

Thus the section in the yz-plane is an ellipse. Similarly, the sections in the xz- and xy-planes are ellipses with respective equations

$$\frac{x^2}{a^2} + \frac{z^2}{c^2} = 1 \qquad \text{and} \qquad \frac{x^2}{a^2} + \frac{y^2}{b^2} = 1.$$

Actually, it is easy to verify that the section of 12·15 in a plane parallel to a coordinate plane is an ellipse. For example, the equation of the section in the plane $x = k$ (a plane parallel to the yz-plane) is obtained by replacing x by k in 12·15. The resulting equation can be written in the form

$$\frac{y^2}{b^2} + \frac{z^2}{c^2} = 1 - \frac{k^2}{a^2}.$$

If $k^2 < a^2$, this is the equation of an ellipse; if $k^2 > a^2$, the equation has no graph.

If $a = b$ in 12·15, the sections of the ellipsoid in planes parallel to the xy-plane are circles. Since in this case the ellipsoid may be thought of as being formed by rotating the ellipse

$$\frac{x^2}{a^2} + \frac{z^2}{c^2} = 1$$

in the xz-plane about the z-axis, it is called an **ellipsoid of revolution.** Similarly, the graph of 12·15 is an ellipsoid of revolution if $a = c$ or $b = c$. In the special case in which $a = b = c$, the graph is a sphere.

82. THE PARABOLOIDS

The graph of an equation of the form

12·16
$$\frac{x^2}{a^2} + \frac{y^2}{b^2} = cz$$

is called an **elliptic paraboloid.** The name stems from the fact that plane sections of the graph parallel to two coordinate planes are parabolas, whereas plane sections parallel to the other coordinate plane are ellipses. Thus, in the plane $z = k$ the section has the equation

$$\frac{x^2}{a^2} + \frac{y^2}{b^2} = ck,$$

which is an ellipse if $ck > 0$, and which has no graph if $ck < 0$. In the planes $x = k$ and $y = k$, the sections are parabolas with respective equations

$$\frac{y^2}{b^2} = cz - \frac{k^2}{a^2} \quad \text{and} \quad \frac{x^2}{a^2} = cz - \frac{k^2}{b^2}.$$

The elliptic paraboloid with equation 12·16 is symmetric with respect to the yz- and xz-planes, and hence also with respect to the z-axis. The

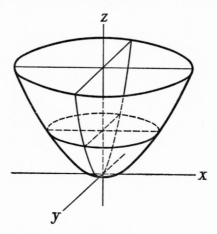

Figure 168

graph is above or below the xy-plane according as $c > 0$ or $c < 0$. The case in which $c > 0$ is indicated in Figure 168.

If $a = b$ in 12·16, the graph is called a **paraboloid of revolution.** Each section in a plane parallel to the xy-plane is a circle, and the surface may be thought of as being generated by a rotation of the parabola

$$\frac{x^2}{a^2} = cz$$

in the xz-plane about the z-axis. A parabolic reflector, such as is used in a reflecting telescope, has the shape of a paraboloid of revolution.

The graph of an equation of the form

12·17
$$\frac{x^2}{a^2} - \frac{y^2}{b^2} = cz$$

is called a **hyperbolic paraboloid.** Each section of this surface in a plane parallel to the xy-plane is a hyperbola, whereas each section in a plane parallel to the xz- or yz-plane is a parabola. The surface itself may be described as "saddle-shaped," and is sketched in Figure 169. It also is symmetric with respect to the yz-plane, the xz-plane, and the z-axis.

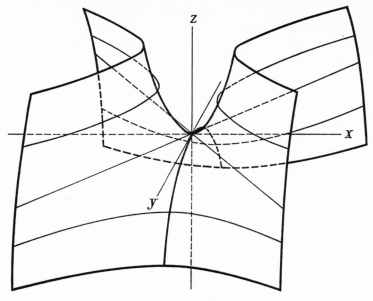

Figure 169

83. THE HYPERBOLOIDS

A surface with an equation of the form

12·18
$$\frac{x^2}{a^2} + \frac{y^2}{b^2} - \frac{z^2}{c^2} = 1,$$

or of the form

12·19
$$\frac{x^2}{a^2} + \frac{y^2}{b^2} - \frac{z^2}{c^2} = -1,$$

is called a **hyperboloid.** In either case, the section (if it exists) of the surface in the plane $z = k$ is an ellipse, and the section in the plane $x = k$ or $y = k$ is a hyperbola. The graph of 12·18, sketched in Figure 170, is called a **hyperboloid of one sheet,** and the graph of 12·19, shown in Figure 171, is called a **hyperboloid of two sheets.** Both surfaces are symmetric with respect to all coordinate planes and axes.

If $a = b$ in 12·18 or 12·19, the sections of the surface in planes parallel to the xy-plane are circles. In this case the surface is formed by rotating one of the hyperbolas

$$\frac{x^2}{a^2} - \frac{z^2}{c^2} = 1 \qquad \text{or} \qquad \frac{x^2}{a^2} - \frac{z^2}{c^2} = -1$$

in the xz-plane about the z-axis, and is called a **hyperboloid of revolution.**

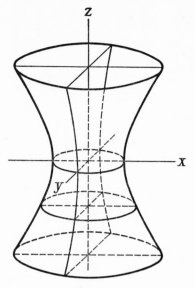

Figure 170

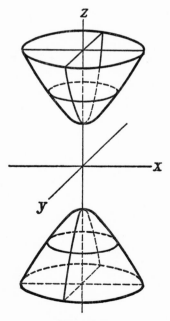

Figure 171

84.   THE ELLIPTIC CONE

The graph of an equation of the form

12·20
$$\frac{x^2}{a^2} + \frac{y^2}{b^2} = cz^2 \qquad\qquad (c > 0)$$

is called an **elliptic cone.**

In general, a **cone** is a surface having a fixed point V (called the **vertex**) on it such that for every other point P on the surface the line on P and V lies entirely on the surface. A cone may be thought of as

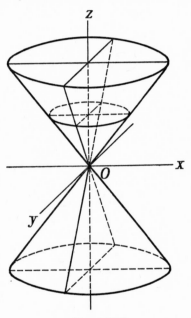

Figure 172

being generated by a line on the vertex which moves along some curve in a plane.

We now prove that the graph of Equation 12·20 is a cone with vertex at the origin. Let $P(x_1, y_1, z_1)$ be any point on this surface other than the origin. The line l on P and the origin then has direction numbers x_1, y_1, z_1, and hence has parametric equations

$$x = x_1 t, \qquad y = y_1 t, \qquad z = z_1 t.$$

Since P is on the surface, we have –

$$\frac{x_1{}^2}{a^2} + \frac{y_1{}^2}{b^2} = cz_1{}^2,$$

and therefore, when both sides of this equation are multiplied by t^2, it follows that

$$\frac{(x_1 t)^2}{a^2} + \frac{(y_1 t)^2}{b^2} = c(z_1 t)^2.$$

Clearly, then, every point on l has coordinates that satisfy Equation 12·20, and thus every point on l is also on the surface.

Each section of the cone 12·20 in a plane parallel to the xy-plane is an ellipse, and hence the name *elliptic cone*. The surface is sketched in Figure 172.

If $a = b$ in 12·20, the sections in planes parallel to the xy-plane are circles. The surface then is a familiar **right circular cone**.

85. SIMPLIFICATION BY TRANSLATION OF AXES

It can be shown that by suitable rotation and translation of axes, the equation of any quadric surface can be reduced to one of the simple types discussed in the preceding sections. The rotation of axes is used to eliminate all cross-product terms, that is, all terms involving xy, xz, and yz. By completing squares and using the formulas for translation of axes, we may then easily identify the graph. We shall not discuss rotation of axes, but in this section we shall illustrate how to identify the graph of an equation of the second degree in which there are no cross-product terms.

Example 17

Identify the graph of the equation

$$x^2 - 9y^2 - 4z^2 - 6x + 18y + 16z + 20 = 0.$$

Solution: By completing squares, we may write this equation in the form

$$(x - 3)^2 - 9(y - 1)^2 - 4(z - 2)^2 = -36.$$

Upon dividing both sides by -36, we obtain

$$\frac{(y - 1)^2}{4} + \frac{(z - 2)^2}{9} - \frac{(x - 3)^2}{36} = 1.$$

We now translate the axes to the new origin $(3, 1, 2)$ by Formulas 12·3, to get the simplified equation

$$\frac{y'^2}{4} + \frac{z'^2}{9} - \frac{x'^2}{36} = 1.$$

This is now of the form 12·18 with the x-, y-, and z-axes replaced respectively by the y'-, z'-, and x'-axes. The surface is therefore a hyperboloid of one sheet.

Example 18

Identify the graph of the equation

$$z^2 - 4y^2 - 16x - 16y - 2z + 49 = 0.$$

Solution: By completing the squares on the terms involving z and on those involving y, we may write this equation in the form

$$(z - 1)^2 - 4(y + 2)^2 = 16x - 64,$$

or

$$\frac{(z - 1)^2}{4} - \frac{(y + 2)^2}{1} = 4(x - 4).$$

By translation of axes to the new origin $(4, -2, 1)$, the equation of the surface becomes

$$\frac{z'^2}{4} - \frac{y'^2}{1} = 4x'.$$

By comparison with 12·17, this is seen to be a hyperbolic paraboloid.

EXERCISES

Discuss and sketch the graph of each of the following equations:

1. $x^2 + y^2 + z^2 - 4x + 2y = 11.$

2. $x^2 + y^2 + z^2 + 6x - 4y + 2z + 13 = 0.$

3. $4x^2 + 4y^2 + 4z^2 - 4x + 16y + 12z + 1 = 0.$

4. $4x^2 + 4y^2 + 4z^2 + 4x - 8y - 11 = 0.$

5. $4x^2 + 9y^2 + 36z^2 = 36.$

6. $x^2 + y^2 + z^2 = 36.$

7. $x^2 + y^2 - 4z^2 = 0.$

8. $4x^2 + z^2 = 4y.$

9. $x^2 + y^2 - z^2 = 4.$

10. $x^2 + y^2 + 9z^2 = 9.$

11. $x^2 + 9y^2 = 36 - 9z^2.$

12. $4x^2 - y^2 - z^2 = 4.$

13. $y^2 + z^2 - 4x = 0.$

14. $x^2 = y^2 + 25z^2.$

15. $x^2 + 4y^2 = z^2 - 4.$

16. $x^2 = y + 4z^2.$

17. $9x^2 - 4y = 9z^2.$

18. $x^2 - y^2 + z^2 = 0.$

19. $x - y^2 - z^2 = 0.$

20. $x^2 + 4y^2 + 16z^2 = 16.$

21. $x^2 + y^2 = 2x - z^2.$

22. $x^2 + 4y^2 = 16 + 16z^2.$

23. $x^2 + 4y^2 = 4 - z.$

24. $y^2 = -2x - z^2.$

25. $x^2 + 4y^2 = 4x - 4z^2.$

26. $x^2 + y^2 = 6x - 8y - z^2.$

27. $z = xy.$

28. $x^2 + y^2 = (z - 1)^2.$

29. $100x^2 + 25y^2 + 100 = 4z^2.$

30. $x^2 + z^2 + 1 = x.$

86. CYLINDRICAL AND SPHERICAL COORDINATES (OPTIONAL)

In addition to the rectangular coordinate system, two other coordinate systems are sometimes used in solid analytic geometry. We conclude our introduction to solid analytic geometry by defining these coordinate systems.

If P is a point in space with rectangular coordinates (x, y, z), then the projection M of P on the xy-plane has rectangular coordinates (x, y) in that plane (Figure 173). If M has polar coordinates (r, θ) in the xy-

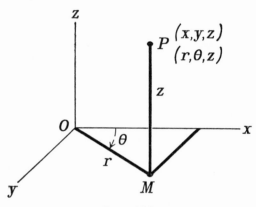

Figure 173

plane, then P is said to have **cylindrical coordinates** (r, θ, z), and we may write $P(r, \theta, z)$. Since r and θ are any polar coordinates of M, there is no restriction on the magnitude of either r or θ.

If c is a constant, the graph in space of the equation $r = c$ is a right circular cylinder, the axis of which is the z-axis; the graph of the equation $\theta = c$ is a plane containing the z-axis; and the graph of the equation $z = c$ is a plane parallel to the xy-plane.

If (x, y, z) and (r, θ, z) are rectangular and cylindrical coordinates of the same point P, it follows at once from 9·3 that

12·21 $$x = r \cos \theta, \qquad y = r \sin \theta, \qquad z = z.$$

We now define spherical coordinates of a point P. Again, let M be the projection of P on the xy-plane (Figure 174), and let θ be any angle in standard position in the xy-plane with terminal side OM. Let ϕ be the third direction angle of the half-line OP; that is, ϕ is the angle such that $0 \leqq \phi \leqq 180°$ between the positive half of the z-axis and the half-line OP. If we set $\rho = |OP|$, then the position of P is determined by ρ together with the angles θ and ϕ. We say that P has **spherical coordi-**

nates $(\rho,\ \theta,\ \phi)$, and write $P(\rho,\ \theta,\ \phi)$. The angles θ and ϕ are sometimes called respectively the *longitude* and *co-latitude* of the point P.

If c is a constant, the graph in space of the equation $\rho\ =\ c$ is a sphere with center at the origin, and the graph of the equation $\phi\ =\ c$ is a right circular cone whose axis is the z-axis and whose vertex is the origin.

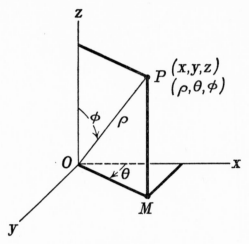

Figure 174

If $(x,\ y,\ z)$ and $(\rho,\ \theta,\ \phi)$ are rectangular and spherical coordinates of the same point P (as in Figure 174), we see that the projection M of P on the xy-plane has polar coordinates $(|OM|,\ \theta)$ in that plane. Since $|OM|\ =\ \rho\ \sin\ \phi$, it is easy to find that

12·22
$$
\begin{aligned}
x &= |OM|\ \cos\ \theta = \rho\ \sin\ \phi\ \cos\ \theta, \\
y &= |OM|\ \sin\ \theta = \rho\ \sin\ \phi\ \sin\ \theta, \\
z &= \rho\ \cos\ \phi.
\end{aligned}
$$

APPENDIX

Facts and Formulas for Reference

1. THE QUADRATIC FORMULA

The solutions of the quadratic equation

$$ax^2 + bx + c = 0 \qquad (a \neq 0)$$

are

$$x = \frac{-b \pm \sqrt{b^2 - 4ac}}{2a}.$$

2. INEQUALITIES

If a and b are real numbers such that $a - b$ is a positive number, we say that "a is greater than b" and indicate this by writing $a > b$. The same relationship also may be expressed by the statement "b is less than a," which is written as $b < a$. Obviously, $c > 0$ means that c is a positive number, and $d < 0$ means that d is a negative number. As examples of the use of this notation, we see that $4 > 2$ since $4 - 2$ is a positive number; likewise $-2 > -4$ since $-2 - (-4)$ is a positive number. Other examples are

$$17 > 4, \qquad -3 > -5, \qquad 2 > 1, \qquad -13 < 0.$$

Some simple rules for manipulating inequalities are the following:

If $a > b$, then $a + c > b + c$ for any real number c.
If $a > b$ and c is any *positive* number, then $ac > bc$.
If $a > b$ and c is any *negative* number, then $ac < bc$.
If $a > b$ and $b > c$, then $a > c$.

These rules also hold if the symbols $>$ and $<$ are interchanged throughout.

If we wish to indicate that either $a > b$ or $a = b$ (without specifying which), we write $a \geq b$. Similarly, $b \leq a$ means that b is either less than a or equal to a. The rules given above remain valid if the symbols $>$ and $<$ are replaced by $\geq$ and $\leq$, respectively.

If $a < b$ and $b < c$, we may write

$$a < b < c.$$

Similarly,

$$a \leqq b \leqq c$$

means that $a \leqq b$ and $b \leqq c$.

3.   ABSOLUTE VALUES

If a is any nonzero real number, the *absolute value* of a is the positive one of the two numbers a, $-a$.   The absolute value of zero is zero.   The absolute value of the number a is denoted by $|a|$.   As examples of this notation, we have

$$|-3| = 3, \qquad |3| = 3, \qquad |-2| = 2, \qquad |0| = 0.$$

For any numbers a and b, it is clear that

$$|a - b| = |b - a|;$$

also that

$$a^2 = b^2 \qquad \text{if and only if} \qquad |a| = |b|.$$

If c is any positive number, so that c has real square roots, the symbol $\sqrt{c}$ always means the *positive* square root of c.   It follows that

$$\sqrt{c^2} = |c|.$$

4.   ANGLES

By a *half-line* we mean that portion of a line extending indefinitely in one direction from a fixed point, called the *endpoint*, on it.   An *angle* is considered to be generated by a rotation of a half-line about its endpoint, now called the *vertex* of the angle.   The direction of rotation is usually indicated by an arrowhead, and it is agreed that an angle generated by a counterclockwise rotation has *positive* measure, whereas an angle gen-

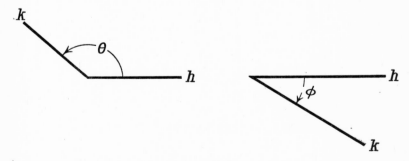

Appendix I

erated by a clockwise rotation has *negative* measure.   In Figure I, the angle θ has positive measure, whereas the angle ϕ has negative measure.

The half-line at which the rotation begins is called the *initial side* of the angle, and the half-line at which the rotation ends is called the *ter-minal side* of the angle. In Figure I, the initial side of each angle is designated by h and the terminal side by k.

5. THE TRIGONOMETRIC FUNCTIONS

If one has coordinate axes, an angle θ is said to be in *standard position* if its vertex is at the origin and its initial side is the positive half of the x-axis.

Now, let θ be any angle in standard position, as in Figure II, and P

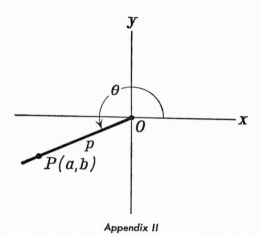

Appendix II

any point other than the origin on the terminal side of angle θ. If P has x-coordinate a and y-coordinate b, and if the distance (always considered to be positive) between P and the origin is p, then by definition

$$\sin \theta = \frac{b}{p}, \qquad \csc \theta = \frac{p}{b},$$

$$\cos \theta = \frac{a}{p}, \qquad \sec \theta = \frac{p}{a},$$

$$\tan \theta = \frac{b}{a}, \qquad \cot \theta = \frac{a}{b}.$$

6. THE FUNDAMENTAL IDENTITIES

$$\sin \theta \csc \theta = 1, \qquad \sin^2 \theta + \cos^2 \theta = 1,$$
$$\cos \theta \sec \theta = 1, \qquad 1 + \tan^2 \theta = \sec^2 \theta,$$
$$\tan \theta \cot \theta = 1, \qquad 1 + \cot^2 \theta = \csc^2 \theta,$$
$$\tan \theta = \frac{\sin \theta}{\cos \theta}, \qquad \cot \theta = \frac{\cos \theta}{\sin \theta}.$$

7. THE ADDITION FORMULAS

$$\sin (\theta + \phi) = \sin \theta \cos \phi + \cos \theta \sin \phi,$$
$$\sin (\theta - \phi) = \sin \theta \cos \phi - \cos \theta \sin \phi,$$
$$\cos (\theta + \phi) = \cos \theta \cos \phi - \sin \theta \sin \phi,$$
$$\cos (\theta - \phi) = \cos \theta \cos \phi + \sin \theta \sin \phi,$$

$$\tan (\theta + \phi) = \frac{\tan \theta + \tan \phi}{1 - \tan \theta \tan \phi},$$
$$\tan (\theta - \phi) = \frac{\tan \theta - \tan \phi}{1 + \tan \theta \tan \phi}.$$

8. SOME REDUCTION FORMULAS

$$\sin (-\theta) = -\sin \theta, \qquad \sin (90° - \theta) = \cos \theta,$$
$$\cos (-\theta) = \cos \theta, \qquad \cos (90° - \theta) = \sin \theta,$$
$$\tan (-\theta) = -\tan \theta, \qquad \tan (90° - \theta) = \cot \theta,$$
$$\sin (90° + \theta) = \cos \theta, \qquad \sin (180° - \theta) = \sin \theta,$$
$$\cos (90° + \theta) = -\sin \theta, \qquad \cos (180° - \theta) = -\cos \theta,$$
$$\tan (90° + \theta) = -\cot \theta, \qquad \tan (180° - \theta) = -\tan \theta,$$

$$\sin (180° + \theta) = -\sin \theta,$$
$$\cos (180° + \theta) = -\cos \theta,$$
$$\tan (180° + \theta) = \tan \theta.$$

9. DOUBLE-ANGLE AND HALF-ANGLE FORMULAS

$$\sin 2\theta = 2 \sin \theta \cos \theta,$$
$$\cos 2\theta = \cos^2 \theta - \sin^2 \theta = 2 \cos^2 \theta - 1 = 1 - 2 \sin^2 \theta,$$
$$\tan 2\theta = \frac{2 \tan \theta}{1 - \tan^2 \theta},$$
$$\sin \frac{\theta}{2} = \pm \sqrt{\frac{1 - \cos \theta}{2}},$$
$$\cos \frac{\theta}{2} = \pm \sqrt{\frac{1 + \cos \theta}{2}},$$
$$\tan \frac{\theta}{2} = \frac{1 - \cos \theta}{\sin \theta} = \frac{\sin \theta}{1 + \cos \theta}.$$

10. TRIANGLE FORMULAS

If the angles of a triangle are A, B, C, and the respective opposite sides have lengths a, b, c, then

Law of Sines: $\dfrac{\sin A}{a} = \dfrac{\sin B}{b} = \dfrac{\sin C}{c}.$

Law of Cosines: $a^2 = b^2 + c^2 - 2bc \cos A.$

11. RADIAN MEASURE

If an angle θ is at the center of a circle of radius r, and the intercepted arc is of length s, the angle is said to have measure s/r *radians* if θ is generated by a counterclockwise rotation, and measure $-s/r$ *radians* if θ is generated

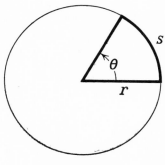

Appendix III

by a clockwise rotation. Frequently, the same symbol is used for an angle and its measure. Thus, if θ, r, s are related as in Figure III, and θ is expressed in radians, we have $\theta = s/r$, or

$$s = r\theta.$$

The relationship between degree and radian measure is obtained easily by observing that the complete angle about a point has radian measure $2\pi r/r$, since the circumference of the circle is $2\pi r$. Thus

$$360° = 2\pi \text{ radians,}$$

or

$$180° = \pi \text{ radians.}$$

Angles, other than simple multiples or fractions of π radians can be changed from degrees to radians or vice versa by use of Table I (page 277).

In advanced mathematics, radian measure is almost always used, but the word "radian" is usually omitted.

12. EXACT VALUES OF FUNCTIONS OF SPECIAL ANGLES

Radians	Degrees	Sin	Cos	Tan	Cot	Sec	Csc
0	0	0	1	0	—	1	—
$\dfrac{\pi}{6}$	30	$\dfrac{1}{2}$	$\dfrac{\sqrt{3}}{2}$	$\dfrac{\sqrt{3}}{3}$	$\sqrt{3}$	$\dfrac{2\sqrt{3}}{3}$	2
$\dfrac{\pi}{4}$	45	$\dfrac{\sqrt{2}}{2}$	$\dfrac{\sqrt{2}}{2}$	1	1	$\sqrt{2}$	$\sqrt{2}$
$\dfrac{\pi}{3}$	60	$\dfrac{\sqrt{3}}{2}$	$\dfrac{1}{2}$	$\sqrt{3}$	$\dfrac{\sqrt{3}}{3}$	2	$\dfrac{2\sqrt{3}}{3}$
$\dfrac{\pi}{2}$	90	1	0	—	0	—	1
$\dfrac{2\pi}{3}$	120	$\dfrac{\sqrt{3}}{2}$	$-\dfrac{1}{2}$	$-\sqrt{3}$	$-\dfrac{\sqrt{3}}{3}$	-2	$\dfrac{2\sqrt{3}}{3}$
$\dfrac{3\pi}{4}$	135	$\dfrac{\sqrt{2}}{2}$	$-\dfrac{\sqrt{2}}{2}$	-1	-1	$-\sqrt{2}$	$\sqrt{2}$
$\dfrac{5\pi}{6}$	150	$\dfrac{1}{2}$	$-\dfrac{\sqrt{3}}{2}$	$-\dfrac{\sqrt{3}}{3}$	$-\sqrt{3}$	$-\dfrac{2\sqrt{3}}{3}$	2
π	180	0	-1	0	—	-1	—
$\dfrac{7\pi}{6}$	210	$-\dfrac{1}{2}$	$-\dfrac{\sqrt{3}}{2}$	$\dfrac{\sqrt{3}}{3}$	$\sqrt{3}$	$-\dfrac{2\sqrt{3}}{3}$	-2
$\dfrac{5\pi}{4}$	225	$-\dfrac{\sqrt{2}}{2}$	$-\dfrac{\sqrt{2}}{2}$	1	1	$-\sqrt{2}$	$-\sqrt{2}$
$\dfrac{4\pi}{3}$	240	$-\dfrac{\sqrt{3}}{2}$	$-\dfrac{1}{2}$	$\sqrt{3}$	$\dfrac{\sqrt{3}}{3}$	-2	$-\dfrac{2\sqrt{3}}{3}$
$\dfrac{3\pi}{2}$	270	-1	0	—	0	—	-1
$\dfrac{5\pi}{3}$	300	$-\dfrac{\sqrt{3}}{2}$	$\dfrac{1}{2}$	$-\sqrt{3}$	$-\dfrac{\sqrt{3}}{3}$	2	$-\dfrac{2\sqrt{3}}{3}$
$\dfrac{7\pi}{4}$	315	$-\dfrac{\sqrt{2}}{2}$	$\dfrac{\sqrt{2}}{2}$	-1	-1	$\sqrt{2}$	$-\sqrt{2}$
$\dfrac{11\pi}{6}$	330	$-\dfrac{1}{2}$	$\dfrac{\sqrt{3}}{2}$	$-\dfrac{\sqrt{3}}{3}$	$-\sqrt{3}$	$\dfrac{2\sqrt{3}}{3}$	-2

13. LOGARITHMS

Let a be a fixed positive real number not equal to 1. Then, by definition, the following equations are equivalent:

$$u = \log_a v, \qquad a^u = v.$$

The principal laws of logarithms are as follows:

$$\log_a xy = \log_a x + \log_a y,$$
$$\log_a \frac{x}{y} = \log_a x - \log_a y,$$
$$\log_a x^k = k \log_a x,$$
$$(\log_a b)(\log_b a) = 1,$$
$$(\log_a b)(\log_c a) = \log_c b.$$

In the above, a, b, and c are positive numbers not equal to 1; k is an arbitrary real number; x and y are arbitrary positive numbers.

14. LOWER CASE GREEK LETTERS

Letters	*Names*	*Letters*	*Names*	*Letters*	*Names*
α	Alpha	ι	Iota	ρ	Rho
β	Beta	κ	Kappa	σ	Sigma
γ	Gamma	λ	Lambda	τ	Tau
δ	Delta	μ	Mu	υ	Upsilon
ϵ	Epsilon	ν	Nu	ϕ	Phi
ζ	Zeta	ξ	Xi	χ	Chi
η	Eta	o	Omicron	ψ	Psi
θ	Theta	π	Pi	ω	Omega

TABLE I
Values of Trigonometric Functions

Degrees	Radians	Sine	Tangent	Cotangent	Cosine		
0° 00′	.0000	.0000	.0000		1.0000	1.5708	90° 00′
10′	.0029	.0029	.0029	343.77	1.0000	1.5679	50′
20′	.0058	.0058	.0058	171.89	1.0000	1.5650	40′
30′	.0087	.0087	.0087	114.59	1.0000	1.5621	30′
40′	.0116	.0116	.0116	85.940	.9999	1.5592	20′
50′	.0145	.0145	.0145	68.750	.9999	1.5563	10′
1° 00′	.0175	.0175	.0175	57.290	.9998	1.5533	89° 00′
10′	.0204	.0204	.0204	49.104	.9998	1.5504	50′
20′	.0233	.0233	.0233	42.964	.9997	1.5475	40′
30′	.0262	.0262	.0262	38.188	.9997	1.5446	30′
40′	.0291	.0291	.0291	34.368	.9996	1.5417	20′
50′	.0320	.0320	.0320	31.242	.9995	1.5388	10′
2° 00′	.0349	.0349	.0349	28.636	.9994	1.5359	88° 00′
10′	.0378	.0378	.0378	26.432	.9993	1.5330	50′
20′	.0407	.0407	.0407	24.542	.9992	1.5301	40′
30′	.0436	.0436	.0437	22.904	.9990	1.5272	30′
40′	.0465	.0465	.0466	21.470	.9989	1.5243	20′
50′	.0495	.0494	.0495	20.206	.9988	1.5213	10′
3° 00′	.0524	.0523	.0524	19.081	.9986	1.5184	87° 00′
10′	.0553	.0552	.0553	18.075	.9985	1.5155	50′
20′	.0582	.0581	.0582	17.169	.9983	1.5126	40′
30′	.0611	.0610	.0612	16.350	.9981	1.5097	30′
40′	.0640	.0640	.0641	15.605	.9980	1.5068	20′
50′	.0669	.0669	.0670	14.924	.9978	1.5039	10′
4° 00′	.0698	.0698	.0699	14.301	.9976	1.5010	86° 00′
10′	.0727	.0727	.0729	13.727	.9974	1.4981	50′
20′	.0756	.0756	.0758	13.197	.9971	1.4952	40′
30′	.0785	.0785	.0787	12.706	.9969	1.4923	30′
40′	.0814	.0814	.0816	12.251	.9967	1.4893	20′
50′	.0844	.0843	.0846	11.826	.9964	1.4864	10′
5° 00′	.0873	.0872	.0875	11.430	.9962	1.4835	85° 00′
10′	.0902	.0901	.0904	11.059	.9959	1.4806	50′
20′	.0931	.0929	.0934	10.712	.9957	1.4777	40′
30′	.0960	.0958	.0963	10.385	.9954	1.4748	30′
40′	.0989	.0987	.0992	10.078	.9951	1.4719	20′
50′	.1018	.1016	.1022	9.7882	.9948	1.4690	10′
6° 00′	.1047	.1045	.1051	9.5144	.9945	1.4661	84° 00′
10′	.1076	.1074	.1080	9.2553	.9942	1.4632	50′
20′	.1105	.1103	.1110	9.0098	.9939	1.4603	40′
30′	.1134	.1132	.1139	8.7769	.9936	1.4573	30′
40′	.1164	.1161	.1169	8.5555	.9932	1.4544	20′
50′	.1193	.1190	.1198	8.3450	.9929	1.4515	10′
7° 00′	.1222	.1219	.1228	8.1443	.9925	1.4486	83° 00′
10′	.1251	.1248	.1257	7.9530	.9922	1.4457	50′
20′	.1280	.1276	.1287	7.7704	.9918	1.4428	40′
30′	.1309	.1305	.1317	7.5958	.9914	1.4399	30′
40′	.1338	.1334	.1346	7.4287	.9911	1.4370	20′
50′	.1367	.1363	.1376	7.2687	.9907	1.4341	10′
8° 00′	.1396	.1392	.1405	7.1154	.9903	1.4312	82° 00′
10′	.1425	.1421	.1435	6.9682	.9899	1.4283	50′
20′	.1454	.1449	.1465	6.8269	.9894	1.4254	40′
30′	.1484	.1478	.1495	6.6912	.9890	1.4224	30′
40′	.1513	.1507	.1524	6.5606	.9886	1.4195	20′
50′	.1542	.1536	.1554	6.4348	.9881	1.4166	10′
9° 00′	.1571	.1564	.1584	6.3138	.9877	1.4137	81° 00′
		Cosine	Cotangent	Tangent	Sine	Radians	Degrees

TABLE I (Continued)
Values of Trigonometric Functions

Degrees	Radians	Sine	Tangent	Cotangent	Cosine		
9° 00′	.1571	.1564	.1584	6.3138	.9877	1.4137	81° 00′
10′	.1600	.1593	.1614	6.1970	.9872	1.4108	50′
20′	.1629	.1622	.1644	6.0844	.9868	1.4079	40′
30′	.1658	.1650	.1673	5.9758	.9863	1.4050	30′
40′	.1687	.1679	.1703	5.8708	.9858	1.4021	20′
50′	.1716	.1708	.1733	5.7694	.9853	1.3992	10′
10° 00′	.1745	.1736	.1763	5.6713	.9848	1.3963	80° 00′
10′	.1774	.1765	.1793	5.5764	.9843	1.3934	50′
20′	.1804	.1794	.1823	5.4845	.9838	1.3904	40′
30′	.1833	.1822	.1853	5.3955	.9833	1.3875	30′
40′	.1862	.1851	.1883	5.3093	.9827	1.3846	20′
50′	.1891	.1880	.1914	5.2257	.9822	1.3817	10′
11° 00′	.1920	.1908	.1944	5.1446	.9816	1.3788	79° 00′
10′	.1949	.1937	.1974	5.0658	.9811	1.3759	50′
20′	.1978	.1965	.2004	4.9894	.9805	1.3730	40′
30′	.2007	.1994	.2035	4.9152	.9799	1.3701	30′
40′	.2036	.2022	.2065	4.8430	.9793	1.3672	20′
50′	.2065	.2051	.2095	4.7729	.9787	1.3643	10′
12° 00′	.2094	.2079	.2126	4.7046	.9781	1.3614	78° 00′
10′	.2123	.2108	.2156	4.6382	.9775	1.3584	50′
20′	.2153	.2136	.2186	4.5736	.9769	1.3555	40′
30′	.2182	.2164	.2217	4.5107	.9763	1.3526	30′
40′	.2211	.2193	.2247	4.4494	.9757	1.3497	20′
50′	.2240	.2221	.2278	4.3897	.9750	1.3468	10′
13° 00′	.2269	.2250	.2309	4.3315	.9744	1.3439	77° 00′
10′	.2298	.2278	.2339	4.2747	.9737	1.3410	50′
20′	.2327	.2306	.2370	4.2193	.9730	1.3381	40′
30′	.2356	.2334	.2401	4.1653	.9724	1.3352	30′
40′	.2385	.2363	.2432	4.1126	.9717	1.3323	20′
50′	.2414	.2391	.2462	4.0611	.9710	1.3294	10′
14° 00′	.2443	.2419	.2493	4.0108	.9703	1.3265	76° 00′
10′	.2473	.2447	.2524	3.9617	.9696	1.3235	50′
20′	.2502	.2476	.2555	3.9136	.9689	1.3206	40′
30′	.2531	.2504	.2586	3.8667	.9681	1.3177	30′
40′	.2560	.2532	.2617	3.8208	.9674	1.3148	20′
50′	.2589	.2560	.2648	3.7760	.9667	1.3119	10′
15° 00′	.2618	.2588	.2679	3.7321	.9659	1.3090	75° 00′
10′	.2647	.2616	.2711	3.6891	.9652	1.3061	50′
20′	.2676	.2644	.2742	3.6470	.9644	1.3032	40′
30′	.2705	.2672	.2773	3.6059	.9636	1.3003	30′
40′	.2734	.2700	.2805	3.5656	.9628	1.2974	20′
50′	.2763	.2728	.2836	3.5261	.9621	1.2945	10′
16° 00′	.2793	.2756	.2867	3.4874	.9613	1.2915	74° 00′
10′	.2822	.2784	.2899	3.4495	.9605	1.2886	50′
20′	.2851	.2812	.2931	3.4124	.9596	1.2857	40′
30′	.2880	.2840	.2962	3.3759	.9588	1.2828	30′
40′	.2909	.2868	.2994	3.3402	.9580	1.2799	20′
50′	.2938	.2896	.3026	3.3052	.9572	1.2770	10′
17° 00′	.2967	.2924	.3057	3.2709	.9563	1.2741	73° 00′
10′	.2996	.2952	.3089	3.2371	.9555	1.2712	50′
20′	.3025	.2979	.3121	3.2041	.9546	1.2683	40′
30′	.3054	.3007	.3153	3.1716	.9537	1.2654	30′
40′	.3083	.3035	.3185	3.1397	.9528	1.2625	20′
50′	.3113	.3062	.3217	3.1084	.9520	1.2595	10′
18° 00′	.3142	.3090	.3249	3.0777	.9511	1.2566	72° 00′
		Cosine	Cotangent	Tangent	Sine	Radians	Degrees

TABLE I (Continued)
Values of Trigonometric Functions

Degrees	Radians	Sine	Tangent	Cotangent	Cosine		
18° 00′	.3142	.3090	.3249	3.0777	.9511	1.2566	72° 00′
10′	.3171	.3118	.3281	3.0475	.9502	1.2537	50′
20′	.3200	.3145	.3314	3.0178	.9492	1.2508	40′
30′	.3229	.3173	.3346	2.9887	.9483	1.2479	30′
40′	.3258	.3201	.3378	2.9600	.9474	1.2450	20′
50′	.3287	.3228	.3411	2.9319	.9465	1.2421	10′
19° 00′	.3316	.3256	.3443	2.9042	.9455	1.2392	71° 00′
10′	.3345	.3283	.3476	2.8770	.9446	1.2363	50′
20′	.3374	.3311	.3508	2.8502	.9436	1.2334	40′
30′	.3403	.3338	.3541	2.8239	.9426	1.2305	30′
40′	.3432	.3365	.3574	2.7980	.9417	1.2275	20′
50′	.3462	.3393	.3607	2.7725	.9407	1.2246	10′
20° 00′	.3491	.3420	.3640	2.7475	.9397	1.2217	70° 00′
10′	.3520	.3448	.3673	2.7228	.9387	1.2188	50′
20′	.3549	.3475	.3706	2.6985	.9377	1.2159	40′
30′	.3578	.3502	.3739	2.6746	.9367	1.2130	30′
40′	.3607	.3529	.3772	2.6511	.9356	1.2101	20′
50′	.3636	.3557	.3805	2.6279	.9346	1.2072	10′
21° 00′	.3665	.3584	.3839	2.6051	.9336	1.2043	69° 00′
10′	.3694	.3611	.3872	2.5826	.9325	1.2014	50′
20′	.3723	.3638	.3906	2.5605	.9315	1.1985	40′
30′	.3752	.3665	.3939	2.5386	.9304	1.1956	30′
40′	.3782	.3692	.3973	2.5172	.9293	1.1926	20′
50′	.3811	.3719	.4006	2.4960	.9283	1.1897	10′
22° 00′	.3840	.3746	.4040	2.4751	.9272	1.1868	68° 00′
10′	.3869	.3773	.4074	2.4545	.9261	1.1839	50′
20′	.3898	.3800	.4108	2.4342	.9250	1.1810	40′
30′	.3927	.3827	.4142	2.4142	.9239	1.1781	30′
40′	.3956	.3854	.4176	2.3945	.9228	1.1752	20′
50′	.3985	.3881	.4210	2.3750	.9216	1.1723	10′
23° 00′	.4014	.3907	.4245	2.3559	.9205	1.1694	67° 00′
10′	.4043	.3934	.4279	2.3369	.9194	1.1665	50′
20′	.4072	.3961	.4314	2.3183	.9182	1.1636	40′
30′	.4102	.3987	.4348	2.2998	.9171	1.1606	30′
40′	.4131	.4014	.4383	2.2817	.9159	1.1577	20′
50′	.4160	.4041	.4417	2.2637	.9147	1.1548	10′
24° 00′	.4189	.4067	.4452	2.2460	.9135	1.1519	66° 00′
10′	.4218	.4094	.4487	2.2286	.9124	1.1490	50′
20′	.4247	.4120	.4522	2.2113	.9112	1.1461	40′
30′	.4276	.4147	.4557	2.1943	.9100	1.1432	30′
40′	.4305	.4173	.4592	2.1775	.9088	1.1403	20′
50′	.4334	.4200	.4628	2.1609	.9075	1.1374	10′
25° 00′	.4363	.4226	.4663	2.1445	.9063	1.1345	65° 00′
10′	.4392	.4253	.4699	2.1283	.9051	1.1316	50′
20′	.4422	.4279	.4734	2.1123	.9038	1.1286	40′
30′	.4451	.4305	.4770	2.0965	.9026	1.1257	30′
40′	.4480	.4331	.4806	2.0809	.9013	1.1228	20′
50′	.4509	.4358	.4841	2.0655	.9001	1.1199	10′
26° 00′	.4538	.4384	.4877	2.0503	.8988	1.1170	64° 00′
10′	.4567	.4410	.4913	2.0353	.8975	1.1141	50′
20′	.4596	.4436	.4950	2.0204	.8962	1.1112	40′
30′	4625	.4462	.4986	2.0057	.8949	1.1083	30′
40′	.4654	.4488	.5022	1.9912	.8936	1.1054	20′
50′	.4683	.4514	.5059	1.9768	.8923	1.1025	10′
27° 00′	.4712	.4540	.5095	1.9626	.8910	1.0996	63° 00′
		Cosine	Cotangent	Tangent	Sine	Radians	Degrees

TABLE I (Continued)
Values of Trigonometric Functions

Degrees	Radians	Sine	Tangent	Cotangent	Cosine		
27° 00′	.4712	.4540	.5095	1.9626	.8910	1.0996	63° 00′
10′	.4741	.4566	.5132	1.9486	.8897	1.0966	50′
20′	.4771	.4592	.5169	1.9347	.8884	1.0937	40′
30′	.4800	.4617	.5206	1.9210	.8870	1.0908	30′
40′	.4829	.4643	.5243	1.9074	.8857	1.0879	20′
50′	.4858	.4669	.5280	1.8940	.8843	1.0850	10′
28° 00′	.4887	.4695	.5317	1.8807	.8829	1.0821	62° 00′
10′	.4916	.4720	.5354	1.8676	.8816	1.0792	50′
20′	.4945	.4746	.5392	1.8546	.8802	1.0763	40′
30′	.4974	.4772	.5430	1.8418	.8788	1.0734	30′
40′	.5003	.4797	.5467	1.8291	.8774	1.0705	20′
50′	.5032	.4823	.5505	1.8165	.8760	1.0676	10′
29° 00′	.5061	.4848	.5543	1.8040	.8746	1.0647	61° 00′
10′	.5091	.4874	.5581	1.7917	.8732	1.0617	50′
20′	.5120	.4899	.5619	1.7796	.8718	1.0588	40′
30′	.5149	.4924	.5658	1.7675	.8704	1.0559	30′
40′	.5178	.4950	.5696	1.7556	.8689	1.0530	20′
50′	.5207	.4975	.5735	1.7437	.8675	1.0501	10′
30° 00′	.5236	.5000	.5774	1.7321	.8660	1.0472	60° 00′
10′	.5265	.5025	.5812	1.7205	.8646	1.0443	50′
20′	.5294	.5050	.5851	1.7090	.8631	1.0414	40′
30′	.5323	.5075	.5890	1.6977	.8616	1.0385	30′
40′	.5352	.5100	.5930	1.6864	.8601	1.0356	20′
50′	.5381	.5125	.5969	1.6753	.8587	1.0327	10′
31° 00′	.5411	.5150	.6009	1.6643	.8572	1.0297	59° 00′
10′	.5440	.5175	.6048	1.6534	.8557	1.0268	50′
20′	.5469	.5200	.6088	1.6426	.8542	1.0239	40′
30′	.5498	.5225	.6128	1.6319	.8526	1.0210	30′
40′	.5527	.5250	.6168	1.6212	.8511	1.0181	20′
50′	.5556	.5275	.6208	1.6107	.8496	1.0152	10′
32° 00′	.5585	.5299	.6249	1.6003	.8480	1.0123	58° 00′
10′	.5614	.5324	.6289	1.5900	.8465	1.0094	50′
20′	.5643	.5348	.6330	1.5798	.8450	1.0065	40′
30′	.5672	.5373	.6371	1.5697	.8434	1.0036	30′
40′	.5701	.5398	.6412	1.5597	.8418	1.0007	20′
50′	.5730	.5422	.6453	1.5497	.8403	.9977	10′
33° 00′	.5760	.5446	.6494	1.5399	.8387	.9948	57° 00′
10′	.5789	.5471	.6536	1.5301	.8371	.9919	50′
20′	.5818	.5495	.6577	1.5204	.8355	.9890	40′
30′	.5847	.5519	.6619	1.5108	.8339	.9861	30′
40′	.5876	.5544	.6661	1.5013	.8323	.9832	20′
50′	.5905	.5568	.6703	1.4919	.8307	.9803	10′
34° 00′	.5934	.5592	.6745	1.4826	.8290	.9774	56° 00′
10′	.5963	.5616	.6787	1.4733	.8274	.9745	50′
20′	.5992	.5640	.6830	1.4641	.8258	.9716	40′
30′	.6021	.5664	.6873	1.4550	.8241	.9687	30′
40′	.6050	.5688	.6916	1.4460	.8225	.9657	20′
50′	.6080	.5712	.6959	1.4370	.8208	.9628	10′
35° 00′	.6109	.5736	.7002	1.4281	.8192	.9599	55° 00′
10′	.6138	.5760	.7046	1.4193	.8175	.9570	50′
20′	.6167	.5783	.7089	1.4106	.8158	.9541	40′
30′	.6196	.5807	.7133	1.4019	.8141	.9512	30′
40′	.6225	.5831	.7177	1.3934	.8124	.9483	20′
50′	.6254	.5854	.7221	1.3848	.8107	.9454	10′
36° 00′	.6283	.5878	.7265	1.3764	.8090	.9425	54° 00′
		Cosine	Cotangent	Tangent	Sine	Radians	Degrees

TABLE I (Continued)
Values of Trigonometric Functions

Degrees	Radians	Sine	Tangent	Cotangent	Cosine		
36° 00′	.6283	.5878	.7265	1.3764	.8090	.9425	54° 00′
10′	.6312	.5901	.7310	1.3680	.8073	.9396	50′
20′	.6341	.5925	.7355	1.3597	.8056	.9367	40′
30′	.6370	.5948	.7400	1.3514	.8039	.9338	30′
40′	.6400	.5972	.7445	1.3432	.8021	.9308	20′
50′	.6429	.5995	.7490	1.3351	.8004	.9279	10′
37° 00′	.6458	.6018	.7536	1.3270	.7986	.9250	53° 00′
10′	.6487	.6041	.7581	1.3190	.7969	.9221	50′
20′	.6516	.6065	.7627	1.3111	.7951	.9192	40′
30′	.6545	.6088	.7673	1.3032	.7934	.9163	30′
40′	.6574	.6111	.7720	1.2954	.7916	.9134	20′
50′	.6603	.6134	.7766	1.2876	.7898	.9105	10′
38° 00′	.6632	.6157	.7813	1.2799	.7880	.9076	52° 00′
10′	.6661	.6180	.7860	1.2723	.7862	.9047	50′
20′	.6690	.6202	.7907	1.2647	.7844	.9018	40′
30′	.6720	.6225	.7954	1.2572	.7826	.8988	30′
40′	.6749	.6248	.8002	1.2497	.7808	.8959	20′
50′	.6778	.6271	.8050	1.2423	.7790	.8930	10′
39° 00′	.6807	.6293	.8098	1.2349	.7771	.8901	51° 00′
10′	.6836	.6316	.8146	1.2276	.7753	.8872	50′
20′	.6865	.6338	.8195	1.2203	.7735	.8843	40′
30′	.6894	.6361	.8243	1.2131	.7716	.8814	30′
40′	.6923	.6383	.8292	1.2059	.7698	.8785	20′
50′	.6952	.6406	.8342	1.1988	.7679	.8756	10′
40° 00′	.6981	.6428	.8391	1.1918	.7660	.8727	50° 00′
10′	.7010	.6450	.8441	1.1847	.7642	.8698	50′
20′	.7039	.6472	.8491	1.1778	.7623	.8668	40′
30′	.7069	.6494	.8541	1.1708	.7604	.8639	30′
40′	.7098	.6517	.8591	1.1640	.7585	.8610	20′
50′	.7127	.6539	.8642	1.1571	.7566	.8581	10′
41° 00′	.7156	.6561	.8693	1.1504	.7547	.8552	49° 00′
10′	.7185	.6583	.8744	1.1436	.7528	.8523	50′
20′	.7214	.6604	.8796	1.1369	.7509	.8494	40′
30′	.7243	.6626	.8847	1.1303	.7490	.8465	30′
40′	.7272	.6648	.8899	1.1237	.7470	.8436	20′
50′	.7301	.6670	.8952	1.1171	.7451	.8407	10′
42° 00′	.7330	.6691	.9004	1.1106	.7431	.8378	48° 00′
10′	.7359	.6713	.9057	1.1041	.7412	.8348	50′
20′	.7389	.6734	.9110	1.0977	.7392	.8319	40′
30′	.7418	.6756	.9163	1.0913	.7373	.8290	30′
40′	.7447	.6777	.9217	1.0850	.7353	.8261	20′
50′	.7476	.6799	.9271	1.0786	.7333	.8232	10′
43° 00′	.7505	.6820	.9325	1.0724	.7314	.8203	47° 00′
10′	.7534	.6841	.9380	1.0661	.7294	.8174	50′
20′	.7563	.6862	.9435	1.0599	.7274	.8145	40′
30′	.7592	.6884	.9490	1.0538	.7254	.8116	30′
40′	.7621	.6905	.9545	1.0477	.7234	.8087	20′
50′	.7650	.6926	.9601	1.0416	.7214	.8058	10′
44° 00′	.7679	.6947	.9657	1.0355	.7193	.8029	46° 00′
10′	.7709	.6967	.9713	1.0295	.7173	.7999	50′
20′	.7738	.6988	.9770	1.0235	.7153	.7970	40′
30′	.7767	.7009	.9827	1.0176	.7133	.7941	30′
40′	.7796	.7030	.9884	1.0117	.7112	.7912	20′
50′	.7825	.7050	.9942	1.0058	.7092	.7883	10′
45° 00′	.7854	.7071	1.0000	1.0000	.7071	.7854	45° 00′
		Cosine	Cotangent	Tangent	Sine	Radians	Degrees

TABLE II
Logarithms of Numbers

N	0	1	2	3	4	5	6	7	8	9
1.0	.0000	.0043	.0086	.0128	.0170	.0212	.0253	.0294	.0334	.0374
1.1	.0414	.0453	.0492	.0531	.0569	.0607	.0645	.0682	.0719	.0755
1.2	.0792	.0828	.0864	.0899	.0934	.0969	.1004	.1038	.1072	.1106
1.3	.1139	.1173	.1206	.1239	.1271	.1303	.1335	.1367	.1399	.1430
1.4	.1461	.1492	.1523	.1553	.1584	.1614	.1644	.1673	.1703	.1732
1.5	.1761	.1790	.1818	.1847	.1875	.1903	.1931	.1959	.1987	.2014
1.6	.2041	.2068	.2095	.2122	.2148	.2175	.2201	.2227	.2253	.2279
1.7	.2304	.2330	.2355	.2380	.2405	.2430	.2455	.2480	.2504	.2529
1.8	.2553	.2577	.2601	.2625	.2648	.2672	.2695	.2718	.2742	.2765
1.9	.2788	.2810	.2833	.2856	.2878	.2900	.2923	.2945	.2967	.2989
2.0	.3010	.3032	.3054	.3075	.3096	.3118	.3139	.3160	.3181	.3201
2.1	.3222	.3243	.3263	.3284	.3304	.3324	.3345	.3365	.3385	.3404
2.2	.3424	.3444	.3464	.3483	.3502	.3522	.3541	.3560	.3579	.3598
2.3	.3617	.3636	.3655	.3674	.3692	.3711	.3729	.3747	.3766	.3784
2.4	.3802	.3820	.3838	.3856	.3874	.3892	.3909	.3927	.3945	.3962
2.5	.3979	.3997	.4014	.4031	.4048	.4065	.4082	.4099	.4116	.4133
2.6	.4150	.4166	.4183	.4200	.4216	.4232	.4249	.4265	.4281	.4298
2.7	.4314	.4330	.4346	.4362	.4378	.4393	.4409	.4425	.4440	.4456
2.8	.4472	.4487	.4502	.4518	.4533	.4548	.4564	.4579	.4594	.4609
2.9	.4624	.4639	.4654	.4669	.4683	.4698	.4713	.4728	.4742	.4757
3.0	.4771	.4786	.4800	.4814	.4829	.4843	.4857	.4871	.4886	.4900
3.1	.4914	.4928	.4942	.4955	.4969	.4983	.4997	.5011	.5024	.5038
3.2	.5051	.5065	.5079	.5092	.5105	.5119	.5132	.5145	.5159	.5172
3.3	.5185	.5198	.5211	.5224	.5237	.5250	.5263	.5276	.5289	.5302
3.4	.5315	.5328	.5340	.5353	.5366	.5378	.5391	.5403	.5416	.5428
3.5	.5441	.5453	.5465	.5478	.5490	.5502	.5514	.5527	.5539	.5551
3.6	.5563	.5575	.5587	.5599	.5611	.5623	.5635	.5647	.5658	.5670
3.7	.5682	.5694	.5705	.5717	.5729	.5740	.5752	.5763	.5775	.5786
3.8	.5798	.5809	.5821	.5832	.5843	.5855	.5866	.5877	.5888	.5899
3.9	.5911	.5922	.5933	.5944	.5955	.5966	.5977	.5988	.5999	.6010
4.0	.6021	.6031	.6042	.6053	.6064	.6075	.6085	.6096	.6107	.6117
4.1	.6128	.6138	.6149	.6160	.6170	.6180	.6191	.6201	.6212	.6222
4.2	.6232	.6243	.6253	.6263	.6274	.6284	.6294	.6304	.6314	.6325
4.3	.6335	.6345	.6355	.6365	.6375	.6385	.6395	.6405	.6415	.6425
4.4	.6435	.6444	.6454	.6464	.6474	.6484	.6493	.6503	.6513	.6522
4.5	.6532	.6542	.6551	.6561	.6571	.6580	.6590	.6599	.6609	.6618
4.6	.6628	.6637	.6646	.6656	.6665	.6675	.6684	.6693	.6702	.6712
4.7	.6721	.6730	.6739	.6749	.6758	.6767	.6776	.6785	.6794	.6803
4.8	.6812	.6821	.6830	.6839	.6848	.6857	.6866	.6875	.6884	.6893
4.9	.6902	.6911	.6920	.6928	.6937	.6946	.6955	.6964	.6972	.6981
5.0	.6990	.6998	.7007	.7016	.7024	.7033	.7042	.7050	.7059	.7067
5.1	.7076	.7084	.7093	.7101	.7110	.7118	.7126	.7135	.7143	.7152
5.2	.7160	.7168	.7177	.7185	.7193	.7202	.7210	.7218	.7226	.7235
5.3	.7243	.7251	.7259	.7267	.7275	.7284	.7292	.7300	.7308	.7316
5.4	.7324	.7332	.7340	.7348	.7356	.7364	.7372	.7380	.7388	.7396
N	0	1	2	3	4	5	6	7	8	9

TABLE II (Continued)
Logarithms of Numbers

N	0	1	2	3	4	5	6	7	8	9
5.5	.7404	.7412	.7419	.7427	.7435	.7443	.7451	.7459	.7466	.7474
5.6	.7482	.7490	.7497	.7505	.7513	.7520	.7528	.7536	.7543	.7551
5.7	.7559	.7566	.7574	.7582	.7589	.7597	.7604	.7612	.7619	.7627
5.8	.7634	.7642	.7649	.7657	.7664	.7672	.7679	.7686	.7694	.7701
5.9	.7709	.7716	.7723	.7731	.7738	.7745	.7752	.7760	.7767	.7774
6.0	.7782	.7789	.7796	.7803	.7810	.7818	.7825	.7832	.7839	.7846
6.1	.7853	.7860	.7868	.7875	.7882	.7889	.7896	.7903	.7910	.7917
6.2	.7924	.7931	.7938	.7945	.7952	.7959	.7966	.7973	.7980	.7987
6.3	.7993	.8000	.8007	.8014	.8021	.8028	.8035	.8041	.8048	.8055
6.4	.8062	.8069	.8075	.8082	.8089	.8096	.8102	.8109	.8116	.8122
6.5	.8129	.8136	.8142	.8149	.8156	.8162	.8169	.8176	.8182	.8189
6.6	.8195	.8202	.8209	.8215	.8222	.8228	.8235	.8241	.8248	.8254
6.7	.8261	.8267	.8274	.8280	.8287	.8293	.8299	.8306	.8312	.8319
6.8	.8325	.8331	.8338	.8344	.8351	.8357	.8363	.8370	.8376	.8382
6.9	.8388	.8395	.8401	.8407	.8414	.8420	.8426	.8432	.8439	.8445
7.0	.8451	.8457	.8463	.8470	.8476	.8482	.8488	.8494	.8500	.8506
7.1	.8513	.8519	.8525	.8531	.8537	.8543	.8549	.8555	.8561	.8567
7.2	.8573	.8579	.8585	.8591	.8597	.8603	.8609	.8615	.8621	.8627
7.3	.8633	.8639	.8645	.8651	.8657	.8663	.8669	.8675	.8681	.8686
7.4	.8692	.8698	.8704	.8710	.8716	.8722	.8727	.8733	.8739	.8745
7.5	.8751	.8756	.8762	.8768	.8774	.8779	.8785	.8791	.8797	.8802
7.6	.8808	.8814	.8820	.8825	.8831	.8837	.8842	.8848	.8854	.8859
7.7	.8865	.8871	.8876	.8882	.8887	.8893	.8899	.8904	.8910	.8915
7.8	.8921	.8927	.8932	.8938	.8943	.8949	.8954	.8960	.8965	.8971
7.9	.8976	.8982	.8987	.8993	.8998	.9004	.9009	.9015	.9020	.9025
8.0	.9031	.9036	.9042	.9047	.9053	.9058	.9063	.9069	.9074	.9079
8.1	.9085	.9090	.9096	.9101	.9106	.9112	.9117	.9122	.9128	.9133
8.2	.9138	.9143	.9149	.9154	.9159	.9165	.9170	.9175	.9180	.9186
8.3	.9191	.9196	.9201	.9206	.9212	.9217	.9222	.9227	.9232	.9238
8.4	.9243	.9248	.9253	.9258	.9263	.9269	.9274	.9279	.9284	.9289
8.5	.9294	.9299	.9304	.9309	.9315	.9320	.9325	.9330	.9335	.9340
8.6	.9345	.9350	.9355	.9360	.9365	.9370	.9375	.9380	.9385	.9390
8.7	.9395	.9400	.9405	.9410	.9415	.9420	.9425	.9430	.9435	.9440
8.8	.9445	.9450	.9455	.9460	.9465	.9469	.9474	.9479	.9484	.9489
8.9	.9494	.9499	.9504	.9509	.9513	.9518	.9523	.9528	.9533	.9538
9.0	.9542	.9547	.9552	.9557	.9562	.9566	.9571	.9576	.9581	.9586
9.1	.9590	.9595	.9600	.9605	.9609	.9614	.9619	.9624	.9628	.9633
9.2	.9638	.9643	.9647	.9652	.9657	.9661	.9666	.9671	.9675	.9680
9.3	.9685	.9689	.9694	.9699	.9703	.9708	.9713	.9717	.9722	.9727
9.4	.9731	.9736	.9741	.9745	.9750	.9754	.9759	.9763	.9768	.9773
9.5	.9777	.9782	.9786	.9791	.9795	.9800	.9805	.9809	.9814	.9818
9.6	.9823	.9827	.9832	.9836	.9841	.9845	.9850	.9854	.9859	.9863
9.7	.9868	.9872	.9877	.9881	.9886	.9890	.9894	.9899	.9903	.9908
9.8	.9912	.9917	.9921	.9926	.9930	.9934	.9939	.9943	.9948	.9952
9.9	.9956	.9961	.9965	.9969	.9974	.9978	.9983	.9987	.9991	.9996
N	0	1	2	3	4	5	6	7	8	9

Answers to Odd-numbered Exercises

CHAPTER ONE

Page 5

1. $-5, 5, 5, -\dfrac{4}{3}, \dfrac{1}{2}, 3, 2, -\dfrac{2}{3}, 0, -\dfrac{13}{3}$

3. $11, \dfrac{29}{6}, -\dfrac{7}{4}, \dfrac{25}{4}; -\dfrac{1}{3}, \dfrac{25}{3}, \dfrac{34}{3}; 0, \dfrac{211}{12}, 11$

Page 8

1. $\dfrac{7}{2}$ 3. $-\dfrac{7}{3}$ and $\dfrac{4}{3}$ 5. $8\sqrt{2} - 14$ 7. -295 9. $-\dfrac{11}{3}$

11. 4 13. -1 15. $3\sqrt{3} - 2$ 17. -11 19. $-\dfrac{5}{2}$

23. $\dfrac{r}{1+r}$

Page 13

7. 36 9. $(-1, 1), (4, -2)$ 11. If (x, y) is a point on the line, $y = 2$.

Page 17

1. $\sqrt{85}$ 3. $\dfrac{\sqrt{2533}}{12}$ 5. $\sqrt{82}$ 7. $\sqrt{17}, 2\sqrt{10}, \sqrt{29}$
9. $\sqrt{122}, \sqrt{146}, 6$ 11. isosceles   13. right, area 10
15. right, area 10   17. both, area 26   19. right, area $2\sqrt{3}$
23. yes   25. -9 27. $(-3, 4), (-4, 3), (\sqrt{21}, -2); x^2 + y^2 = 25$

Page 23

1. $(5, 1), (6, 3)$ 3. $\left(-\dfrac{3}{2}, -\dfrac{25}{6}\right), \left(-\dfrac{1}{2}, -\dfrac{4}{3}\right)$ 5. $\left(-\dfrac{11}{6}, -3\right)$

7. $(10, 1)$ 9. $\left(\dfrac{9}{4}, 0\right)$ 11. $\sqrt{26}, 4\sqrt{2}, \sqrt{26}$

13. $\dfrac{\sqrt{410}}{2}; \dfrac{\sqrt{137}}{2}; \dfrac{\sqrt{653}}{2}$ 15. $\dfrac{3}{2}; -\dfrac{5}{2}$

17. $\dfrac{r}{r+1}; -(r+1)$ 19. $\dfrac{ac}{8}$

CHAPTER TWO

Page 30

9. $5; 78° 41'$ **11.** $0; 0°$ **13.** $1; 45°$ **15.** $-1; 135°$

17. $2, -\dfrac{3}{2}, -5; -\dfrac{1}{3}, -\dfrac{8}{3}$, no slope **19.** $150°; -\dfrac{\sqrt{3}}{3}$

Page 33

1. $-\dfrac{4}{7}, \dfrac{1}{2}, -2$ **3.** $\dfrac{2}{3}, \dfrac{1}{5}, -\dfrac{1}{2}$ **5.** $-2, -\dfrac{1}{3}, -\dfrac{3}{4}$

7. $-\dfrac{41}{45}, \dfrac{4}{5}, -\dfrac{2}{3}$ **11.** yes; no **15.** 5 **19.** $-\dfrac{1}{4}$

Page 37

1. $A = 37° 53', B = 81° 52', C = 60° 15'$
3. $A = 63°26', B = 26° 34', C = 90°$
5. $A = 53° 50', B = 94° 24', C = 31° 46'$

7. $72° 21'$ **11.** $85°, 15°, 170°$ **13.** $\dfrac{59}{7}$

Page 43

1. $5y - x - 11 = 0$ **3.** $2y - 3x + 10 = 0$ **5.** $y - mx + am = 0$
7. $y + x - 1 = 0$ **9.** $bx + ay = ab$ **11.** $y = 3x$
13. $y = -1$ **15.** $18x - 30y - 19 = 0$
17. sides: $3y - 4x - 15 = 0, 3y + x = 0, y + 2x - 5 = 0$;
medians: $9y - 2x - 15 = 0, x = 0, 9y + 8x - 15 = 0$;
altitudes: $2y - x - 5 = 0, y - 3x - 5 = 0, 4y + 3x - 5 = 0$;
perpendicular bisectors: $8y + 6x - 15 = 0, y - 3x = 0$,
$4y - 2x - 5 = 0$
19. sides: $3x - 5y - 8 = 0, 4x + 5y + 1 = 0, x - 6 = 0$;
medians: $x + 10y + 9 = 0, 2x - y - 10 = 0, 11x + 5y - 41 = 0$;
altitudes: $5x - 4y - 22 = 0, y + 1 = 0, 5x + 3y - 15 = 0$;
perpendicular bisectors: $2y + 3 = 0, 10x - 8y - 59 = 0$,
$5x + 3y - 19 = 0$
21. sides: $6x - 5y + 14 = 0, 3x + 2y - 11 = 0, y + 2 = 0$;
medians: $3x - 7y - 2 = 0, 12x - y - 8 = 0, 6x + 13y - 4 = 0$;
altitudes: $2x - 3y + 2 = 0, x - 1 = 0, 5x + 6y - 13 = 0$;
perpendicular bisectors: $2x - 1 = 0, 2x - 3y - 3 = 0$,
$10x + 12y + 3 = 0$
23. $3y - 4x = 0$

Page 46

1. intercepts $-\dfrac{3}{2}$ and $-\dfrac{3}{5}$; $y = -\dfrac{2}{5}x - \dfrac{3}{5}$; $-\dfrac{2}{5}$

3. intercepts -1 and -1; $y = -x - 1$; -1

5. intercepts -12 and 12; $y = x + 12$; 1

7. intercepts 0 and 0; $y = -\dfrac{5}{2}x$; $-\dfrac{5}{2}$

9. intercepts 2 and $\dfrac{1}{2}$; $y = -\dfrac{1}{4}x + \dfrac{1}{2}$; $-\dfrac{1}{4}$

11. $3x - 7y + 23 = 0$, $7x + 3y + 15 = 0$ 13. $x = 3$, $y = -2$

15. $5x + y + 7 = 0$, $x - 5y + 17 = 0$ 21. $86°\ 38'$

Page 49

1. below, above, above   3. below, above, below

5. above, below, above   7. above, on, above

9. above, below, above

Page 51

1. $(1, 3)$ 3. $(2, 1)$ 5. $\left(-\dfrac{1}{9}, \dfrac{8}{9}\right)$ 7. meet on $\left(\dfrac{31}{16}, \dfrac{15}{8}\right)$

9. $(-1, 2)$, $(4, 3)$, $(2, -6)$ 11. $\left(-\dfrac{5}{2}, 3\right)$, $\left(4, \dfrac{3}{2}\right)$, $\left(0, -\dfrac{5}{3}\right)$

13. $\left(5, \dfrac{1}{2}\right)$, $\left(-2, \dfrac{5}{2}\right)$, $\left(1, -\dfrac{3}{2}\right)$ 15. $\left(\dfrac{14}{3}, 3\right)$

Page 54

1. $\dfrac{18}{5}$ 3. $\dfrac{14\sqrt{13}}{13}$ 5. $\dfrac{6}{13}$ 7. $\dfrac{4}{5}$ 9. $\dfrac{15}{2}$

11. $\dfrac{8\sqrt{5}}{5}$, area 8 13. $\dfrac{39}{2}$ 15. 27 17. $\dfrac{9}{10}$

19. $3x - 4y - 3 = 0$, $3x - 4y - 43 = 0$

Page 58

1. $\sqrt{3}x + y - 8 = 0$ 3. $y + 5 = 0$ 5. $\sqrt{2}x - \sqrt{2}y + 2 = 0$

7. $x + \sqrt{3}y + 6 = 0$ 9. $\dfrac{x}{\sqrt{2}} + \dfrac{y}{\sqrt{2}} - \dfrac{3}{\sqrt{2}} = 0$, $\alpha = 45°$, $p = \dfrac{3}{\sqrt{2}}$

11. $-\dfrac{3x}{5} + \dfrac{4y}{5} - \dfrac{7}{5} = 0$, $\alpha = 126°\ 52'$, $p = \dfrac{7}{5}$

13. $y - \dfrac{2}{3} = 0$, $\alpha = 90°$, $p = \dfrac{2}{3}$

15. $-\dfrac{5x}{13} + \dfrac{12y}{13} = 0$, $\alpha = 112° \, 37'$. $p = 0$

17. $\dfrac{x}{2} + \dfrac{\sqrt{3}y}{2} - 2 = 0$, $\alpha = 60°$, $p = 2$

19. $\dfrac{3x}{5} + \dfrac{4y}{5} - 10 = 0$ **21.** $3x - y - 2\sqrt{10} = 0$

CHAPTER THREE

Page 73

1. $(0, 1)$, $(-1, 4)$ **3.** $(1, 2)$, $(0, \sqrt{2})$ **5.** $(0, 1)$, $\left(\dfrac{2\sqrt{14}}{3}, 8\right)$

7. 7   **9.** $A = -\dfrac{11}{5}$, $B = \dfrac{1}{5}$ **11.** x−axis; $(-1, -4)$, $(-3, 7)$,

$(2, -4)$, $(1, 3)$: y−axis; $(1, 4)$, $(3, -7)$, $(-2, 4)$, $(-1, -3)$: origin;
$(1, -4)$, $(3, 7)$, $(-2, -4)$, $(-1, 3)$ **13.** $(3, 9)$, $(-3, -9)$,$(-7, 9)$,
$(-3, 7)$, $(-9, 3)$
15. $(2, -5)$, $(4, 5)$, $(-2, -3)$, $(4, -19)$, $(-4, -7)$

Page 76

1. $(9, 6)$, $(1, 2)$ **3.** $(1, 1)$, $(-1, -1)$ **5.** $(1, -2)$, $(2, 1)$

7. $(3, -2)$, $\left(-\dfrac{4}{3}, \dfrac{9}{2}\right)$ **9.** none

11. $(-1 + 2\sqrt{2}, 2\sqrt{2})$, $(-1 - 2\sqrt{2}, -2\sqrt{2})$
13. $(3 + 2\sqrt{2}, 3 - 2\sqrt{2})$, $(3 - 2\sqrt{2}, 3 + 2\sqrt{2})$,
$(-3 + 2\sqrt{2}, -3 - 2\sqrt{2})$, $(-3 - 2\sqrt{2}, -3 + 2\sqrt{2})$

Page 79

1. $x^2 + y^2 + 2x - 4y - 4 = 0$ **3.** $y^2 - 4y - 8x + 20 = 0$
5. $x^2 - 4y + 4 = 0$ **7.** $x^2 - 3y^2 + 8y = 0$
9. $xy = 4$, $xy = -4$ **11.** $y^2 - 8x = 0$
13. $y = 4$ with the point $(0, 4)$ missing
15. $x^2 + 2xy + y^2 + 8x - 8y + 16 = 0$
17. $16x^2 + 25y^2 - 96x - 50y - 231 = 0$
19. $x^2 + y^2 + x + 4y - 23 = 0$

Page 82

1. $3x - y - 6 = 0$, $x + 3y - 8 = 0$
3. $\dfrac{3x - 2y + 3}{\sqrt{13}} = \pm\dfrac{x + y - 4}{\sqrt{2}}$

5. $2x + 14y - 7 = 0$, $14x - 2y + 1 = 0$

7. $\dfrac{2x - 5y - 1}{\sqrt{29}} = \dfrac{y - 5x - 9}{\sqrt{26}}$

9. $3x - y - 11 = 0$ 11. $8y - 5 = 0$, $27y - 99x + 38 = 0$,

    $77y + 99x - 103 = 0$; $\left(\dfrac{439}{792}, \dfrac{5}{8}\right)$

CHAPTER FOUR

Page 86

1. $x^2 + y^2 - 4x + 2y - 4 = 0$ 3. $x^2 + y^2 + 10y = 0$

5. $x^2 + y^2 - 6x + 4y - 12 = 0$ 7. $x^2 + y^2 - 8y - 16 = 0$

9. $x^2 + y^2 + 4x + 4y = 0$ 11. $\left(\dfrac{3}{2}, 0\right)$, $r = \sqrt{2}$

13. $(-1, -1)$, $r = 2$ 15. $(5, -5)$, $r = 5\sqrt{2}$

17. $\left(-\dfrac{1}{2}, \dfrac{5}{2}\right)$, $r = 1$ 19. $\left(0, \dfrac{4}{5}\right)$, $r = \dfrac{\sqrt{61}}{5}$

21. $\left(-\dfrac{1}{2}, -1\right)$, $r = \dfrac{\sqrt{5}}{2}$

23. $3x^2 + 3y^2 - 24x - 38y + 135 = 0$

Page 90

1. $3x^2 + 3y^2 - 10x - 16y + 8 = 0$

3. $3x^2 + 3y^2 + 2x - 8y - 16 = 0$

5. $7x^2 + 7y^2 - 109x - 65y + 472 = 0$

7. $(x - 1)^2 + (y - 6)^2 = 25$, $(x - 2)^2 + (y + 1)^2 = 25$

9. $x^2 + y^2 + 6x - 10y + 14 = 0$

11. $3x^2 + 3y^2 + 16x - 44y - 34 = 0$

13. $(x - 3)^2 + (y + 5)^2 = 25$, $(x - 23)^2 + (y + 145)^2 = 21{,}025$

15. $x^2 + y^2 - 2x - 2y + 1 = 0$, $x^2 + y^2 - 10x - 10y + 25 = 0$

17. $x^2 + y^2 - 8x + 14y + 1 = 0$, $x^2 + y^2 - 8x + 14y - 79 = 0$

19. $11x + 2y + 5 = 0$ 21. $5x + 4y - 24 = 0$

23. $6x + y + 30 = 0$

Page 93

1. $5x^2 + 5y^2 + 7x - 3y - 14 = 0$ 3. $x^2 + y^2 + 11x - 5y - 6 = 0$

5. $9x^2 + 9y^2 - 18x - 10y + 1 = 0$ 7. $x^2 + y^2 + 10x + 8y + 23 = 0$

CHAPTER FIVE

Page 98

1. focus $(0, -3)$; directrix $y = 3$; length of l.r. 12
3. focus $(2, 0)$; directrix $x = -2$; length of l.r. 8
5. focus $\left(0, -\dfrac{3}{8}\right)$; directrix $y = \dfrac{3}{8}$; length of l.r. $\dfrac{3}{2}$
7. focus $\left(0, \dfrac{7}{2}\right)$; directrix $y = -\dfrac{7}{2}$; length of l.r. 14
9. focus $\left(\dfrac{1}{4}, 0\right)$; directrix $x = -\dfrac{1}{4}$; length of l.r. 1
11. focus $\left(0, -\dfrac{3}{2}\right)$; directrix $y = \dfrac{3}{2}$; length of l.r. 6
13. $y^2 = 16x$ 15. $x^2 = -12y$ 17. $y^2 = -2x$
19. $x^2 = 4\sqrt{2}y$ 21. $x^2 - 8y + 16 = 0$ 23. $y^2 - 4x - 4 = 0$
25. $y^2 - 4x - 12y + 48 = 0$
27. $x^2 - 2xy + y^2 - 4x - 4y + 4 = 0$
29. $x^2 + y^2 + 8y - 48 = 0$ 31. $(-1, -1), (3, -9)$

Page 104

1. vertices $(\pm 3, 0)$; foci $(\pm \sqrt{5}, 0)$ 3. vertices $(0, \pm 5)$;
   foci $(0, \pm 4)$
5. vertices $\left(0, \pm \dfrac{5}{3}\right)$; foci $\left(0, \pm \dfrac{4}{3}\right)$ 7. vertices $(\pm 5, 0)$;
   foci $(\pm 2\sqrt{6}, 0)$
9. vertices $(0, \pm 1)$; foci $\left(0, \pm \dfrac{\sqrt{3}}{2}\right)$ 11. circle, radius $\dfrac{5}{2}$
13. $9x^2 + 25y^2 = 225$ 15. $x^2 + 4y^2 = 16$
17. $2x^2 + y^2 = 8$ 19. $4x^2 + 3y^2 = 192$
21. $16x^2 + 25y^2 - 192x - 250y + 801 = 0$
23. $2x^2 + 2y^2 - 5y - 18 = 0$

Page 108

1. $\dfrac{3}{5}$; $(\pm 3, 0)$; $x = \pm \dfrac{25}{3}$ 3. $\dfrac{1}{2}$; $(0, \pm 1)$; $y = \pm 4$
5. $\dfrac{2}{3}$; $\left(\pm \dfrac{1}{3}, 0\right)$; $x = \pm \dfrac{3}{4}$
7. $\dfrac{2\sqrt{2}}{3}$; $\left(0, \pm \dfrac{2\sqrt{2}}{3}\right)$; $y = \pm \dfrac{3\sqrt{2}}{4}$
9. $3x^2 + 4y^2 = 48$ 11. $4x^2 + y^2 = 12$
13. $8x^2 + 9y^2 = 128$ 15. $16x^2 + 25y^2 = 1600$

17. $\dfrac{x^2}{64} + \dfrac{y^2}{48} = 1$ or $\dfrac{x^2}{32(7 - \sqrt{13})} + \dfrac{y^2}{24(\sqrt{13} - 1)} = 1$

Page 116

3. vertices $(0, \pm 2)$; foci $(0, \pm 2\sqrt{2})$; asymptotes $y = \pm x$
5. vertices $(0, \pm 12)$; foci $(0, \pm 13)$; asymptotes $5y \pm 12x = 0$
7. vertices $(\pm 3, 0)$; foci $(\pm \sqrt{13}, 0)$; asymptotes $3y \pm 2x = 0$
9. vertices $(\pm \sqrt{3}, 0)$; foci $(\pm \sqrt{7}, 0)$; asymptotes $\sqrt{3}y \pm 2x = 0$
11. vertices $(0, \pm 1)$; foci $(0, \pm \sqrt{5})$; asymptotes $2y \pm x = 0$
13. vertices $(\pm 1, 0)$; foci $(\pm \sqrt{2}, 0)$; asymptotes $y \pm x = 0$
15. $16x^2 - 9y^2 = 144$ **17.** $x^2 - 4y^2 = 16$
19. $4x^2 - 9y^2 = 36$ **21.** $x^2 - y^2 = \pm 25$
23. $16x^2 - 9y^2 - 128x + 36y + 76 = 0$

Page 118

1. $\dfrac{5}{3}$; $(\pm 5, 0)$; $x = \pm \dfrac{9}{5}$ **3.** $\sqrt{2}$; $(0, \pm 2\sqrt{2})$; $y = \pm \sqrt{2}$

5. $\sqrt{10}$; $(\pm \sqrt{10}, 0)$; $x = \pm \dfrac{\sqrt{10}}{10}$ **7.** $\dfrac{\sqrt{10}}{3}$; $\left(0, \pm \dfrac{\sqrt{10}}{3}\right)$;

   $y = \pm \dfrac{3\sqrt{10}}{10}$

9. $3x^2 - y^2 = 48$ **11.** $8y^2 - x^2 = 1152$
13. $20x^2 - 16y^2 = 405$ **15.** $16y^2 - 9x^2 = 576$

CHAPTER SIX

Page 131

1. $x^2 - 6x - 8y + 25 = 0$ **3.** $x^2 - y^2 - 4x + 2y - 1 = 0$
5. $3x^2 + 4y^2 - 36x - 16y + 76 = 0$ **7.** $x^2 + 10x + 8y - 15 = 0$
9. $4x^2 + 3y^2 - 16x - 24y + 52 = 0$

11. $4x^2 + 3y^2 + 8x - 16y + 20 = 0$; $\left(-1, \dfrac{10}{3}\right)$ and $(-1, 2)$

13. $x^2 + y^2 - 7x + 6y + 15 = 0$ **15.** $\dfrac{(y - 2)^2}{1} - \dfrac{(x - 2)^2}{4} = 1$

17. $\dfrac{x^2}{1} + \dfrac{(y + 1)^2}{2} = 1$ **19.** $\dfrac{(y + 1)^2}{1} - \dfrac{(x - 3)^2}{4} = 1$

21. $4x - 3y - 4 = 0, 4x + 3y - 4 = 0$
23. $(x - 1)^2 = 2(y - 4)$
25. $\dfrac{(x - 1)^2}{4} + \dfrac{(y + 1)^2}{3} = 1$ **27.** $\left(y - \dfrac{1}{3}\right)^2 = x + \dfrac{2}{3}$

Page 135

1. $\dfrac{x'^2}{4} - \dfrac{y'^2}{12} = 1$ 3. $x'^2 + 4y'^2 = 4$

5. $\dfrac{(x'-3)^2}{4} + \dfrac{(y'+2)^2}{16} = 1$ 7. $y'^2 = -x'$

CHAPTER SEVEN

Page 141

1. $\dfrac{x'^2}{1} + \dfrac{y'^2}{6} = 1$ 3. $(x'-2)^2 = 3\left(y' + \dfrac{4}{3}\right)$

5. $y'^2 = 2\left(x' - \dfrac{1}{2}\right)$ 7. $\dfrac{x'^2}{1} + \dfrac{y'^2}{11} = 1$

9. $\dfrac{(x'+\sqrt{2})^2}{2} - \dfrac{y'^2}{2} = 1$ 11. $\dfrac{y'^2}{90} - \dfrac{x'^2}{10} = 1$

13. $\dfrac{(x'-1)^2}{1} + \dfrac{(y'+2)^2}{4} = 1$ 15. $\dfrac{x'^2}{1} - \dfrac{(y'+1)^2}{1} = 1$

CHAPTER NINE

Page 185

1. $r = 4$ 3. $r^2 \cos 2\theta = 1$ 5. $r^2 \sin 2\theta = 18$
7. $r = 2 \cos \theta - 4 \sin \theta$ 9. $x^2 + y^2 - 4y = 0$
11. $x = 0$ 13. $(x^2 + y^2 - ax)^2 = a^2(x^2 + y^2)$
15. $x^4 - a^2(x^2 + y^2) = 0$

Page 192

1. parabola; vertex $(1, 0)$ 3. ellipse; vertices $\left(2, \dfrac{\pi}{2}\right)$ and $\left(6, \dfrac{3\pi}{2}\right)$

5. hyperbola; vertices $\left(-\sqrt{2} - 1, \dfrac{\pi}{2}\right)$ and $\left(\sqrt{2} - 1, \dfrac{3\pi}{2}\right)$

7. hyperbola; vertices $(-8, 0)$ and $\left(\dfrac{24}{5}, \pi\right)$

9. ellipse; vertices $(3, 0)$ and $(6, \pi)$

11. $r = \dfrac{2}{1 - \cos \theta}$ 13. $r = \dfrac{10}{3 - 2 \sin \theta}$

15. $r = \dfrac{4}{1 - \cos \theta}$ 17. $r = \dfrac{6}{1 + 2 \cos \theta}$

19. $r = \dfrac{8}{1 - \cos \theta}$

23. $\left| \dfrac{2eq}{1 - e^2} \right|$

Page 196

1. $\left(\dfrac{4}{3}, 60°\right)$, $(4, 240°)$ **3.** $(-24, 210°)$, $\left(\dfrac{24}{5}, 30°\right)$

5. $(0, 0°)$, $\left(\dfrac{3\sqrt{2}}{2}, 45°\right)$ **7.** $(0, 0°)$, $\left(\dfrac{1}{2}, 60°\right)$, $\left(\dfrac{1}{2}, -60°\right)$

9. $(-3, 180°)$, $(4, 41° \; 25')$, $(4, -41° \; 25')$

11. $(2 + \sqrt{2}, 45°)$, $(2 + \sqrt{2}, 135°)$, $(2 - \sqrt{2}, 225°)$, $(2 - \sqrt{2}, 315°)$,
$(\sqrt{2}, 17° \; 2')$, $(\sqrt{2}, 162° \; 58')$

CHAPTER TEN

Page 200

1. $3x + 2y - 2 = 0$ **3.** $x - y + 1 = 0$

5. $y^2 - 2y - x + 2 = 0$ **7.** $x^2 + xy - 2x - y = 0$

9. $x^3 - 4y = 0.$ **11.** $x^2 - y - 1 = 0$

13. $x^2 + y^2 = 4$ **15.** $\dfrac{25\sqrt{2}}{4} = 8.8$ sec.; 1250 ft.

17. yes   **19.** 108 ft.

Page 208

1. $x^2 + y^2 = 9$ **3.** $\dfrac{x^2}{16} + \dfrac{y^2}{4} = 1$

5. $(x - 1)^2 + (y - 2)^2 = 1$ **7.** $\sqrt{x} + \sqrt{y} = 1$

9. $\dfrac{y^2}{16} - \dfrac{x^2}{9} = 1$

CHAPTER ELEVEN

Page 217

1. $12x - y - 12 = 0$ **3.** $x + 2y + 2 = 0$

5. $2x - \sqrt{3}y - 4 = 0$ **7.** $3x + 4y - 18 = 0$

9. $4x - 5y + 31 = 0$ **11.** $3x + y + 6 = 0$

19. $4x + y - 8 = 0$ **21.** $x - 4y + 14 = 0$

CHAPTER TWELVE

Page 228

5. 48   **7.** 48   **9.** isosceles   **11.** right   **13.** isosceles
15. right   **19.** $2x - 3y + 2z = 0$

Page 235

1. $\dfrac{1}{2}, \dfrac{1}{2}, \dfrac{\sqrt{2}}{2}$; 60°, 60°, 45°

3. $-\dfrac{1}{2}, \dfrac{1}{2}, \dfrac{\sqrt{2}}{2}$; 120°, 60°, 45°

5. $\dfrac{\sqrt{3}}{3}, \dfrac{\sqrt{3}}{3}, \dfrac{\sqrt{3}}{3}$; 54° 44′, 54° 44′, 54° 44′

7. $4, -8, 1; \dfrac{4}{9}, -\dfrac{8}{9}, \dfrac{1}{9}$; 63° 37′, 152° 44′, 83° 37′

9. $1, 2, -2; \dfrac{1}{3}, \dfrac{2}{3}, -\dfrac{2}{3}$; 70° 32′, 48° 11′, 131° 49′

11. $1, 0, 1; \dfrac{\sqrt{2}}{2}, 0, \dfrac{\sqrt{2}}{2}$; 45°, 90°, 45°

15. $\dfrac{\pi}{3}$ or $\dfrac{2\pi}{3}$

Page 239

1. $x = 1 + t, y = 1 - t, z = 1 - t$; $(2, 0, 0), (0, 2, 2)$

3. $x = 2 + t, y = -3 - 3t, z = -11 - 8t; \left(\dfrac{5}{8}, \dfrac{9}{8}, 0\right), (1, 0, -3),$
  $(0, 3, 5)$

5. $x = 1, y = 1 + t, z = -t$; $(1, 1, 0), (1, 0, 1),$ none
7. $x = -2 + t, y = 2 + t, z = 4 - t$; $(2, 6, 0), (-4, 0, 6), (0, 4, 2)$
9. $x = 6 + 2t, y = 5 + 5t, z = -6 - 3t$; $(2, -5, 0), (4, 0, -3),$
  $(0, -10, 3)$
11. $(2, 0, 1), (-1, 3, 2), (4, 1, -1)$
13. $(3, 4, -2), (1, 1, 3), (7, -6, 4)$

15. $\dfrac{x - 3}{1} = \dfrac{y - 4}{-2} = \dfrac{z + 1}{5}$

17. $\dfrac{x}{2} = \dfrac{y}{3} = \dfrac{z - 4}{-2}$ **19.** $\dfrac{x - 7}{5} = \dfrac{y - 4}{-1} = \dfrac{z - 3}{5}$

21. $x = t, y = 0, z = 0; x = 0, y = t, z = 0; x = 0, y = 0, z = t$

Page 243

1. 51° 20'   **3.** 78° 54'   **5.** 61° 19'
7. $x = 11 + 4t, y = 4 + 3t, z = -6 - 2t$
9. $x = 13 + 7t, y = 9 - 3t, z = -1 + t$
11. $x = 5 + 3t, y = -4 + t, z = 4$
13. $x = 2 + 2t, y = 2 + t, z = -3 - t$
15. $x = 3 + 2t, y = 4 - t, z = -1 - 3t$
17. 39° 46'

Page 249

1. $4x + y + 3z - 5 = 0$ 3. $x + y - 2z + 4 = 0$
5. $x - 4z - 5 = 0$ 7. $x - 2y + 4z - 4 = 0$
9. $x - 4y - 5 = 0$ 11. $x - y + 5z - 3 = 0$
19. $2x - y + 3z - 5 = 0$
21. $x = 1 + t, y = -2 - 3t, z = -2t$
23. $x - 2y - 5 = 0$

Page 251

1. 4   3. 2   5. $\dfrac{\sqrt{3}}{3}$ 7. $\dfrac{39}{9}$

9. $\dfrac{3\sqrt{2}}{2}$ 11. 1   13. $\dfrac{13}{6}$ 15. 32

Page 264

1. sphere, center $(2, -1, 0), r = 4$
3. sphere, center $\left(\dfrac{1}{2}, -2, -\dfrac{3}{2}\right), r = \dfrac{5}{2}$
5. ellipsoid   **7.** circular cone
9. hyperboloid (of revolution) of one sheet
11. ellipsoid of revolution   13. paraboloid of revolution
15. hyperboloid of two sheets   17. hyperbolic paraboloid
19. paraboloid of revolution   21. sphere, center $(1, 0, 0), r = 1$
23. elliptic paraboloid   25. ellipsoid of revolution, center $(2, 0, 0)$
27. hyperbolic paraboloid   29. hyperboloid of two sheets

Index

Index